Now you can modify the data in this book using your own labor and markup rates ... And instantly generate your own "customized" version that you can download, save and print!

Dear valued customer:

Your paid purchase of this 2010 NEC Costbook entitles you to create a custom, PDF (Adobe Acrobat format) version of the entire book with all unit costs adjusted to reflect your labor rates. You can even create a customized title page of the book!

The wage rates used in this book reflect national averages and are applicable for a wide range of estimating needs. But as you know, actual rates can vary significantly from state to state, as well as in open-shop environments.

Now this problem is solved!

Starting right now, you can simply plug-in your own rates for 13 different labor classifications – and have every unit cost in the entire book completely recalculated! And then you can generate a PDF version to print and/or share with the other members of your staff.

TRY IT FREE!

This new service is available exclusively to paid buyers of this book. And you can generate a 32-page sample document for Free! An online demo/tutorial guides you every step of the way.

All you need to get started is a User id and a PIN number. To get your PIN number and temporary User Id, just go to www.bnibooks.com/costbooks and enter your BNI Invoice Number. If you don't have your invoice number (or if you purchased this book from one of our associates), just call us at 1.888.BNI.BOOK and we'll get you set up right away.

Then, for just $9.95, you can create a complete, customized version of this book that you can print, share, or save to your PC. We're providing this value-added service to help our customers extend the value of this book with faster and more accurate estimates.

Sincerely,

William D. Mahoney, P.E.
Editor-in-Chief

PS: If you received this book on a courtesy free preview basis, you can get your PIN number right away by calling us with your credit card payment information at 1.888.BNI.BOOK

 **Building News**

990 Park Center Drive, Suite E, Vista, CA 92081-8352

nec 2010

NATIONAL ELECTRICAL CODE®

COSTBOOK

EDITOR-IN-CHIEF
William D. Mahoney, P.E.

TECHNICAL SERVICES
Andrew Atkinson
Edward B. Wetherill, CSI
Anthony Jackson
Ana Varela
Sara Gustafson

GRAPHIC DESIGN
Robert O. Wright Jr.

BNI Publications, Inc.

LOS ANGELES
10801 NATIONAL BLVD. SUITE 100, LOS ANGELES, CA 90064

NEW ENGLAND
1800 MINERAL SPRING AVE. #101 NORTH PROVIDENCE, RI 02901-3927

ANAHEIM
1612 S. CLEMENTINE STREET, ANAHEIM, CA 92802

VISTA
990 PARK CENTER DRIVE, SUITE E, VISTA, CA 92081

1-888-BNI-BOOK (1-888-264-2665)
www.bnibooks.com

ISBN 978-1-55701-672-0

Cover photos provided by shutterstock.com

PREFACE

For over 60 years, BNi Building News has been dedicated to providing construction professionals with timely and reliable information. Based on this experience, our staff has researched and compiled thousands of up-to-the-minute costs for the **NEC 2010 Costbook**. This book is an essential reference for contractors, engineers, architects, facility managers — any construction professional who must provide an estimate for any type of building project.

Whether working up a preliminary estimate or submitting a formal bid, the costs listed here can quickly and easily be tailored to your needs. All costs are based on your company's labor rates. Overhead and profit should be included in all costs. Man-hours are also provided.

All data is categorized according to the Construction Specifications Institute (CSI). This industry standard provides an all-inclusive checklist to ensure that no element of a project is overlooked. In addition, to make specific items even easier to locate, there is a complete alphabetical index.

The "Features of this Book" section presents a clear overview of the many features of this book. Included is an explanation of the data, sample page layout and discussion of how to best use the information in the book.

Of course, all buildings and construction projects are unique. The information provided in this book is based on averages from well-managed projects with good labor productivity under normal working conditions (eight hours a day). Other circumstances affecting costs such as overtime, unusual working conditions, savings from buying bulk quantities for large projects, and unusual or hidden costs must be factored in as they arise.

The data provided in this book is for estimating purposes only. Check all applicable federal, state and local codes and regulations for local requirements.

BNi. Building News

TABLE OF CONTENTS

BNi® Building News

FEATURES OF THIS BOOK

The construction estimating information in this book is divided into two main sections: Costbook Pages and Man-Hour Tables. Each section is organized according to the 16 divisions of the MASTERFORMAT. In addition, there are NEC Handbook Reference tables, Geographic Costs Modifiers and a detailed Index.

Sample pages with graphic explanations are included before the Costbook pages and Man-Hour tables. These explanations, along with the discussions below, will provide a good understanding of what is included in this book and how it can best be used in construction estimating.

Hours (Man-Hours)
The man-hour data used to develop the labor costs are listed in the second main section of this book, the "Man-Hour Tables." These productivities represent typical installation labor for thousands of construction items. The data takes into account all activities involved in normal construction under commonly experienced working conditions such as site movement, material handling, start-up, etc.

Material Costs
The material costs used in this book represent national averages for prices that a contractor would expect to pay plus an allowance for freight (if applicable) and handling and storage. These costs reflect neither the lowest or highest prices, but rather a typical average cost over time. Periodic fluctuations in availability and in certain commodities (e.g. copper, conduit) can significantly affect local material pricing. In the final estimating and bidding stages of a project when the highest degree of accuracy is required, it is best to check local, current prices.

Labor Costs
Labor costs include the basic wage, plus commonly applicable taxes, insurance and markups for overhead and profit. The labor rates used here to develop the costs are typical average prevailing wage rates. Rates for different trades are used where appropriate for each type of work.

Fixed government rates and average allowances for taxes and insurance are included in the labor costs. These include employer-paid Social Security/Medicare taxes (FICA), Worker's Compensation insurance, state and federal unemployment taxes, and business insurance.

Please note, however, most of these items vary significantly from state to state and within states. For more specific data, local agencies and sources should be consulted.

Equipment Costs
Costs for various types and pieces of equipment are included in Division 1 - General Requirements and can be included in an estimate when required either as a total "Equipment" category or with specific appropriate trades. Costs for equipment are included when appropriate in the installation costs in the Costbook pages.

Overhead and Profit
Included in the labor costs are allowances for overhead and profit for the contractor/employer whose workers are performing the specific tasks. No cost allowances or fees are included for management of subcontractors by the general contractor or construction manager. These costs, where appropriate, must be added to the costs as listed in the book.

FEATURES OF THIS BOOK (*Continued*)

The allowance for overhead is included to account for office overhead, the contractors' typical costs of doing business. These costs normally include in-house office staff salaries and benefits, office rent and operating expenses, professional fees, vehicle costs and other operating costs which are not directly applicable to specific jobs. It should be noted for this book that office overhead as included should be distinguished from project overhead, the General Requirements (CSI Division 1) which are specific to particular projects. Project overhead should be included on an item by item basis for each job.

Depending on the trade, an allowance of 10-15 percent is incorporated into the labor/installation costs to account for typical profit of the installing contractor. See Division 1, General Requirements, for a more detailed review of typical profit allowances.

Adjustments to Costs

The costs as presented in this book attempt to represent national averages. Costs, however, vary among regions, states and even between adjacent localities.

In order to more closely approximate the probable costs for specific locations throughout the U.S., a table of City Multipliers is provided. These adjustment factors are used to modify costs obtained from this book to help account for regional variations of construction costs. Whenever local current costs are known, whether material or equipment prices or labor rates, they should be used if more accuracy is required.

Editor's Note: This **2010 Costbook** is intended to provide accurate, reliable, average costs and typical productivities for thousands of common construction components. The data is developed and compiled from various industry sources, including government, manufacturers, suppliers and working professionals. The intent of the information is to provide assistance and guidelines to construction professionals in estimating. The user should be aware that local conditions, material and labor availability and cost variations, economic considerations, weather, local codes and regulations, etc., all affect the actual cost of construction. These and other such factors must be considered and incorporated into any and all construction estimates.

SAMPLE COSTBOOK PAGE

In order to best use the information in this book, please review this sample page and read the "Features of This Book" section.

CSI MASTERFORMAT Division

Man-Hours
Man-hour quantities represent typical installation times and take into account all activities involved in normal construction under commonly experienced working conditions.

CSI Broadscope Category

CSI Mediumscope Category

Material Cost
Material cost represent average contractor prices plus an allowance for freight, handling and storage.

Detailed Descriptions
Complete descriptions of items may include information listed above a particular line. Review of the whole category is recommended for a complete description.

Installation Cost
Installation cost includes basic wage rates, markups for taxes, insurance overhead and profit and also includes equipment costs where appropriate.

Total Cost
The total cost is the sum of material and installation costs. This total represents typical contractors' costs including overhead and profit, but does not include markups for the general contractor or construction management fees.

Unit of Measurement
Each item (and cost) is defined in terms of the common estimating unit. All costs are listed in dollars per unit.

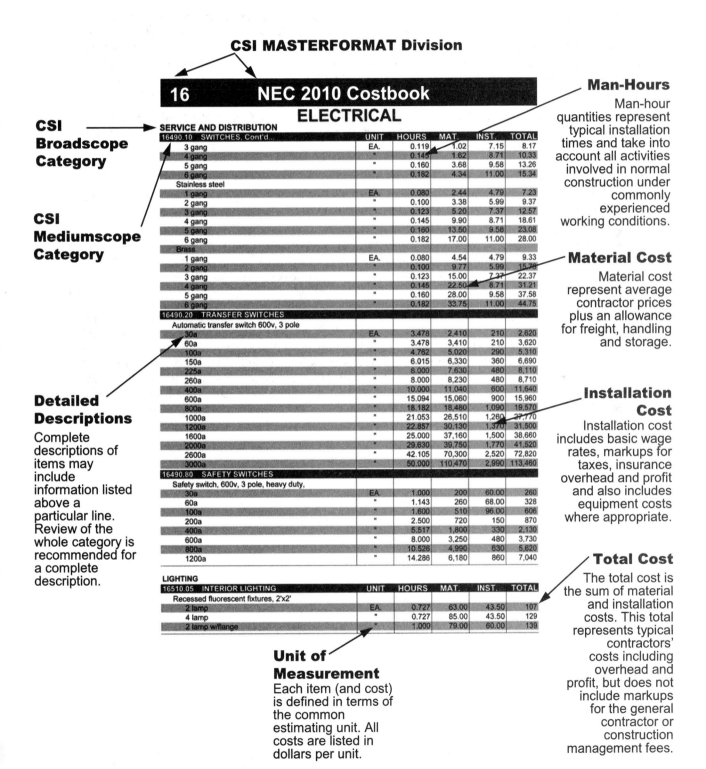

16   NEC 2010 Costbook
ELECTRICAL

SERVICE AND DISTRIBUTION

16490.10 SWITCHES, Cont'd...	UNIT	HOURS	MAT.	INST.	TOTAL
3 gang	EA.	0.119	1.02	7.15	8.17
4 gang	"	0.145	1.62	8.71	10.33
5 gang	"	0.160	3.68	9.58	13.26
6 gang	"	0.182	4.34	11.00	15.34
Stainless steel					
1 gang	EA.	0.080	2.44	4.79	7.23
2 gang	"	0.100	3.38	5.99	9.37
3 gang	"	0.123	5.20	7.37	12.57
4 gang	"	0.145	9.90	8.71	18.61
5 gang	"	0.160	13.50	9.58	23.08
6 gang	"	0.182	17.00	11.00	28.00
Brass					
1 gang	EA.	0.080	4.54	4.79	9.33
2 gang	"	0.100	9.77	5.99	15.76
3 gang	"	0.123	15.00	7.37	22.37
4 gang	"	0.145	22.50	8.71	31.21
5 gang	"	0.160	28.00	9.58	37.58
6 gang	"	0.182	33.75	11.00	44.75

16490.20 TRANSFER SWITCHES					
Automatic transfer switch 600v, 3 pole					
30a	EA.	3.478	2,410	210	2,620
60a	"	3.478	3,410	210	3,620
100a	"	4.762	5,020	290	5,310
150a	"	6.015	6,330	360	6,690
225a	"	8.000	7,630	480	8,110
260a	"	8.000	8,230	480	8,710
400a	"	10.000	11,040	600	11,640
600a	"	15.094	15,060	900	15,960
800a	"	18.182	18,480	1,090	19,570
1000a	"	21.053	26,510	1,260	27,770
1200a	"	22.857	30,130	1,370	31,500
1600a	"	25.000	37,160	1,500	38,660
2000a	"	29.630	39,750	1,770	41,520
2600a	"	42.105	70,300	2,520	72,820
3000a	"	50.000	110,470	2,990	113,460

16490.80 SAFETY SWITCHES					
Safety switch, 600v, 3 pole, heavy duty,					
30a	EA.	1.000	200	60.00	260
60a	"	1.143	260	68.00	328
100a	"	1.600	510	96.00	606
200a	"	2.500	720	150	870
400a	"	5.517	1,800	330	2,130
600a	"	8.000	3,250	480	3,730
800a	"	10.526	4,990	630	5,620
1200a	"	14.286	6,180	860	7,040

LIGHTING

16510.05 INTERIOR LIGHTING	UNIT	HOURS	MAT.	INST.	TOTAL
Recessed fluorescent fixtures, 2'x2'					
2 lamp	EA.	0.727	63.00	43.50	107
4 lamp	"	0.727	85.00	43.50	129
2 lamp w/flange	"	1.000	79.00	60.00	139

REQUIREMENTS

01010.00 ALLOWANCES	UNIT	HOURS	MAT.	INST.	TOTAL
Overhead					
$20,000 project					
Minimum	PCT.				15.00
Average	"				20.00
Maximum	"				40.00
$100,000 project					
Minimum	PCT.				12.00
Average	"				15.00
Maximum	"				25.00
$500,000 project					
Minimum	PCT.				10.00
Average	"				12.00
Maximum	"				20.00
Profit					
$20,000 project					
Minimum	PCT.				10.00
Average	"				15.00
Maximum	"				25.00
$100,000 project					
Minimum	PCT.				10.00
Average	"				12.00
Maximum	"				20.00
$500,000 project					
Minimum	PCT.				5.00
Average	"				10.00
Maximum	"				15.00
Taxes					
Sales tax					
Minimum	PCT.				4.00
Average	"				5.00
Maximum	"				10.00
Unemployment					
Minimum	PCT.				3.00
Average	"				6.50
Maximum	"				8.00
Social security (FICA)	"				7.85
01050.10 FIELD STAFF					
Superintendent					
Minimum	YEAR				78,600
Average	"				115,000
Maximum	"				165,000
Foreman					
Minimum	YEAR				43,700
Average	"				71,000
Maximum	"				104,000
Bookkeeper/timekeeper					
Minimum	YEAR				25,000
Average	"				33,000
Maximum	"				54,600
Watchman					
Minimum	YEAR				17,500
Average	"				21,900
Maximum	"				35,000

REQUIREMENTS

01310.10 SCHEDULING	UNIT	HOURS	MAT.	INST.	TOTAL
Scheduling for					
$100,000 project					
Minimum	PCT.				1.09
Average	"				2.18
Maximum	"				4.36
$500,000 project					
Minimum	PCT.				0.55
Average	"				1.10
Maximum	"				2.19
Scheduling software					
Minimum	EA.				420
Average	"				2,400
Maximum	"				48,050
01380.10 JOB REQUIREMENTS					
Job photographs, small jobs					
Minimum	EA.				120
Average	"				170
Maximum	"				400
Large projects					
Minimum	EA.				580
Average	"				870
Maximum	"				2,890
Welding, per test					
Minimum	EA.				19.00
Average	"				31.75
Maximum	"				130
01500.10 TEMPORARY FACILITIES					
Barricades, temporary					
Highway					
Concrete	L.F.	0.080	11.25	3.94	15.19
Wood	"	0.032	3.67	1.57	5.24
Steel	"	0.027	3.93	1.31	5.24
Pedestrian barricades					
Plywood	S.F.	0.027	2.62	1.31	3.93
Chain link fence	"	0.027	2.95	1.31	4.26
Trailers, general office type, per month					
Minimum	EA.				200
Average	"				330
Maximum	"				660
Crew change trailers, per month					
Minimum	EA.				120
Average	"				130
Maximum	"				200
01505.10 MOBILIZATION					
Equipment mobilization					
Bulldozer					
Minimum	EA.				180
Average	"				380
Maximum	"				630
Backhoe/front-end loader					
Minimum	EA.				110
Average	"				190
Maximum	"				410

REQUIREMENTS

01505.10 MOBILIZATION, Cont'd...	UNIT	HOURS	MAT.	INST.	TOTAL
Crane, crawler type					
Minimum	EA.				1,990
Average	"				4,880
Maximum	"				10,480
Truck crane					
Minimum	EA.				470
Average	"				700
Maximum	"				1,210
01525.10 CONSTRUCTION AIDS					
Scaffolding/staging, rent per month					
Measured by lineal feet of base					
10' high	L.F.				11.50
20' high	"				20.75
30' high	"				29.00
40' high	"				33.50
50' high	"				40.00
Measured by square foot of surface					
Minimum	S.F.				0.51
Average	"				0.87
Maximum	"				1.57
Safety nets, heavy duty, per job					
Minimum	S.F.				0.33
Average	"				0.40
Maximum	"				0.89
01570.10 SIGNS					
Construction signs, temporary					
Signs, 2' x 4'					
Minimum	EA.				33.25
Average	"				80.00
Maximum	"				280
Signs, 4' x 8'					
Minimum	EA.				70.00
Average	"				180
Maximum	"				780
Signs, 8' x 8'					
Minimum	EA.				90.00
Average	"				280
Maximum	"				2,900
01600.10 EQUIPMENT					
Air compressor					
60 cfm					
By day	EA.				88.00
By week	"				260
By month	"				790
Air tools, per compressor, per day					
Minimum	EA.				33.75
Average	"				42.25
Maximum	"				59.00
Generators, 5 kw					
By day	EA.				85.00
By week	"				250
By month	"				770
Heaters, salamander type, per week					

REQUIREMENTS

01600.10 EQUIPMENT, Cont'd...	UNIT	HOURS	MAT.	INST.	TOTAL
Minimum	EA.				100
Average	"				140
Maximum	"				300
Pumps, submersible					
50 gpm					
By day	EA.				68.00
By week	"				200
By month	"				610
Diaphragm pump, by week					
Minimum	EA.				120
Average	"				200
Maximum	"				420
Pickup truck					
By day	EA.				130
By week	"				370
By month	"				1,150
Dump truck					
6 cy truck					
By day	EA.				340
By week	"				1,010
By month	"				3,040
Backhoe/loader, rubber tired					
1/2 cy capacity					
By day	EA.				420
By week	"				1,270
By month	"				3,800
Bulldozer					
75 hp					
By day	EA.				590
By week	"				1,770
By month	"				5,320
Cranes, crawler type					
15 ton capacity					
By day	EA.				760
By week	"				2,280
By month	"				6,840
Truck mounted, hydraulic					
15 ton capacity					
By day	EA.				720
By week	"				2,150
By month	"				6,210
Loader, rubber tired					
1 cy capacity					
By day	EA.				510
By week	"				1,520
By month	"				4,560
01740.10 BONDS					
Performance bonds					
Minimum	PCT.				0.64
Average	"				2.01
Maximum	"				3.18

DEMOLITION

02220.00 SELECTIVE BUILDING DEMOLITION	UNIT	HOURS	MAT.	INST.	TOTAL
Cut-outs					
Concrete, elevated slabs, mesh reinforcing					
Under 5 cf	C.F.	0.800		39.50	39.50
Over 5 cf	"	0.667		32.75	32.75
Bar reinforcing					
Under 5 cf	C.F.	1.333		66.00	66.00
Over 5 cf	"	1.000		49.25	49.25
Rubbish handling					
Load in dumpster or truck					
Minimum	C.F.	0.018		0.87	0.87
Maximum	"	0.027		1.31	1.31
For use of elevators, add					
Minimum	C.F.	0.004		0.19	0.19
Maximum	"	0.008		0.39	0.39
Rubbish hauling					
Hand loaded on trucks, 2 mile trip	C.Y.	0.320		33.50	33.50
Machine loaded on trucks, 2 mile trip	"	0.240		21.75	21.75
02225.13 CORE DRILLING					
Concrete					
6" thick					
3" dia.	EA.	0.571		36.75	36.75
4" dia.	"	0.667		42.75	42.75
6" dia.	"	0.800		51.00	51.00
8" dia.	"	1.333		86.00	86.00
8" thick					
3" dia.	EA.	0.800		51.00	51.00
4" dia.	"	1.000		64.00	64.00
6" dia.	"	1.143		73.00	73.00
8" dia.	"	1.600		100	100
10" thick					
3" dia.	EA.	1.000		64.00	64.00
4" dia.	"	1.143		73.00	73.00
6" dia.	"	1.333		86.00	86.00
8" dia.	"	2.000		130	130
12" thick					
3" dia.	EA.	1.333		86.00	86.00
4" dia.	"	1.600		100	100
6" dia.	"	2.000		130	130
8" dia.	"	2.667		170	170
02250.10 TRENCH SHEETING					
Closed timber, including pull and salvage,					
8' deep	S.F.	0.064	3.24	7.55	10.79
20' deep	"	0.098	3.24	11.50	14.74

EARTHWORK, EXCAVATION & FILL

02315.30 BULK EXCAVATION	UNIT	HOURS	MAT.	INST.	TOTAL
Hydraulic excavator					
1 cy capacity					
Light material	C.Y.	0.040		3.61	3.61
Medium material	"	0.048		4.34	4.34
Wet material	"	0.060		5.42	5.42
Blasted rock	"	0.069		6.20	6.20

EARTHWORK, EXCAVATION & FILL

02315.30 BULK EXCAVATION, Cont'd...	UNIT	HOURS	MAT.	INST.	TOTAL
Wheel mounted front-end loader					
7/8 cy capacity					
Light material	C.Y.	0.020		2.89	2.89
Medium material	"	0.023		3.30	3.30
Wet material	"	0.027		3.85	3.85
Blasted rock	"	0.032		4.62	4.62
Track mounted front-end loader					
1-1/2 cy capacity					
Light material	C.Y.	0.013		1.92	1.92
Medium material	"	0.015		2.10	2.10
Wet material	"	0.016		2.31	2.31
Blasted rock	"	0.018		2.56	2.56
02315.40 BUILDING EXCAVATION					
Structural excavation, unclassified earth					
3/8 cy backhoe	C.Y.	0.107		15.50	15.50
3/4 cy backhoe	"	0.080		11.50	11.50
1 cy backhoe	"	0.067		9.63	9.63
Foundation backfill and compaction by	"	0.160		23.00	23.00
02315.45 HAND EXCAVATION					
Excavation					
To 2' deep					
Normal soil	C.Y.	0.889		43.75	43.75
Sand and gravel	"	0.800		39.50	39.50
Medium clay	"	1.000		49.25	49.25
Heavy clay	"	1.143		56.00	56.00
Loose rock	"	1.333		66.00	66.00
To 6' deep					
Normal soil	C.Y.	1.143		56.00	56.00
Sand and gravel	"	1.000		49.25	49.25
Medium clay	"	1.333		66.00	66.00
Heavy clay	"	1.600		79.00	79.00
Loose rock	"	2.000		99.00	99.00
Compaction of backfill around structures or in					
By hand with air tamper	C.Y.	0.571		28.25	28.25
By hand with vibrating plate tamper	"	0.533		26.25	26.25
1 ton roller	"	0.400		42.00	42.00
Miscellaneous hand labor					
Trim slopes, sides of excavation	S.F.	0.001		0.06	0.06
Trim bottom of excavation	"	0.002		0.07	0.07
Excavation around obstructions and	C.Y.	2.667		130	130
02315.60 TRENCHING					
Trenching and continuous footing excavation					
By gradall					
1 cy capacity					
Light soil	C.Y.	0.023		3.30	3.30
Medium soil	"	0.025		3.55	3.55
Heavy/wet soil	"	0.027		3.85	3.85
Loose rock	"	0.029		4.20	4.20
Blasted rock	"	0.031		4.44	4.44
By hydraulic excavator					
1/2 cy capacity					
Light soil	C.Y.	0.027		3.85	3.85
Medium soil	"	0.029		4.20	4.20

EARTHWORK, EXCAVATION & FILL

02315.60 TRENCHING, Cont'd...	UNIT	HOURS	MAT.	INST.	TOTAL
Heavy/wet soil	C.Y.	0.032		4.62	4.62
Loose rock	"	0.036		5.13	5.13
Blasted rock	"	0.040		5.78	5.78
Hand excavation					
Bulk, wheeled 100'					
Normal soil	C.Y.	0.889		43.75	43.75
Sand or gravel	"	0.800		39.50	39.50
Medium clay	"	1.143		56.00	56.00
Heavy clay	"	1.600		79.00	79.00
Loose rock	"	2.000		99.00	99.00
Trenches, up to 2' deep					
Normal soil	C.Y.	1.000		49.25	49.25
Sand or gravel	"	0.889		43.75	43.75
Medium clay	"	1.333		66.00	66.00
Heavy clay	"	2.000		99.00	99.00
Loose rock	"	2.667		130	130
Trenches, to 6' deep					
Normal soil	C.Y.	1.143		56.00	56.00
Sand or gravel	"	1.000		49.25	49.25
Medium clay	"	1.600		79.00	79.00
Heavy clay	"	2.667		130	130
Loose rock	"	4.000		200	200
Backfill trenches					
With compaction					
By hand	C.Y.	0.667		32.75	32.75
By 60 hp tracked dozer	"	0.020		2.10	2.10
By 200 hp tracked dozer	"	0.009		1.28	1.28
By small front-end loader	"	0.023		2.40	2.40
Backfill trenches, sand bedding, no					
By hand	C.Y.	0.667	13.00	32.75	45.75
By small front-end loader	"	0.023	13.00	3.30	16.30
02315.70 UTILITY EXCAVATION					
Trencher, sandy clay, 8" wide trench					
18" deep	L.F.	0.018		1.86	1.86
24" deep	"	0.020		2.10	2.10
36" deep	"	0.023		2.40	2.40
Trench backfill, 95% compaction					
Tamp by hand	C.Y.	0.500		24.50	24.50
Vibratory compaction	"	0.400		19.75	19.75
Trench backfilling, with borrow sand, place &	"	0.400	13.00	19.75	32.75
02315.80 HAULING MATERIAL					
Haul material by 10 cy dump truck, round trip					
1 mile	C.Y.	0.044		4.66	4.66
2 mile	"	0.053		5.60	5.60
5 mile	"	0.073		7.63	7.63
10 mile	"	0.080		8.40	8.40
20 mile	"	0.089		9.33	9.33
30 mile	"	0.107		11.25	11.25
Site grading, cut & fill, sandy clay, 200' haul,	"	0.032		3.36	3.36
Spread topsoil by equipment on site	"	0.036		3.73	3.73
Site grading (cut and fill to 6") less than 1 acre					
75 hp dozer	C.Y.	0.053		5.60	5.60
1.5 cy backhoe/loader	"	0.080		8.40	8.40

SOIL STABILIZATION & TREATMENT

02340.05 SOIL STABILIZATION	UNIT	HOURS	MAT.	INST.	TOTAL
Straw bale secured with rebar	L.F.	0.027	6.05	1.31	7.36
Filter barrier, 18" high filter fabric	"	0.080	1.82	3.94	5.76
Sediment fence, 36" fabric with 6" mesh	"	0.100	4.32	4.92	9.24

SANITARY SEWER

02530.30 MANHOLES	UNIT	HOURS	MAT.	INST.	TOTAL
Precast sections, 48" dia.					
Base section	EA.	2.000	330	180	510
1'0" riser	"	1.600	93.00	140	233
1'4" riser	"	1.714	110	160	270
2'8" riser	"	1.846	170	170	340
4'0" riser	"	2.000	310	180	490
2'8" cone top	"	2.400	200	220	420
Precast manholes, 48" dia.					
4' deep	EA.	4.800	760	430	1,190
6' deep	"	6.000	1,160	540	1,700
7' deep	"	6.857	1,320	620	1,940
8' deep	"	8.000	1,490	720	2,210
10' deep	"	9.600	1,670	870	2,540
Cast-in-place, 48" dia., with frame and cover					
5' deep	EA.	12.000	570	1,080	1,650
6' deep	"	13.714	750	1,240	1,990
8' deep	"	16.000	1,090	1,450	2,540
10' deep	"	19.200	1,270	1,740	3,010
Brick manholes, 48" dia. with cover, 8" thick					
4' deep	EA.	8.000	670	490	1,160
6' deep	"	8.889	840	540	1,380
8' deep	"	10.000	1,080	610	1,690
10' deep	"	11.429	1,350	700	2,050
12' deep	"	13.333	1,690	820	2,510
14' deep	"	16.000	2,050	980	3,030
Frames and covers, 24" diameter					
300 lb	EA.	0.800	390	39.50	430
400 lb	"	0.889	410	43.75	454
500 lb	"	1.143	480	56.00	536
Watertight, 350 lb	"	2.667	500	130	630
For heavy equipment, 1200 lb	"	4.000	1,080	200	1,280
Steps for manholes					
7" x 9"	EA.	0.160	13.25	7.88	21.13
8" x 9"	"	0.178	16.75	8.75	25.50

POWER & COMMUNICATIONS

02580.20 HIGH VOLTAGE CABLE	UNIT	HOURS	MAT.	INST.	TOTAL
High voltage XLP copper cable, shielded,					
#6 awg	L.F.	0.013	2.25	0.84	3.09
#4 awg	"	0.016	2.58	1.03	3.61
#2 awg	"	0.019	3.37	1.23	4.60
#1 awg	"	0.021	3.56	1.36	4.92
#1/0 awg	"	0.024	4.22	1.54	5.76
#2/0 awg	"	0.029	7.10	1.88	8.98
#3/0 awg	"	0.034	7.22	2.20	9.42
#4/0 awg	"	0.036	7.60	2.35	9.95

POWER & COMMUNICATIONS

02580.20 HIGH VOLTAGE CABLE, Cont'd...	UNIT	HOURS	MAT.	INST.	TOTAL
#250 awg	L.F.	0.043	8.81	2.80	11.61
#300 awg	"	0.048	10.00	3.14	13.14
#350 awg	"	0.053	11.25	3.45	14.70
#500 awg	"	0.073	16.25	4.71	20.96
#750 awg	"	0.080	23.75	5.18	28.93
Ungrounded, 15,000v					
#1 awg	L.F.	0.031	5.39	1.99	7.38
#1/0 awg	"	0.034	6.36	2.20	8.56
#2/0 awg	"	0.036	7.29	2.35	9.64
#3/0 awg	"	0.040	8.43	2.59	11.02
#4/0 awg	"	0.046	9.31	2.96	12.27
#250 awg	"	0.048	10.50	3.14	13.64
#300 awg	"	0.053	11.75	3.45	15.20
#350 awg	"	0.062	13.25	3.98	17.23
#500 awg	"	0.080	17.25	5.18	22.43
#750 awg	"	0.098	25.75	6.32	32.07
#1000 awg	"	0.123	37.75	7.97	45.72
Aluminum cable, shielded, 5000v					
#6 awg	L.F.	0.011	1.83	0.71	2.54
#4 awg	"	0.013	1.99	0.84	2.83
#2 awg	"	0.015	2.21	0.96	3.17
#1 awg	"	0.017	2.43	1.10	3.53
#1/0 awg	"	0.019	2.66	1.23	3.89
#2/0 awg	"	0.020	2.95	1.29	4.24
#3/0 awg	"	0.021	3.36	1.36	4.72
#4/0 awg	"	0.024	3.72	1.54	5.26
#250 awg	"	0.026	3.97	1.67	5.64
#300 awg	"	0.031	4.33	1.99	6.32
#350 awg	"	0.034	4.69	2.20	6.89
#500 awg	"	0.036	5.65	2.35	8.00
#750 awg	"	0.044	7.31	2.88	10.19
#1000 awg	"	0.050	8.25	3.24	11.49
Ungrounded, 15,000v					
#1 awg	L.F.	0.021	3.32	1.36	4.68
#1/0 awg	"	0.025	3.50	1.62	5.12
#2/0 awg	"	0.027	3.78	1.75	5.53
#3/0 awg	"	0.028	4.13	1.81	5.94
#4/0 awg	"	0.029	4.48	1.88	6.36
#250 awg	"	0.031	4.80	1.99	6.79
#300 awg	"	0.032	5.20	2.07	7.27
#350 awg	"	0.036	5.59	2.35	7.94
#500 awg	"	0.043	6.56	2.80	9.36
#750 awg	"	0.052	8.60	3.34	11.94
#1000 awg	"	0.064	11.25	4.14	15.39
Indoor terminations, 5000v					
#6 - #4	EA.	0.157	69.00	10.25	79.25
#2 - #2/0	"	0.157	81.00	10.25	91.25
#3/0 - #250	"	0.157	100	10.25	110
#300 - #750	"	2.759	120	180	300
#1000	"	3.810	140	250	390
In-line splice, 5000v					
#6 - #4/0	EA.	3.810	150	250	400
#250 - #500	"	10.000	160	650	810

POWER & COMMUNICATIONS

02580.20 HIGH VOLTAGE CABLE, Cont'd...	UNIT	HOURS	MAT.	INST.	TOTAL
#750 - #1000	EA.	13.008	220	840	1,060
T-splice, 5000v					
#2 - #4/0	EA.	11.994	150	780	930
#250 - #500	"	20.000	160	1,300	1,460
#750 - #1000	"	25.000	220	1,620	1,840
Indoor terminations, 15,000v					
#2 - #2/0	EA.	3.478	92.00	230	322
#3/0 - #500	"	5.333	120	350	470
#750 - #1000	"	6.154	140	400	540
In-line splice, 15,000v					
#2 - #4/0	EA.	8.999	160	580	740
#250 - #500	"	11.994	220	780	1,000
#750 - #1000	"	18.018	280	1,170	1,450
T-splice, 15,000v					
#4	EA.	18.018	160	1,170	1,330
#250 - #500	"	29.963	220	1,940	2,160
#750 - #1000	"	44.944	280	2,910	3,190
Compression lugs, 15,000v					
#4	EA.	0.400	11.00	26.00	37.00
#2	"	0.533	12.50	34.50	47.00
#1	"	0.533	13.75	34.50	48.25
#1/0	"	0.667	21.00	43.25	64.25
#2/0	"	0.667	22.00	43.25	65.25
#3/0	"	0.851	24.75	55.00	79.75
#4/0	"	0.851	27.25	55.00	82.25
#250	"	0.952	31.75	62.00	93.75
#300	"	0.952	37.00	62.00	99.00
#350	"	1.159	38.00	75.00	113
#500	"	1.250	58.00	81.00	139
#750	"	1.509	92.00	98.00	190
#1000	"	1.905	130	120	250
Compression splices, 15,000v					
#4	EA.	0.667	12.25	43.25	55.50
#2	"	0.727	13.50	47.00	60.50
#1	"	0.899	15.25	58.00	73.25
#1/0	"	1.000	16.25	65.00	81.25
#2/0	"	1.159	17.50	75.00	92.50
#3/0	"	1.250	19.00	81.00	100
#4/0	"	1.404	20.75	91.00	112
#250	"	1.509	22.75	98.00	121
#350	"	1.739	25.75	110	136
#500	"	2.000	38.25	130	168
#750	"	2.500	63.00	160	223
02580.40 SUPPORTS & CONNECTORS					
Cable supports for conduit					
1-1/2"	EA.	0.348	70.00	22.50	92.50
2"	"	0.348	97.00	22.50	120
2-1/2"	"	0.400	110	26.00	136
3"	"	0.400	140	26.00	166
3-1/2"	"	0.500	180	32.50	213
4"	"	0.500	220	32.50	253
5"	"	0.667	400	43.25	443
6"	"	0.727	840	47.00	887

POWER & COMMUNICATIONS

02580.40 SUPPORTS & CONNECTORS, Cont'd...	UNIT	HOURS	MAT.	INST.	TOTAL
Split bolt connectors					
#10	EA.	0.200	2.14	13.00	15.14
#8	"	0.200	2.53	13.00	15.53
#6	"	0.200	2.79	13.00	15.79
#4	"	0.400	3.25	26.00	29.25
#3	"	0.400	4.65	26.00	30.65
#2	"	0.400	5.26	26.00	31.26
#1/0	"	0.667	6.85	43.25	50.10
#2/0	"	0.667	10.75	43.25	54.00
#3/0	"	0.667	16.50	43.25	59.75
#4/0	"	0.667	18.75	43.25	62.00
#250	"	1.000	19.25	65.00	84.25
#350	"	1.000	34.25	65.00	99.25
#500	"	1.000	44.75	65.00	110
#750	"	1.509	76.00	98.00	174
#1000	"	1.509	100	98.00	198
Single barrel lugs					
#6	EA.	0.250	0.75	16.25	17.00
#1/0	"	0.500	1.48	32.50	33.98
#250	"	0.667	3.58	43.25	46.83
#350	"	0.667	4.65	43.25	47.90
#500	"	0.667	8.99	43.25	52.24
#600	"	0.899	9.52	58.00	67.52
#800	"	0.899	10.75	58.00	68.75
#1000	"	0.899	13.00	58.00	71.00
Double barrel lugs					
#1/0	EA.	0.899	2.92	58.00	60.92
#250	"	1.290	8.54	84.00	92.54
#350	"	1.290	12.25	84.00	96.25
#600	"	1.905	18.50	120	139
#800	"	1.905	21.00	120	141
#1000	"	1.905	21.50	120	142
Three barrel lugs					
#2/0	EA.	1.290	23.50	84.00	108
#250	"	1.905	45.00	120	165
#350	"	1.905	74.00	120	194
#600	"	2.667	81.00	170	251
#800	"	2.667	130	170	300
#1000	"	2.667	180	170	350
Four barrel lugs					
#250	EA.	2.759	50.00	180	230
#350	"	2.759	84.00	180	264
#600	"	3.478	91.00	230	321
#800	"	3.478	140	230	370
Compression conductor adapters					
#6	EA.	0.296	6.49	19.25	25.74
#4	"	0.348	6.85	22.50	29.35
#2	"	0.444	7.15	28.75	35.90
#1	"	0.444	8.23	28.75	36.98
#1/0	"	0.533	8.54	34.50	43.04
#250	"	0.800	16.25	52.00	68.25
#350	"	0.851	19.25	55.00	74.25
#500	"	1.096	25.25	71.00	96.25

POWER & COMMUNICATIONS

02580.40 SUPPORTS & CONNECTORS, Cont'd...	UNIT	HOURS	MAT.	INST.	TOTAL
#750	EA.	1.143	34.50	74.00	109
Terminal blocks, 2 screw					
3 circuit	EA.	0.200	18.75	13.00	31.75
6 circuit	"	0.200	25.75	13.00	38.75
8 circuit	"	0.200	30.00	13.00	43.00
10 circuit	"	0.296	34.75	19.25	54.00
12 circuit	"	0.296	39.25	19.25	58.50
18 circuit	"	0.296	53.00	19.25	72.25
24 circuit	"	0.348	67.00	22.50	89.50
36 circuit	"	0.348	94.00	22.50	117
Compression splice					
#8 awg	EA.	0.381	3.16	24.75	27.91
#6 awg	"	0.276	3.76	17.75	21.51
#4 awg	"	0.276	3.98	17.75	21.73
#2 awg	"	0.533	6.17	34.50	40.67
#1 awg	"	0.533	8.67	34.50	43.17
#1/0 awg	"	0.533	10.50	34.50	45.00
#2/0 awg	"	0.851	11.25	55.00	66.25
#3/0 awg	"	0.851	13.25	55.00	68.25
#4/0 awg	"	0.851	14.00	55.00	69.00
#250 awg	"	1.356	14.75	88.00	103
#300 awg	"	1.356	16.25	88.00	104
#350 awg	"	1.404	16.50	91.00	108
#400 awg	"	1.404	22.25	91.00	113
#500 awg	"	1.509	26.25	98.00	124
#600 awg	"	1.509	39.75	98.00	138
#750 awg	"	1.739	42.00	110	152
#1000 awg	"	1.739	54.00	110	164

FORMWORK

03100.00 ELEVATED SLAB FORMWORK	UNIT	HOURS	MAT.	INST.	TOTAL
Elevated slab formwork					
Slab, with drop panels					
1 use	S.F.	0.064	3.56	4.05	7.61
5 uses	"	0.055	1.27	3.49	4.76
Floor slab, hung from steel beams					
1 use	S.F.	0.062	2.86	3.89	6.75
5 uses	"	0.053	1.06	3.37	4.43
Floor slab, with pans or domes					
1 use	S.F.	0.073	5.10	4.60	9.70
5 uses	"	0.062	2.55	3.89	6.44
Equipment curbs, 12" high					
1 use	L.F.	0.080	2.64	5.06	7.70
5 uses	"	0.067	1.11	4.22	5.33
03110.25 EQUIPMENT PAD FORMWORK					
Equipment pad, job built					
1 use	S.F.	0.100	3.46	6.33	9.79
2 uses	"	0.094	2.07	5.96	8.03
3 uses	"	0.089	1.66	5.63	7.29
4 uses	"	0.084	1.29	5.33	6.62
5 uses	"	0.080	1.05	5.06	6.11
03110.35 FOOTING FORMWORK					
Wall footings, job built, continuous					
1 use	S.F.	0.080	1.62	5.06	6.68
5 uses	"	0.067	0.72	4.22	4.94
Column footings, spread					
1 use	S.F.	0.100	1.71	6.33	8.04
5 uses	"	0.080	0.69	5.06	5.75
03110.55 SLAB / MAT FORMWORK					
Edge forms					
6" high					
1 use	L.F.	0.073	2.54	4.60	7.14
5 uses	"	0.062	0.72	3.89	4.61
12" high					
1 use	L.F.	0.080	2.38	5.06	7.44
5 uses	"	0.067	0.68	4.22	4.90
Formwork for openings					
1 use	S.F.	0.160	3.47	10.25	13.72
5 uses	"	0.114	1.06	7.24	8.30
03110.65 WALL FORMWORK					
Wall forms, exterior, job built					
Up to 8' high wall					
1 use	S.F.	0.080	2.81	5.06	7.87
5 uses	"	0.067	1.02	4.22	5.24
Over 8' high wall					
1 use	S.F.	0.100	3.09	6.33	9.42
5 uses	"	0.080	1.27	5.06	6.33
Column pier and pilaster					
1 use	S.F.	0.160	3.09	10.25	13.34
5 uses	"	0.114	1.39	7.24	8.63
Interior wall forms					
Up to 8' high					
1 use	S.F.	0.073	2.81	4.60	7.41

FORMWORK

03110.65 WALL FORMWORK, Cont'd...	UNIT	HOURS	MAT.	INST.	TOTAL
5 uses	S.F.	0.062	1.01	3.89	4.90
Over 8' high					
1 use	S.F.	0.089	3.09	5.63	8.72
5 uses	"	0.073	1.28	4.60	5.88

REINFORCEMENT

03210.20 ELEVATED SLAB REINFORCING	UNIT	HOURS	MAT.	INST.	TOTAL
Elevated slab					
#3 - #4	TON	10.000	1,220	700	1,920
#5 - #6	"	8.889	1,070	630	1,700
Galvanized					
#3 - #4	TON	10.000	1,990	700	2,690
#5 - #6	"	8.889	1,960	630	2,590

03210.25 EQUIP. PAD REINFORCING	UNIT	HOURS	MAT.	INST.	TOTAL
Equipment pad					
#3 - #4	TON	16.000	1,220	1,130	2,350
#5 - #6	"	14.545	1,070	1,030	2,100
#7 - #8	"	13.333	1,020	940	1,960
#9 - #10	"	12.308	1,020	870	1,890
#11 - #12	"	11.429	1,020	810	1,830

03210.35 FOOTING REINFORCING	UNIT	HOURS	MAT.	INST.	TOTAL
Footings					
#3 - #4	TON	13.333	1,220	940	2,160
#5 - #6	"	11.429	1,070	810	1,880
Straight dowels, 24" long					
1" dia. (#8)	EA.	0.080	3.79	5.64	9.43
3/4" dia. (#6)	"	0.080	3.42	5.64	9.06
5/8" dia. (#5)	"	0.067	2.95	4.70	7.65
1/2" dia. (#4)	"	0.057	2.22	4.02	6.24

03210.55 SLAB / MAT REINFORCING	UNIT	HOURS	MAT.	INST.	TOTAL
Bars, slabs					
#3 - #4	TON	13.333	1,220	940	2,160
#5 - #6	"	11.429	1,070	810	1,880
#7 - #8	"	10.000	1,020	700	1,720
Galvanized					
#3 - #4	TON	13.333	2,080	940	3,020
#5 - #6	"	11.429	1,960	810	2,770
Wire mesh, slabs					
Galvanized					
4x4					
W1.4xW1.4	S.F.	0.005	0.30	0.37	0.67
W2.0xW2.0	"	0.006	0.39	0.40	0.79
W2.9xW2.9	"	0.006	0.55	0.43	0.98
W4.0xW4.0	"	0.007	0.81	0.47	1.28
6x6					
W1.4xW1.4	S.F.	0.004	0.28	0.28	0.56
W2.0xW2.0	"	0.004	0.39	0.31	0.70
W2.9xW2.9	"	0.005	0.53	0.33	0.86
W4.0xW4.0	"	0.005	0.57	0.37	0.94

REINFORCEMENT

03210.65 WALL REINFORCING	UNIT	HOURS	MAT.	INST.	TOTAL
Walls					
#3 - #4	TON	11.429	1,220	810	2,030
#5 - #6	"	10.000	1,070	700	1,770
Galvanized					
#3 - #4	TON	11.429	2,080	810	2,890
#5 - #6	"	10.000	1,960	700	2,660
Masonry wall (horizontal)					
#3 - #4	TON	32.000	1,220	2,260	3,480
#5 - #6	"	26.667	1,070	1,880	2,950
Galvanized					
#3 - #4	TON	32.000	2,080	2,260	4,340
#5 - #6	"	26.667	1,960	1,880	3,840
Masonry wall (vertical)					
#3 - #4	TON	40.000	1,220	2,820	4,040
#5 - #6	"	32.000	1,070	2,260	3,330
Galvanized					
#3 - #4	TON	40.000	2,080	2,820	4,900
#5 - #6	"	32.000	1,960	2,260	4,220

PLACING CONCRETE

03380.20 ELEVATED SLAB CONCRETE	UNIT	HOURS	MAT.	INST.	TOTAL
Elevated slab					
2500# or 3000# concrete					
By crane	C.Y.	0.480	110	39.25	149
By pump	"	0.369	110	30.00	140
By hand buggy	"	0.800	110	39.50	150
5000# concrete					
By crane	C.Y.	0.480	120	39.25	159
By pump	"	0.369	120	30.00	150
By hand buggy	"	0.800	120	39.50	160
03380.25 EQUIPMENT PAD CONCRETE					
Equipment pad					
2500# or 3000# concrete					
By chute	C.Y.	0.267	110	13.25	123
By pump	"	0.686	110	56.00	166
By crane	"	0.800	110	65.00	175
3500# or 4000# concrete					
By chute	C.Y.	0.267	110	13.25	123
By pump	"	0.686	110	56.00	166
By crane	"	0.800	110	65.00	175
5000# concrete					
By chute	C.Y.	0.267	120	13.25	133
By pump	"	0.686	120	56.00	176
By crane	"	0.800	120	65.00	185
03380.35 FOOTING CONCRETE					
Continuous footing					
2500# or 3000# concrete					
By chute	C.Y.	0.267	110	13.25	123
By pump	"	0.600	110	49.00	159
By crane	"	0.686	110	56.00	166
5000# concrete					
By chute	C.Y.	0.267	120	13.25	133

PLACING CONCRETE

03380.35 FOOTING CONCRETE, Cont'd...	UNIT	HOURS	MAT.	INST.	TOTAL
By pump	C.Y.	0.600	120	49.00	169
By crane	"	0.686	120	56.00	176
Spread footing					
2500# or 3000# concrete					
Under 5 cy					
By chute	C.Y.	0.267	100	13.25	113
By pump	"	0.640	100	52.00	152
By crane	"	0.738	100	60.00	160
5000# concrete					
Under 5 c.y.					
By chute	C.Y.	0.267	120	13.25	133
By pump	"	0.640	120	52.00	172
By crane	"	0.738	120	60.00	180
03380.55 SLAB / MAT CONCRETE					
Slab on grade					
2500# or 3000# concrete					
By chute	C.Y.	0.200	110	9.85	120
By crane	"	0.400	110	32.50	143
By pump	"	0.343	110	28.00	138
By hand buggy	"	0.533	110	26.25	136
5000# concrete					
By chute	C.Y.	0.200	120	9.85	130
By crane	"	0.400	120	32.50	153
By pump	"	0.343	120	28.00	148
By hand buggy	"	0.533	120	26.25	146
03380.65 WALL CONCRETE					
Walls					
2500# or 3000# concrete					
To 4'					
By chute	C.Y.	0.229	110	11.25	121
By crane	"	0.800	110	65.00	175
By pump	"	0.738	110	60.00	170
To 8'					
By crane	C.Y.	0.873	110	71.00	181
By pump	"	0.800	110	65.00	175
Filled block (CMU)					
3000# concrete, by pump					
4" wide	S.F.	0.034	0.39	2.79	3.18
6" wide	"	0.040	0.90	3.26	4.16
8" wide	"	0.048	1.40	3.91	5.31
10" wide	"	0.056	1.89	4.60	6.49
12" wide	"	0.069	2.43	5.59	8.02
Pilasters, 3000# concrete	C.F.	0.960	5.50	78.00	83.50
Wall cavity, 2" thick, 3000# concrete	S.F.	0.032	1.02	2.60	3.62

MORTAR AND GROUT

04100.00 MASONRY GROUT	UNIT	HOURS	MAT.	INST.	TOTAL
Grout, non shrink, non-metallic, trowelable	C.F.	0.016	4.95	1.44	6.39
Grout-filled individual CMU cells					
4" wide	L.F.	0.012	0.27	1.08	1.35
8" wide	"	0.012	0.49	1.08	1.57
04150.50 MASONRY FLASHING					
Through-wall flashing					
5 oz. coated copper	S.F.	0.067	3.35	4.08	7.43
0.030" elastomeric	"	0.053	1.10	3.26	4.36

UNIT MASONRY

04210.10 BRICK MASONRY	UNIT	HOURS	MAT.	INST.	TOTAL
Standard size brick, running bond					
Face brick, red (6.4/sf)					
Veneer	S.F.	0.133	5.39	8.17	13.56
Cavity wall	"	0.114	5.39	7.00	12.39
9" solid wall	"	0.229	10.75	14.00	24.75
Chimney, standard brick, including flue					
16" x 16"	L.F.	0.800	37.75	49.00	86.75
20" x 20"	"	1.000	62.00	61.00	123
04220.10 CONCRETE MASONRY UNITS					
Hollow, load bearing					
4"	S.F.	0.059	1.37	3.63	5.00
8"	"	0.067	2.31	4.08	6.39
Solid, load bearing					
4"	S.F.	0.059	2.15	3.63	5.78
8"	"	0.067	3.30	4.08	7.38
Back-up block, 8" x 16"					
4"	S.F.	0.047	1.37	2.88	4.25
8"	"	0.053	2.31	3.26	5.57
Steel angles and plates					
Minimum	Lb.	0.011	1.04	0.70	1.74
Maximum	"	0.020	1.54	1.22	2.76
Various size angle lintels					
1/4" stock					
3" x 3"	L.F.	0.050	5.66	3.06	8.72
3" x 3-1/2"	"	0.050	6.23	3.06	9.29
3/8" stock					
3" x 4"	L.F.	0.050	9.82	3.06	12.88
4" x 4"	"	0.050	11.25	3.06	14.31
1/2" stock					
6" x 4"	L.F.	0.050	15.00	3.06	18.06
04295.10 PARGING / MASONRY PLASTER					
Parging					
1/2" thick	S.F.	0.053	0.29	3.26	3.55
3/4" thick	"	0.067	0.37	4.08	4.45

MASONRY RESTORATION

04520.10 RESTORATION AND CLEANING	UNIT	HOURS	MAT.	INST.	TOTAL
Masonry cleaning					
Washing brick					
Smooth surface	S.F.	0.013	0.42	0.81	1.23
Rough surface	"	0.018	0.59	1.08	1.67

MASONRY RESTORATION

04520.10 RESTORATION AND CLEANING, Cont'd...	UNIT	HOURS	MAT.	INST.	TOTAL
Pointing masonry					
Brick	S.F.	0.032	1.35	1.96	3.31
Concrete block	"	0.023	0.60	1.40	2.00
Brick removal and replacement					
Minimum	EA.	0.100	0.68	6.13	6.81
Average	"	0.133	0.89	8.17	9.06
Maximum	"	0.400	1.80	24.50	26.30
04550.10 REFRACTORIES					
Flue liners					
Rectangular					
8" x 12"	L.F.	0.133	7.53	8.17	15.70
12" x 12"	"	0.145	9.40	8.91	18.31
Round					
18" dia.	L.F.	0.190	34.00	11.75	45.75
24" dia.	"	0.229	67.00	14.00	81.00

METAL FASTENING

05050.00 STRUCTURAL WELDING	UNIT	HOURS	MAT.	INST.	TOTAL
Welding					
Single pass					
1/8"	L.F.	0.040	0.33	2.82	3.15
3/16"	"	0.053	0.55	3.76	4.31
1/4"	"	0.067	0.77	4.70	5.47
Miscellaneous steel shapes					
Plain	Lb.	0.002	1.44	0.11	1.55
Galvanized	"	0.003	1.80	0.18	1.98
Plates					
Plain	Lb.	0.002	1.29	0.14	1.43
Galvanized	"	0.003	1.66	0.22	1.88

05050.90 METAL ANCHORS	UNIT	HOURS	MAT.	INST.	TOTAL
Anchor bolts					
3/8" x					
8" long	EA.				0.97
10" long	"				1.06
12" long	"				1.16
1/2" x					
8" long	EA.				1.46
10" long	"				1.56
12" long	"				1.70
18" long	"				1.85
Add 25% for galvanized anchor bolts					

05050.95 METAL LINTELS	UNIT	HOURS	MAT.	INST.	TOTAL
Lintels, steel					
Plain	Lb.	0.020	1.33	1.41	2.74
Galvanized	"	0.020	2.00	1.41	3.41

COLD FORMED FRAMING

05410.10 METAL FRAMING	UNIT	HOURS	MAT.	INST.	TOTAL
Furring channel, galvanized					
Beams and columns, 3/4"					
12" o.c.	S.F.	0.080	0.51	5.64	6.15
16" o.c.	"	0.073	0.39	5.12	5.51
Walls, 3/4"					
12" o.c.	S.F.	0.040	0.51	2.82	3.33
16" o.c.	"	0.033	0.39	2.35	2.74
Stud, load bearing					
16" o.c.					
16 ga.					
2-1/2"	S.F.	0.036	1.76	2.50	4.26
3-5/8"	"	0.036	1.98	2.50	4.48
24" o.c.					
16 ga.					
2-1/2"	S.F.	0.031	1.23	2.16	3.39
3-5/8"	"	0.031	1.38	2.16	3.54

BNi Building News

FASTENERS AND ADHESIVES

06050.00 ACCESSORIES	UNIT	HOURS	MAT.	INST.	TOTAL
Anchors					
Bolts, threaded two ends, with nuts and					
1/2" dia.					
4" long	EA.	0.050	1.92	3.16	5.08
7-1/2" long	"	0.050	2.03	3.16	5.19
3/4" dia.					
7-1/2" long	EA.	0.050	3.30	3.16	6.46
15" long	"	0.050	4.34	3.16	7.50
Bolts, carriage					
1/4 x 4	EA.	0.080	1.72	5.06	6.78
5/16 x 6	"	0.084	1.80	5.33	7.13
3/8 x 6	"	0.084	2.04	5.33	7.37
1/2 x 6	"	0.084	2.20	5.33	7.53
Joist and beam hangers					
18 ga.					
2 x 4	EA.	0.080	2.14	5.06	7.20
2 x 6	"	0.080	2.79	5.06	7.85
2 x 8	"	0.080	3.24	5.06	8.30
2 x 10	"	0.089	3.74	5.63	9.37
2 x 12	"	0.100	4.34	6.33	10.67
Strap ties, 14 ga., 1-3/8" wide					
12" long	EA.	0.067	1.85	4.22	6.07
18" long	"	0.073	2.03	4.60	6.63
24" long	"	0.080	2.54	5.06	7.60
36" long	"	0.089	3.87	5.63	9.50

ROUGH CARPENTRY

06110.10 BLOCKING	UNIT	HOURS	MAT.	INST.	TOTAL
Steel construction					
Walls					
2x4	L.F.	0.053	0.62	3.37	3.99
2x6	"	0.062	0.88	3.89	4.77
2x8	"	0.067	1.26	4.22	5.48
2x10	"	0.073	1.73	4.60	6.33
2x12	"	0.080	2.29	5.06	7.35
Ceilings					
2x4	L.F.	0.062	0.62	3.89	4.51
2x6	"	0.073	0.88	4.60	5.48
2x8	"	0.080	1.26	5.06	6.32
2x10	"	0.089	1.73	5.63	7.36
2x12	"	0.100	2.29	6.33	8.62
Wood construction					
Walls					
2x4	L.F.	0.044	0.62	2.81	3.43
2x6	"	0.050	0.88	3.16	4.04
2x8	"	0.053	1.26	3.37	4.63
2x10	"	0.057	1.73	3.62	5.35
2x12	"	0.062	2.29	3.89	6.18
Ceilings					
2x4	L.F.	0.050	0.62	3.16	3.78
2x6	"	0.057	0.88	3.62	4.50
2x8	"	0.062	1.26	3.89	5.15
2x10	"	0.067	1.73	4.22	5.95

ROUGH CARPENTRY

06110.10 BLOCKING, Cont'd...	UNIT	HOURS	MAT.	INST.	TOTAL
2x12	L.F.	0.073	2.29	4.60	6.89
06110.20 CEILING FRAMING					
Ceiling joists					
12" o.c.					
2x4	S.F.	0.019	0.75	1.20	1.95
2x8	"	0.021	1.55	1.33	2.88
16" o.c.					
2x4	S.F.	0.015	0.62	0.97	1.59
2x8	"	0.017	1.32	1.05	2.37
Sister joists for ceilings					
2x4	L.F.	0.057	0.62	3.62	4.24
2x6	"	0.067	0.88	4.22	5.10
2x8	"	0.080	1.26	5.06	6.32
2x10	"	0.100	1.73	6.33	8.06
2x12	"	0.133	2.29	8.44	10.73
06110.30 FLOOR FRAMING					
Floor joists					
12" o.c.					
2x6	S.F.	0.016	1.10	1.01	2.11
2x8	"	0.016	1.55	1.03	2.58
2x10	"	0.017	2.35	1.05	3.40
2x12	"	0.017	3.12	1.10	4.22
16" o.c.					
2x6	S.F.	0.013	0.94	0.84	1.78
2x8	"	0.014	1.32	0.85	2.17
2x10	"	0.014	1.95	0.87	2.82
2x12	"	0.014	2.53	0.90	3.43
Sister joists for floors					
2x4	L.F.	0.050	0.62	3.16	3.78
2x6	"	0.057	0.88	3.62	4.50
2x8	"	0.067	1.26	4.22	5.48
2x10	"	0.080	1.73	5.06	6.79
2x12	"	0.100	2.29	6.33	8.62
3x6	"	0.080	2.12	5.06	7.18
3x8	"	0.089	2.76	5.63	8.39
3x10	"	0.100	3.44	6.33	9.77
3x12	"	0.114	4.11	7.24	11.35
4x6	"	0.080	2.67	5.06	7.73
4x8	"	0.089	3.68	5.63	9.31
4x10	"	0.100	4.58	6.33	10.91
4x12	"	0.114	5.42	7.24	12.66
06110.40 FURRING					
Furring, wood strips					
Walls					
On masonry or concrete walls					
1x2 furring					
12" o.c.	S.F.	0.025	0.29	1.58	1.87
16" o.c.	"	0.023	0.24	1.44	1.68
24" o.c.	"	0.021	0.20	1.33	1.53
1x3 furring					
12" o.c.	S.F.	0.025	0.42	1.58	2.00
16" o.c.	"	0.023	0.36	1.44	1.80
24" o.c.	"	0.021	0.29	1.33	1.62

ROUGH CARPENTRY

06110.40 FURRING, Cont'd...	UNIT	HOURS	MAT.	INST.	TOTAL
On wood walls					
1x2 furring					
12" o.c.	S.F.	0.018	0.29	1.12	1.41
16" o.c.	"	0.016	0.24	1.01	1.25
24" o.c.	"	0.015	0.20	0.92	1.12
1x3 furring					
12" o.c.	S.F.	0.018	0.42	1.12	1.54
16" o.c.	"	0.016	0.36	1.01	1.37
24" o.c.	"	0.015	0.29	0.92	1.21
Ceilings					
On masonry or concrete ceilings					
1x2 furring					
12" o.c.	S.F.	0.044	0.29	2.81	3.10
16" o.c.	"	0.040	0.24	2.53	2.77
24" o.c.	"	0.036	0.20	2.30	2.50
1x3 furring					
12" o.c.	S.F.	0.044	0.42	2.81	3.23
16" o.c.	"	0.040	0.36	2.53	2.89
24" o.c.	"	0.036	0.29	2.30	2.59
On wood ceilings					
1x2 furring					
12" o.c.	S.F.	0.030	0.29	1.87	2.16
16" o.c.	"	0.027	0.24	1.68	1.92
24" o.c.	"	0.024	0.20	1.53	1.73
1x3					
12" o.c.	S.F.	0.030	0.42	1.87	2.29
16" o.c.	"	0.027	0.36	1.68	2.04
24" o.c.	"	0.024	0.29	1.53	1.82
06110.50 ROOF FRAMING					
Roof framing					
Rafters, gable end					
0-2 pitch (flat to 2-in-12)					
12" o.c.					
2x4	S.F.	0.017	0.75	1.05	1.80
2x6	"	0.017	1.12	1.10	2.22
2x8	"	0.018	1.55	1.15	2.70
16" o.c.					
2x6	S.F.	0.014	0.94	0.90	1.84
2x8	"	0.015	1.32	0.93	2.25
Sister rafters					
2x4	L.F.	0.057	0.62	3.62	4.24
2x6	"	0.067	0.88	4.22	5.10
2x8	"	0.080	1.26	5.06	6.32
2x10	"	0.100	1.73	6.33	8.06
2x12	"	0.133	2.29	8.44	10.73
06110.60 SLEEPERS					
Sleepers, over concrete					
12" o.c.					
1x2	S.F.	0.018	0.26	1.15	1.41
1x3	"	0.019	0.36	1.20	1.56
2x4	"	0.022	0.75	1.40	2.15
2x6	"	0.024	1.10	1.49	2.59
16" o.c.					

ROUGH CARPENTRY

06110.60 SLEEPERS, Cont'd...	UNIT	HOURS	MAT.	INST.	TOTAL
1x2	S.F.	0.016	0.21	1.01	1.22
1x3	"	0.016	0.30	1.01	1.31
2x4	"	0.019	0.62	1.20	1.82
2x6	"	0.020	0.94	1.26	2.20
06110.65 SOFFITS					
Soffit framing					
2x3	L.F.	0.057	0.49	3.62	4.11
2x4	"	0.062	0.62	3.89	4.51
2x6	"	0.067	0.88	4.22	5.10
2x8	"	0.073	1.26	4.60	5.86
06110.70 WALL FRAMING					
Framing wall, studs					
12" o.c.					
2x3	S.F.	0.015	0.53	0.93	1.46
2x4	"	0.015	0.75	0.93	1.68
16" o.c.					
2x3	S.F.	0.013	0.46	0.79	1.25
2x4	"	0.013	0.62	0.79	1.41
24" o.c.					
2x3	S.F.	0.011	0.34	0.68	1.02
2x4	"	0.011	0.50	0.68	1.18
Plates, top or bottom					
2x3	L.F.	0.024	0.49	1.49	1.98
2x4	"	0.025	0.62	1.58	2.20
Headers, door or window					
2x6					
Single					
3' long	EA.	0.400	2.83	25.25	28.08
6' long	"	0.500	5.69	31.75	37.44
Double					
3' long	EA.	0.444	5.69	28.25	33.94
6' long	"	0.571	11.25	36.25	47.50
2x8					
Single					
4' long	EA.	0.500	5.26	31.75	37.01
8' long	"	0.615	10.50	39.00	49.50
Double					
4' long	EA.	0.571	10.50	36.25	46.75
8' long	"	0.727	21.00	46.00	67.00
2x10					
Single					
5' long	EA.	0.615	9.80	39.00	48.80
10' long	"	0.800	19.50	51.00	70.50
Double					
5' long	EA.	0.667	19.50	42.25	61.75
10' long	"	0.800	39.25	51.00	90.25
06115.10 FLOOR SHEATHING					
Sub-flooring, plywood, CDX					
1/2" thick	S.F.	0.010	0.69	0.63	1.32
5/8" thick	"	0.011	0.83	0.72	1.55
3/4" thick	"	0.013	0.98	0.84	1.82
Structural plywood					
1/2" thick	S.F.	0.010	0.77	0.63	1.40

ROUGH CARPENTRY

06115.10 FLOOR SHEATHING, Cont'd...	UNIT	HOURS	MAT.	INST.	TOTAL
Board type subflooring					
1x6					
Minimum	S.F.	0.018	1.02	1.12	2.14
Maximum	"	0.020	1.39	1.26	2.65
1x8					
Minimum	S.F.	0.017	1.23	1.06	2.29
Maximum	"	0.019	1.39	1.19	2.58
1x10					
Minimum	S.F.	0.016	1.45	1.01	2.46
Maximum	"	0.018	1.52	1.12	2.64
Underlayment					
Hardboard, 1/4" tempered	S.F.	0.010	0.49	0.63	1.12
Plywood, CDX					
3/8" thick	S.F.	0.010	0.61	0.63	1.24
1/2" thick	"	0.011	0.70	0.67	1.37
5/8" thick	"	0.011	0.84	0.72	1.56
3/4" thick	"	0.012	1.00	0.77	1.77
06115.20 ROOF SHEATHING					
Sheathing					
Plywood, CDX					
3/8" thick	S.F.	0.010	0.61	0.65	1.26
1/2" thick	"	0.011	0.70	0.67	1.37
5/8" thick	"	0.011	0.84	0.72	1.56
3/4" thick	"	0.012	1.00	0.77	1.77
06115.30 WALL SHEATHING					
Sheathing					
Plywood, CDX					
3/8" thick	S.F.	0.012	0.61	0.75	1.36
1/2" thick	"	0.012	0.70	0.77	1.47
5/8" thick	"	0.013	0.84	0.84	1.68
3/4" thick	"	0.015	1.00	0.92	1.92
06220.10 MILLWORK					
Countertop, laminated plastic					
25" x 7/8" thick					
Minimum	L.F.	0.200	18.00	12.75	30.75
Average	"	0.267	32.25	17.00	49.25
Maximum	"	0.320	54.00	20.25	74.25
25" x 1-1/4" thick					
Minimum	L.F.	0.267	21.50	17.00	38.50
Average	"	0.320	35.75	20.25	56.00
Maximum	"	0.400	57.00	25.25	82.25
Add for cutouts	EA.	0.500		31.75	31.75
Backsplash, 4" high, 7/8" thick	L.F.	0.160	18.00	10.25	28.25
Base cabinets, 34-1/2" high, 24" deep,					
Minimum	L.F.	0.320	68.00	20.25	88.25
Average	"	0.400	120	25.25	145
Maximum	"	0.533	180	33.75	214
Wall cabinets					
Minimum	L.F.	0.267	55.00	17.00	72.00
Average	"	0.320	88.00	20.25	108
Maximum	"	0.400	170	25.25	195

MOISTURE PROTECTION

07100.00 DAMPPROOFING	UNIT	HOURS	MAT.	INST.	TOTAL
Silicone dampproofing, sprayed on					
Concrete surface					
1 coat	S.F.	0.004	0.64	0.21	0.85
2 coats	"	0.006	1.06	0.30	1.36
Concrete block					
1 coat	S.F.	0.005	0.64	0.26	0.90
2 coats	"	0.007	1.06	0.35	1.41
Brick					
1 coat	S.F.	0.006	0.74	0.30	1.04
2 coats	"	0.008	1.15	0.39	1.54
07160.10 BITUMINOUS DAMPPROOFING					
Building paper, asphalt felt					
15 lb	S.F.	0.032	0.15	1.57	1.72
30 lb	"	0.033	0.28	1.64	1.92
07190.10 VAPOR BARRIERS					
Vapor barrier, polyethylene					
2 mil	S.F.	0.004	0.01	0.19	0.20
6 mil	"	0.004	0.05	0.19	0.24
8 mil	"	0.004	0.06	0.21	0.27
10 mil	"	0.004	0.07	0.21	0.28

INSULATION

07210.10 BATT INSULATION	UNIT	HOURS	MAT.	INST.	TOTAL
Ceiling, fiberglass, unfaced					
3-1/2" thick, R11	S.F.	0.009	0.38	0.46	0.84
6" thick, R19	"	0.011	0.50	0.52	1.02
9" thick, R30	"	0.012	1.00	0.60	1.60
Suspended ceiling, unfaced					
3-1/2" thick, R11	S.F.	0.009	0.38	0.43	0.81
6" thick, R19	"	0.010	0.50	0.49	0.99
9" thick, R30	"	0.011	1.00	0.56	1.56
Crawl space, unfaced					
3-1/2" thick, R11	S.F.	0.012	0.38	0.60	0.98
6" thick, R19	"	0.013	0.50	0.65	1.15
9" thick, R30	"	0.015	1.00	0.71	1.71
Wall, fiberglass					
Paper backed					
2" thick, R7	S.F.	0.008	0.25	0.41	0.66
3" thick, R8	"	0.009	0.27	0.43	0.70
4" thick, R11	"	0.009	0.45	0.46	0.91
6" thick, R19	"	0.010	0.67	0.49	1.16
Foil backed, 1 side					
2" thick, R7	S.F.	0.008	0.58	0.41	0.99
3" thick, R11	"	0.009	0.61	0.43	1.04
4" thick, R14	"	0.009	0.64	0.46	1.10
6" thick, R21	"	0.010	0.77	0.49	1.26
Foil backed, 2 sides					
2" thick, R7	S.F.	0.009	0.66	0.46	1.12
3" thick, R11	"	0.010	0.83	0.49	1.32
4" thick, R14	"	0.011	0.99	0.52	1.51
6" thick, R21	"	0.011	1.06	0.56	1.62
Unfaced					

INSULATION

07210.10 BATT INSULATION, Cont'd...	UNIT	HOURS	MAT.	INST.	TOTAL
2" thick, R7	S.F.	0.008	0.37	0.41	0.78
3" thick, R9	"	0.009	0.41	0.43	0.84
4" thick, R11	"	0.009	0.45	0.46	0.91
6" thick, R19	"	0.010	0.58	0.49	1.07
Mineral wool batts					
Paper backed					
2" thick, R6	S.F.	0.008	0.24	0.41	0.65
4" thick, R12	"	0.009	0.52	0.43	0.95
6" thick, R19	"	0.010	0.67	0.49	1.16
Fasteners, self adhering, attached to ceiling					
2-1/2" long	EA.	0.013	0.19	0.65	0.84
4-1/2" long	"	0.015	0.22	0.71	0.93
Capped, self-locking washers for fastening	"	0.008	0.19	0.39	0.58
07210.20 BOARD INSULATION					
Insulation, rigid					
Fiberglass, roof					
0.75" thick, R2.78	S.F.	0.007	0.50	0.35	0.85
1.06" thick, R4.17	"	0.008	0.77	0.37	1.14
1.31" thick, R5.26	"	0.008	1.03	0.39	1.42
1.63" thick, R6.67	"	0.008	1.27	0.41	1.68
2.25" thick, R8.33	"	0.009	1.39	0.43	1.82
Perlite board, roof					
1.00" thick, R2.78	S.F.	0.007	0.58	0.32	0.90
1.50" thick, R4.17	"	0.007	0.90	0.34	1.24
2.00" thick, R5.92	"	0.007	1.11	0.35	1.46
2.50" thick, R6.67	"	0.008	1.35	0.37	1.72
3.00" thick, R8.33	"	0.008	1.70	0.39	2.09
4.00" thick, R10.00	"	0.008	1.89	0.41	2.30
5.25" thick, R14.29	"	0.009	2.07	0.43	2.50
07210.60 LOOSE FILL INSULATION					
Blown-in type					
Fiberglass					
5" thick, R11	S.F.	0.007	0.36	0.32	0.68
6" thick, R13	"	0.008	0.41	0.39	0.80
9" thick, R19	"	0.011	0.50	0.56	1.06
Rockwool, attic application					
6" thick, R13	S.F.	0.008	0.33	0.39	0.72
8" thick, R19	"	0.010	0.39	0.49	0.88
10" thick, R22	"	0.012	0.47	0.60	1.07
12" thick, R26	"	0.013	0.59	0.65	1.24
15" thick, R30	"	0.016	0.71	0.78	1.49
Poured type					
Fiberglass					
1" thick, R4	S.F.	0.005	0.33	0.24	0.57
2" thick, R8	"	0.006	0.61	0.28	0.89
3" thick, R12	"	0.007	0.90	0.32	1.22
4" thick, R16	"	0.008	1.18	0.39	1.57
Mineral wool					
1" thick, R3	S.F.	0.005	0.36	0.24	0.60
2" thick, R6	"	0.006	0.67	0.28	0.95
3" thick, R9	"	0.007	1.02	0.32	1.34
4" thick, R12	"	0.008	1.18	0.39	1.57
Vermiculite or perlite					

INSULATION

07210.60 LOOSE FILL INSULATION, Cont'd...	UNIT	HOURS	MAT.	INST.	TOTAL
2" thick, R4.8	S.F.	0.006	0.77	0.28	1.05
3" thick, R7.2	"	0.007	1.10	0.32	1.42
4" thick, R9.6	"	0.008	1.43	0.39	1.82
Masonry, poured vermiculite or perlite					
4" block	S.F.	0.004	0.33	0.19	0.52
6" block	"	0.005	0.41	0.24	0.65
8" block	"	0.006	0.60	0.28	0.88
10" block	"	0.006	0.71	0.30	1.01
12" block	"	0.007	0.88	0.32	1.20
07210.70 SPRAYED INSULATION					
Foam, sprayed on					
Polystyrene					
1" thick, R4	S.F.	0.008	0.61	0.39	1.00
2" thick, R8	"	0.011	1.19	0.52	1.71
Urethane					
1" thick, R4	S.F.	0.008	0.58	0.39	0.97
2" thick, R8	"	0.011	1.11	0.52	1.63
07250.10 FIREPROOFING					
Sprayed on					
1" thick					
On beams	S.F.	0.018	0.71	0.87	1.58
On columns	"	0.016	0.72	0.78	1.50
On decks					
Flat surface	S.F.	0.008	0.72	0.39	1.11
Fluted surface	"	0.010	0.92	0.49	1.41
1-1/2" thick					
On beams	S.F.	0.023	1.28	1.12	2.40
On columns	"	0.020	1.45	0.98	2.43
On decks					
Flat surface	S.F.	0.010	1.08	0.49	1.57
Fluted surface	"	0.013	1.28	0.65	1.93

SHINGLES AND TILES

07310.10 ASPHALT SHINGLES	UNIT	HOURS	MAT.	INST.	TOTAL
Standard asphalt shingles, strip shingles					
210 lb/square	SQ.	0.800	68.00	48.75	117
235 lb/square	"	0.889	72.00	54.00	126
240 lb/square	"	1.000	75.00	61.00	136
260 lb/square	"	1.143	110	70.00	180
300 lb/square	"	1.333	120	81.00	201
385 lb/square	"	1.600	160	97.00	257
Roll roofing, mineral surface					
90 lb	SQ.	0.571	41.75	34.75	76.50
110 lb	"	0.667	69.00	40.50	110
140 lb	"	0.800	72.00	48.75	121
07310.50 METAL SHINGLES					
Aluminum, .020" thick					
Plain	SQ.	1.600	260	97.00	357
Colors	"	1.600	280	97.00	377
Steel, galvanized					
26 ga.					
Plain	SQ.	1.600	260	97.00	357

SHINGLES AND TILES

07310.50 METAL SHINGLES, Cont'd...	UNIT	HOURS	MAT.	INST.	TOTAL
Colors	SQ.	1.600	340	97.00	437
Porcelain enamel, 22 ga.					
Minimum	SQ.	2.000	800	120	920
Average	"	2.000	920	120	1,040
Maximum	"	2.000	1,030	120	1,150
Replacement shingles					
Small jobs	EA.	0.267	12.00	16.25	28.25
Large jobs	S.F.	0.133	9.51	8.11	17.62
07310.70 WOOD SHINGLES					
Wood shingles, on roofs					
White cedar, #1 shingles					
4" exposure	SQ.	2.667	230	160	390
5" exposure	"	2.000	210	120	330
On walls					
White cedar, #1 shingles					
4" exposure	SQ.	4.000	230	240	470
5" exposure	"	3.200	210	190	400
07310.80 WOOD SHAKES					
Shakes, hand split, 24" red cedar, on roofs					
5" exposure	SQ.	4.000	260	240	500
9" exposure	"	2.667	230	160	390

MEMBRANE ROOFING

07510.10 BUILT-UP ASPHALT ROOFING	UNIT	HOURS	MAT.	INST.	TOTAL
Built-up roofing, asphalt felt, including gravel					
2 ply	SQ.	2.000	67.00	120	187
3 ply	"	2.667	91.00	160	251
4 ply	"	3.200	130	190	320
07530.10 SINGLE-PLY ROOFING					
Elastic sheet roofing					
Neoprene, 1/16" thick	S.F.	0.010	2.83	0.60	3.43
EPDM rubber					
45 mil	S.F.	0.010	1.47	0.60	2.07
60 mil	"	0.010	2.02	0.60	2.62
PVC					
45 mil	S.F.	0.010	2.03	0.60	2.63
60 mil	"	0.010	2.42	0.60	3.02
Flashing					
Pipe flashing, 90 mil thick					
1" pipe	EA.	0.200	28.50	12.25	40.75
2" pipe	"	0.200	30.75	12.25	43.00
3" pipe	"	0.211	31.00	12.75	43.75
4" pipe	"	0.211	33.50	12.75	46.25
5" pipe	"	0.222	35.75	13.50	49.25
6" pipe	"	0.222	39.00	13.50	52.50
Neoprene flashing, 60 mil thick strip					
6" wide	L.F.	0.067	1.73	4.05	5.78
12" wide	"	0.100	3.42	6.08	9.50
18" wide	"	0.133	5.02	8.11	13.13
24" wide	"	0.200	6.61	12.25	18.86
Adhesives					
Mastic sealer, applied at joints only					

MEMBRANE ROOFING

07530.10 SINGLE-PLY ROOFING, Cont'd...	UNIT	HOURS	MAT.	INST.	TOTAL
1/4" bead	L.F.	0.004	0.11	0.24	0.35
Ballast, 3/4" through 1-1/2" dia. river gravel,	S.F.	0.800	0.40	48.75	49.15
Walkway for membrane roofs, 1/2" thick	"	0.027	2.13	1.62	3.75

FLASHING AND SHEET METAL

07610.10 METAL ROOFING	UNIT	HOURS	MAT.	INST.	TOTAL
Sheet metal roofing, copper, 16 oz, batten	SQ.	5.333	1,200	320	1,520
Standing seam	"	5.000	1,170	300	1,470
Aluminum roofing, natural finish					
Corrugated, on steel frame					
.0175" thick	SQ.	2.286	120	140	260
.032" thick	"	2.286	240	140	380
Corrugated galvanized steel roofing, on steel					
28 ga.	SQ.	2.286	140	140	280
22 ga.	"	2.286	200	140	340
07620.10 FLASHING AND TRIM					
Counter flashing					
Aluminum, .032"	S.F.	0.080	1.58	4.86	6.44
Stainless steel, .015"	"	0.080	5.06	4.86	9.92
Copper					
16 oz.	S.F.	0.080	7.49	4.86	12.35
Base flashing					
Aluminum, .040"	S.F.	0.067	2.60	4.05	6.65
Stainless steel, .018"	"	0.067	6.05	4.05	10.10
Copper					
16 oz.	S.F.	0.067	7.49	4.05	11.54
24 oz.	"	0.067	10.75	4.05	14.80
Scupper outlets					
10" x 10" x 4"	EA.	0.200	34.00	12.25	46.25
22" x 4" x 4"	"	0.200	42.00	12.25	54.25
8" x 8" x 5"	"	0.200	34.00	12.25	46.25
Drainage boots, roof, cast iron					
2 x 3	L.F.	0.100	53.00	6.08	59.08
3 x 4	"	0.100	67.00	6.08	73.08
4 x 5	"	0.107	96.00	6.49	102
4 x 6	"	0.107	91.00	6.49	97.49
5 x 7	"	0.114	110	6.95	117
Pitch pocket, copper, 16 oz.					
4 x 4	EA.	0.200	120	12.25	132
6 x 6	"	0.200	130	12.25	142
8 x 8	"	0.200	140	12.25	152
8 x 10	"	0.200	150	12.25	162
8 x 12	"	0.200	180	12.25	192
Reglets, copper 10 oz.	L.F.	0.053	4.88	3.24	8.12
Stainless steel, .020"	"	0.053	2.77	3.24	6.01
07700.10 MANUFACTURED SPECIALTIES					
Ceiling access doors					
Swing up model, metal frame					
Steel door					
2'6" x 2'6"	EA.	0.800	470	48.75	519
2'6" x 3'0"	"	0.800	510	48.75	559
Aluminum door					

FLASHING AND SHEET METAL

07700.10 MANUFACTURED SPECIALTIES, Cont'd...	UNIT	HOURS	MAT.	INST.	TOTAL
2'6" x 2'6"	EA.	0.800	510	48.75	559
2'6" x 3'0"	"	0.800	550	48.75	599
Swing down model, metal frame					
Steel door					
2'6" x 2'6"	EA.	0.800	460	48.75	509
2'6" x 3'0"	"	0.800	490	48.75	539
Aluminum door					
2'6" x 2'6"	EA.	0.800	470	48.75	519
2'6" x 3'0"	"	0.800	510	48.75	559
Gravity ventilators, with curb, base, damper					
Stationary siphon					
6" dia.	EA.	0.533	36.75	32.50	69.25
12" dia.	"	0.533	64.00	32.50	96.50
24" dia.	"	0.800	230	48.75	279
36" dia.	"	0.800	500	48.75	549
Wind driven spinner					
6" dia.	EA.	0.533	56.00	32.50	88.50
12" dia.	"	0.533	75.00	32.50	108
24" dia.	"	0.800	280	48.75	329
36" dia.	"	0.800	580	48.75	629
Stationary mushroom					
16" dia.	EA.	0.800	420	48.75	469
30" dia.	"	1.000	940	61.00	1,001
36" dia.	"	1.333	1,220	81.00	1,301
42" dia.	"	1.600	1,810	97.00	1,907

JOINT SEALERS

07920.10 CAULKING	UNIT	HOURS	MAT.	INST.	TOTAL
Caulk exterior, two component					
1/4 x 1/2	L.F.	0.040	0.39	2.53	2.92
3/8 x 1/2	"	0.044	0.60	2.81	3.41
1/2 x 1/2	"	0.050	0.82	3.16	3.98
Caulk interior, single component					
1/4 x 1/2	L.F.	0.038	0.26	2.41	2.67
3/8 x 1/2	"	0.042	0.37	2.66	3.03
1/2 x 1/2	"	0.047	0.49	2.98	3.47

SPECIALTIES

10100.00 ACCESS & PEDESTAL FLOOR	UNIT	HOURS	MAT.	INST.	TOTAL
Panels, no covering, 2'x2'					
Plain	S.F.	0.010	9.25	0.63	9.88
Perforated	"	0.400	12.50	25.25	37.75
Pedestals					13.50
For 6" to 12" clearance	EA.	0.080	7.07	5.06	12.13
Stringers					
2'	L.F.	0.038	1.92	2.41	4.33
6'	"	0.027	1.92	1.68	3.60
Accessories					
Ramp assembly	S.F.	0.032	43.75	2.02	45.77
Elevated floor assembly	"	0.030	69.00	1.87	70.87
Handrail	L.F.	0.400	54.00	25.25	79.25
Fascia plate	"	0.200	26.00	12.75	38.75
For carpet tiles, add	S.F.				6.97
For vinyl flooring, add	"				7.93
RF shielding components, floor liner					
Hot rolled steel sheet					
14 ga.	S.F.	0.020	3.24	1.26	4.50
11 ga.	"	0.062	3.41	3.89	7.30
10290.10 PEST CONTROL					
Termite control					
Under slab spraying					
Minimum	S.F.	0.002	1.03	0.09	1.12
Average	"	0.004	1.06	0.19	1.25
Maximum	"	0.008	1.15	0.39	1.54
10520.10 FIRE PROTECTION					
Portable fire extinguishers					
Water pump tank type					
2.5 gal.					
Red enameled galvanized	EA.	0.533	120	26.25	146
Red enameled copper	"	0.533	140	26.25	166
Polished copper	"	0.533	210	26.25	236
Carbon dioxide type, red enamel steel					
Squeeze grip with hose and horn					
2.5 lb	EA.	0.533	160	26.25	186
5 lb	"	0.615	170	30.25	200
10 lb	"	0.800	240	39.50	280
15 lb	"	1.000	260	49.25	309
20 lb	"	1.000	340	49.25	389
Wheeled type					
125 lb	EA.	1.600	1,750	79.00	1,829
250 lb	"	1.600	1,810	79.00	1,889
500 lb	"	1.600	3,380	79.00	3,459
Dry chemical, pressurized type					
Red enameled steel					
2.5 lb	EA.	0.533	70.00	26.25	96.25
5 lb	"	0.615	85.00	30.25	115
10 lb	"	0.800	140	39.50	180
20 lb	"	1.000	180	49.25	229
30 lb	"	1.000	430	49.25	479
Chrome plated steel, 2.5 lb	"	0.533	120	26.25	146
Other type extinguishers					
2.5 gal, stainless steel, pressurized water	EA.	0.533	120	26.25	146

SPECIALTIES

10520.10 FIRE PROTECTION, Cont'd...	UNIT	HOURS	MAT.	INST.	TOTAL
Soda and acid type	EA.	0.533	180	26.25	206
Cartridge operated, water type	"	0.533	290	26.25	316
Loaded stream, water type	"	0.533	120	26.25	146
Foam type	"	0.533	130	26.25	156
40 gal, wheeled foam type	"	1.600	4,950	79.00	5,029
Fire extinguisher cabinets					
Enameled steel					
8" x 12" x 27"	EA.	1.600	110	79.00	189
8" x 16" x 38"	"	1.600	130	79.00	209
Aluminum					
8" x 12" x 27"	EA.	1.600	140	79.00	219
8" x 16" x 38"	"	1.600	160	79.00	239
8" x 12" x 27"	"	1.600	170	79.00	249
Stainless steel					
8" x 16" x 38"	EA.	1.600	230	79.00	309
10750.10 TELEPHONE ENCLOSURES					
Telephone enclosure, wall mounted, shelf, 28"	EA.	2.000	1,480	130	1,610
Directory shelf, stainless steel, 3 binders	"	1.333	1,250	84.00	1,334

EQUIPMENT

ARCHITECTURAL EQUIPMENT

11001.00 MAINTENANCE EQUIPMENT	UNIT	HOURS	MAT.	INST.	TOTAL
Vacuum cleaning system					
3 valves					
1.5 hp	EA.	8.889	2,030	560	2,590
2.5 hp	"	11.429	2,290	720	3,010
5 valves	"	16.000	3,050	1,010	4,060
7 valves	"	20.000	3,860	1,270	5,130

11020.10 SECURITY EQUIPMENT	UNIT	HOURS	MAT.	INST.	TOTAL
Bulletproof teller window					
4' x 4'	EA.	13.333	2,140	840	2,980
5' x 4'	"	16.000	2,350	1,010	3,360
Bulletproof partitions					
Up to 12' high, 2.5" thick	S.F.	0.053	170	3.37	173
Counter for banks					
Minimum	L.F.	1.600	760	100	860
Maximum	"	2.667	3,430	170	3,600
Drive-up window					
Minimum	EA.	11.429	4,940	720	5,660
Maximum	"	26.667	5,200	1,690	6,890
Night depository					
Minimum	EA.	11.429	9,010	720	9,730
Maximum	"	26.667	12,690	1,690	14,380
Office safes, 30" x 20" x 20", 1 hr rating	"	2.000	2,200	130	2,330
30" x 16" x 15", 2 hr rating	"	1.600	1,630	100	1,730
30" x 28" x 20", H&G rating	"	1.000	3,740	63.00	3,803
Service windows, pass through painted steel					
24" x 36"	EA.	8.000	3,010	510	3,520
48" x 40"	"	10.000	4,580	630	5,210
72" x 40"	"	16.000	5,730	1,010	6,740
Special doors and windows					
3' x 7' bulletproof door with frame	EA.	11.429	5,970	720	6,690
12" x 12" vision panel	"	5.714	3,410	360	3,770
Surveillance system					
Minimum	EA.	16.000	5,810	1,010	6,820
Maximum	"	80.000	10,520	5,070	15,590
Vault door, 3' wide, 6'6" high					
3-1/2" thick	EA.	100.000	3,690	6,340	10,030
7" thick	"	133.333	5,110	8,450	13,560
10" thick	"	160.000	8,620	10,140	18,760
Insulated vault door					
2 hr rating					
32" wide	EA.	8.000	4,220	510	4,730
40" wide	"	8.421	4,950	530	5,480
4 hr rating					
32" wide	EA.	8.889	4,620	560	5,180
40" wide	"	10.000	5,180	630	5,810
6 hr rating					
32" wide	EA.	8.889	5,450	560	6,010
40" wide	"	10.000	5,920	630	6,550
Insulated file room door					
1 hr rating					
32" wide	EA.	8.000	4,540	510	5,050
40" wide	"	8.889	4,680	560	5,240

ARCHITECTURAL EQUIPMENT

11060.10 THEATER EQUIPMENT	UNIT	HOURS	MAT.	INST.	TOTAL
Roll out stage, steel frame, wood floor					
Manual	S.F.	0.050	39.50	3.16	42.66
Electric	"	0.080	43.00	5.06	48.06
Portable stages					
8" high	S.F.	0.040	20.75	2.53	23.28
18" high	"	0.044	21.75	2.81	24.56
36" high	"	0.047	23.50	2.98	26.48
48" high	"	0.050	35.00	3.16	38.16
Band risers					
Minimum	S.F.	0.040	21.50	2.53	24.03
Maximum	"	0.040	27.00	2.53	29.53
Chairs for risers					
Minimum	EA.	0.036	750	1.79	752
Maximum	"	0.036	910	1.79	912
11080.10 POLICE EQUIPMENT					
Firing range equipment, rifle					
3 position	EA.	26.667	14,760	1,690	16,450
4 position	"	40.000	20,180	2,530	22,710
5 position	"	44.444	25,760	2,820	28,580
6 position	"	47.059	31,350	2,980	34,330
11090.10 CHECKROOM EQUIPMENT					
Motorized checkroom equipment					
No shelf system, 6'4" height					
7'6" length	EA.	8.000	2,760	510	3,270
14'6" length	"	8.000	3,120	510	3,630
28' length	"	8.000	4,310	510	4,820
One shelf, 6'8" height					
7'6" length	EA.	8.000	3,390	510	3,900
14'6" length	"	8.000	4,100	510	4,610
28' length	"	8.000	6,060	510	6,570
Two shelves, 7'5" height					
7'6" length	EA.	8.000	4,100	510	4,610
14'6" length	"	8.000	4,990	510	5,500
28' length	"	8.000	7,130	510	7,640
Three shelves, 8' height					
7'6" length	EA.	16.000	4,280	1,010	5,290
14'6" length	"	16.000	5,170	1,010	6,180
28' length	"	16.000	7,310	1,010	8,320
Four shelves, 8'7" height					
7'6" length	EA.	16.000	4,280	1,010	5,290
14'6" length	"	16.000	5,350	1,010	6,360
28' length	"	16.000	7,310	1,010	8,320
11110.10 LAUNDRY EQUIPMENT					
High capacity, heavy duty					
Washer extractors					
135 lb					
Standard	EA.	6.667	59,290	420	59,710
Pass through	"	6.667	68,240	420	68,660
200 lb					
Standard	EA.	6.667	67,100	420	67,520
Pass through	"	6.667	74,580	420	75,000
110 lb dryer	"	6.667	11,730	420	12,150
Hand operated presser	"	8.889	8,040	560	8,600

ARCHITECTURAL EQUIPMENT

11110.10 LAUNDRY EQUIPMENT, Cont'd...	UNIT	HOURS	MAT.	INST.	TOTAL
Mushroom press	EA.	8.889	5,190	560	5,750
Spreader feeders					
2 station	EA.	8.889	77,090	560	77,650
4 station	"	16.000	84,630	1,010	85,640
Delivery carts					
12 bushel	EA.	0.100	260	6.33	266
16 bushel	"	0.107	300	6.75	307
18 bushel	"	0.114	320	7.24	327
30 bushel	"	0.133	540	8.44	548
40 bushel	"	0.160	640	10.25	650
Low capacity					
Pressers					
Air operated	EA.	3.200	6,370	200	6,570
Hand operated	"	3.200	5,190	200	5,390
Extractor, low capacity	"	3.200	7,460	200	7,660
Ironer, 48"	"	1.600	3,520	100	3,620
Coin washers					
10 lb capacity	EA.	1.600	1,640	100	1,740
20 lb capacity	"	1.600	4,240	100	4,340
Coin dryer	"	1.000	720	63.00	783
Coin dry cleaner, 20 lb	"	3.200	36,790	200	36,990
11161.10 LOADING DOCK EQUIPMENT					
Dock leveler, 10 ton capacity					
6' x 8'	EA.	8.000	4,860	510	5,370
7' x 8'	"	8.000	5,140	510	5,650
Door seal, 12" x 12", vinyl covered	L.F.	0.200	49.75	12.75	62.50
Dock boards, heavy duty, 5' x 5'					
5000 lb					
Minimum	EA.	6.667	1,090	420	1,510
Maximum	"	6.667	1,340	420	1,760
9000 lb					
Minimum	EA.	6.667	1,280	420	1,700
Maximum	"	7.273	1,500	460	1,960
Truck shelters					
Minimum	EA.	6.154	14,260	390	14,650
Maximum	"	11.429	17,820	720	18,540
11170.10 WASTE HANDLING					
Incinerator, electric					
100 lb/hr					
Minimum	EA.	8.000	23,110	520	23,630
Maximum	"	8.000	39,820	520	40,340
400 lb/hr					
Minimum	EA.	16.000	41,030	1,040	42,070
Maximum	"	16.000	79,740	1,040	80,780
1000 lb/hr					
Minimum	EA.	24.242	79,760	1,570	81,330
Maximum	"	24.242	127,610	1,570	129,180
Incinerator, medical-waste					
25 lb/hr, 2-7 x 4-0	EA.	16.000	23,930	1,040	24,970
50 lb/hr, 2-11 x 4-11	"	16.000	25,520	1,040	26,560
75 lb/hr, 3-8 x 5-0	"	32.000	35,090	2,070	37,160
100 lb/hr, 3-8 x 6-0	"	32.000	39,880	2,070	41,950
Industrial compactor					

ARCHITECTURAL EQUIPMENT

11170.10 WASTE HANDLING, Cont'd...	UNIT	HOURS	MAT.	INST.	TOTAL
1 cy	EA.	8.889	12,030	580	12,610
3 cy	"	11.429	23,380	740	24,120
5 cy	"	16.000	30,320	1,040	31,360
Trash chutes steel, including sprinklers					
18" dia.	L.F.	4.000	77.00	250	327
24" dia.	"	4.211	100	270	370
30" dia.	"	4.444	130	280	410
36" dia.	"	4.706	170	300	470
Refuse bottom hopper	EA.	4.444	2,590	280	2,870
11400.10 FOOD SERVICE EQUIPMENT					
Unit kitchens					
30" compact kitchen					
Refrigerator, with range, sink	EA.	4.000	1,680	260	1,940
Sink only	"	2.667	1,550	170	1,720
Range only	"	2.000	1,260	130	1,390
Cabinet for upper wall section	"	1.143	310	74.00	384
Stainless shield, for rear wall	"	0.320	130	20.75	151
Side wall	"	0.320	94.00	20.75	115
42" compact kitchen					
Refrigerator with range, sink	EA.	4.444	1,890	290	2,180
Sink only	"	4.000	1,870	260	2,130
Cabinet for upper wall section	"	1.333	620	86.00	706
Stainless shield, for rear wall	"	0.333	390	21.50	412
Side wall	"	0.333	130	21.50	152
54" compact kitchen					
Refrigerator, oven, range, sink	EA.	5.714	5,550	370	5,920
Cabinet for upper wall section	"	1.600	820	100	920
Stainless shield, for					
Rear wall	EA.	0.364	500	23.50	524
Side wall	"	0.364	140	23.50	164
60" compact kitchen					
Refrigerator, oven, range, sink	EA.	5.714	1,800	370	2,170
Cabinet for upper wall section	"	1.600	140	100	240
Stainless shield, for					
Rear wall	EA.	0.364	590	23.50	614
Side wall	"	0.364	150	23.50	174
72" compact kitchen					
Refrigerator, oven, range, sink	EA.	6.667	3,240	430	3,670
Cabinet for upper wall section	"	1.600	150	100	250
Stainless shield for					
Rear wall	EA.	0.400	640	26.00	666
Side wall	"	0.400	150	26.00	176
Bake oven					
Single deck					
Minimum	EA.	1.000	2,850	65.00	2,915
Maximum	"	2.000	5,370	130	5,500
Double deck					
Minimum	EA.	1.333	5,380	86.00	5,466
Maximum	"	2.000	14,550	130	14,680
Triple deck					
Minimum	EA.	1.333	21,250	86.00	21,336
Maximum	"	2.667	31,340	170	31,510
Convection type oven, electric, 40" x 45" x					

EQUIPMENT

ARCHITECTURAL EQUIPMENT

11400.10 FOOD SERVICE EQUIPMENT, Cont'd...	UNIT	HOURS	MAT.	INST.	TOTAL
Minimum	EA.	1.000	3,390	65.00	3,455
Maximum	"	2.000	7,890	130	8,020
Broiler, without oven, 69" x 26" x 39"					
Minimum	EA.	1.000	3,680	65.00	3,745
Maximum	"	1.333	5,870	86.00	5,956
Coffee urns, 10 gallons					
Minimum	EA.	2.667	6,570	170	6,740
Maximum	"	4.000	10,170	260	10,430
Fryer, with submerger					
Single					
Minimum	EA.	1.600	1,360	100	1,460
Maximum	"	2.667	4,950	170	5,120
Double					
Minimum	EA.	2.000	1,980	130	2,110
Maximum	"	2.667	7,420	170	7,590
Griddle, counter					
3' long					
Minimum	EA.	1.333	1,790	86.00	1,876
Maximum	"	1.600	5,440	100	5,540
5' long					
Minimum	EA.	2.000	4,130	130	4,260
Maximum	"	2.667	7,490	170	7,660
Kettles, steam, jacketed					
20 gallons					
Minimum	EA.	2.000	10,180	130	10,310
Maximum	"	4.000	21,120	260	21,380
40 gallons					
Minimum	EA.	2.000	14,100	130	14,230
Maximum	"	4.000	23,090	260	23,350
60 gallons					
Minimum	EA.	2.000	15,030	130	15,160
Maximum	"	4.000	28,250	260	28,510
Range					
Heavy duty, single oven, open top					
Minimum	EA.	1.000	5,100	65.00	5,165
Maximum	"	2.667	11,890	170	12,060
Fry top					
Minimum	EA.	1.000	7,610	65.00	7,675
Maximum	"	2.667	9,830	170	10,000
Steamers, electric					
27 kw					
Minimum	EA.	2.000	10,660	130	10,790
Maximum	"	2.667	18,430	170	18,600
18 kw					
Minimum	EA.	2.000	5,960	130	6,090
Maximum	"	2.667	11,080	170	11,250
Dishwasher, rack type					
Single tank, 190 racks/hr	EA.	4.000	15,550	260	15,810
Double tank					
234 racks/hr	EA.	4.444	41,000	290	41,290
265 racks/hr	"	5.333	43,870	350	44,220
Dishwasher, automatic 100 meals/hr	"	2.667	12,070	170	12,240
Disposals					

EQUIPMENT

ARCHITECTURAL EQUIPMENT

11400.10 FOOD SERVICE EQUIPMENT, Cont'd...	UNIT	HOURS	MAT.	INST.	TOTAL
100 gal/hr	EA.	2.667	1,330	170	1,500
120 gal/hr	"	2.759	1,410	180	1,590
250 gal/hr	"	2.857	1,800	190	1,990
Exhaust hood for dishwasher, gutter 4 sides,					
4'x4'x2'	EA.	2.963	3,130	190	3,320
4'x7'x2'	"	3.200	4,850	210	5,060
Food preparation machines					
Vertical cutter mixers					
25 quart	EA.	2.667	9,230	170	9,400
40 quart	"	2.667	14,910	170	15,080
80 quart	"	4.000	13,100	260	13,360
130 quart	"	6.667	14,360	430	14,790
Choppers					
5 lb	EA.	2.000	2,360	130	2,490
16 lb	"	2.667	3,160	170	3,330
40 lb	"	4.000	3,560	260	3,820
Mixers, floor models					
20 quart	EA.	1.000	3,880	65.00	3,945
60 quart	"	1.000	15,500	65.00	15,565
80 quart	"	1.143	25,520	74.00	25,594
140 quart	"	1.600	35,640	100	35,740
Ice cube maker					
50 lb per day					
Minimum	EA.	8.000	1,610	520	2,130
Maximum	"	8.000	3,290	520	3,810
500 lb per day					
Minimum	EA.	13.333	4,770	860	5,630
Maximum	"	13.333	5,410	860	6,270
Ice flakers					
300 lb per day	EA.	8.000	4,280	520	4,800
600 lb per day	"	13.333	7,120	860	7,980
1000 lb per day	"	17.778	9,320	1,150	10,470
2000 lb per day	"	20.000	16,800	1,300	18,100
Refrigerated cases					
Dairy products					
Multi deck type	L.F.	0.533	930	34.50	965
For rear sliding doors, add	"				100
Delicatessen case, service deli					
Single deck	L.F.	4.000	840	260	1,100
Multi deck	"	5.000	920	320	1,240
Meat case					
Single deck	L.F.	4.706	580	300	880
Multi deck	"	5.000	670	320	990
Produce case					
Single deck	L.F.	4.706	640	300	940
Multi deck	"	5.000	730	320	1,050
Bottle coolers					
6' long					
Minimum	EA.	16.000	2,360	1,040	3,400
Maximum	"	16.000	3,330	1,040	4,370
10' long					
Minimum	EA.	26.667	2,850	1,730	4,580
Maximum	"	26.667	5,720	1,730	7,450

ARCHITECTURAL EQUIPMENT

11400.10 FOOD SERVICE EQUIPMENT, Cont'd...	UNIT	HOURS	MAT.	INST.	TOTAL
Frozen food cases					
Chest type	L.F.	4.706	570	300	870
Reach-in, glass door	"	5.000	1,210	320	1,530
Island case, single	"	4.706	590	300	890
Multi deck	"	5.000	1,300	320	1,620
Ice storage bins					
500 lb capacity	EA.	11.429	1,770	740	2,510
1000 lb capacity	"	22.857	3,500	1,480	4,980
11450.10 RESIDENTIAL EQUIPMENT					
Compactor, 4 to 1 compaction	EA.	2.000	770	130	900
Dishwasher, built-in					
2 cycles	EA.	4.000	640	260	900
4 or more cycles	"	4.000	2,060	260	2,320
Disposal					
Garbage disposer	EA.	2.667	140	170	310
Heaters, electric, built-in					
Ceiling type	EA.	2.667	390	170	560
Wall type					
Minimum	EA.	2.000	160	130	290
Maximum	"	2.667	300	170	470
Hood for range, 2-speed, vented					
30" wide	EA.	2.667	380	170	550
42" wide	"	2.667	860	170	1,030
Ice maker, automatic					
30 lb per day	EA.	1.143	1,380	74.00	1,454
50 lb per day	"	4.000	1,940	260	2,200
Folding access stairs, disappearing metal					
8' long	EA.	1.143	720	74.00	794
11' long	"	1.143	930	74.00	1,004
12' long	"	1.143	1,230	74.00	1,304
Wood frame, wood stair					
22" x 54" x 8'9" long	EA.	0.800	120	52.00	172
25" x 54" x 10' long	"	0.800	180	52.00	232
Ranges electric					
Built-in, 30", 1 oven	EA.	2.667	1,860	170	2,030
2 oven	"	2.667	2,640	170	2,810
Counter top, 4 burner, standard	"	2.000	1,030	130	1,160
With grill	"	2.000	2,640	130	2,770
Free standing, 21", 1 oven	"	2.667	970	170	1,140
30", 1 oven	"	1.600	1,630	100	1,730
2 oven	"	1.600	3,210	100	3,310
Water softener					
30 grains per gallon	EA.	2.667	960	170	1,130
70 grains per gallon	"	4.000	1,190	260	1,450
11470.10 DARKROOM EQUIPMENT					
Dryers					
36" x 25" x 68"	EA.	4.000	9,570	280	9,850
48" x 25" x 68"	"	4.000	9,890	280	10,170
Processors, film					
Black and white	EA.	4.000	15,250	280	15,530
Color negatives	"	4.000	17,270	280	17,550
Prints	"	4.000	19,800	280	20,080
Transparencies	"	4.000	21,730	280	22,010

ARCHITECTURAL EQUIPMENT

11470.10 DARKROOM EQUIPMENT, Cont'd...	UNIT	HOURS	MAT.	INST.	TOTAL
Sinks with cabinet and/or stand					
5" sink with stand					
24" x 48"	EA.	2.000	1,080	140	1,220
32" x 64"	"	2.667	1,940	190	2,130
38" x 52"	"	2.667	2,120	190	2,310
42" x 132"	"	4.000	3,530	280	3,810
48" x 52"	"	4.000	3,180	280	3,460
5" sink with cabinet					
24" x 48"	EA.	2.000	1,670	140	1,810
32" x 64"	"	2.667	3,030	190	3,220
38" x 52"	"	2.667	3,030	190	3,220
42" x 132"	"	4.000	5,330	280	5,610
48" x 52"	"	4.000	2,970	280	3,250
10" sink with stand					
24" x 48"	EA.	2.000	1,080	140	1,220
32" x 64"	"	2.667	2,010	190	2,200
38" x 52"	"	2.667	2,300	190	2,490
10" sink with cabinet					
24" x 48"	EA.	2.000	2,180	140	2,320
38" x 52"	"	2.667	3,290	190	3,480
11480.10 ATHLETIC EQUIPMENT					
Gym divider curtain					
Minimum	S.F.	0.011	3.57	0.67	4.24
Maximum	"	0.011	13.25	0.67	13.92
Scoreboards, single face					
Minimum	EA.	8.000	5,490	510	6,000
Maximum	"	40.000	28,600	2,530	31,130
11500.10 INDUSTRIAL EQUIPMENT					
Vehicular paint spray booth, solid back, 14'4" x					
24' deep	EA.	8.000	16,040	510	16,550
26'6" deep	"	8.000	16,370	510	16,880
28'6" deep	"	8.000	16,700	510	17,210
Drive through, 14'9" x 9'6"					
24' deep	EA.	8.000	16,300	510	16,810
26'6" deep	"	8.000	16,690	510	17,200
28'6" deep	"	8.000	16,880	510	17,390
Water wash, paint spray booth					
5' x 11'2" x 10'8"	EA.	8.000	8,270	510	8,780
6' x 11'2" x 10'8"	"	8.000	8,460	510	8,970
8' x 11'2" x 10'8"	"	8.000	10,700	510	11,210
10' x 11'2" x 11'2"	"	8.000	11,870	510	12,380
12' x 12'2" x 11'2"	"	8.000	14,500	510	15,010
14' x 12'2" x 11'2"	"	8.000	17,030	510	17,540
16' x 12'2" x 11'2"	"	8.000	19,170	510	19,680
20' x 12'2" x 11'2"	"	8.000	22,960	510	23,470
Dry type spray booth, with paint arrestors					
5'4" x 7'2" x 6'8"	EA.	8.000	3,600	510	4,110
6'4" x 7'2" x 6'8"	"	8.000	4,380	510	4,890
8'4" x 7'2" x 9'2"	"	8.000	4,960	510	5,470
10'4" x 7'2" x 9'2"	"	8.000	5,740	510	6,250
12'4" x 7'6" x 9'2"	"	8.000	5,630	510	6,140
14'4" x 7'6" x 9'8"	"	8.000	7,680	510	8,190
16'4" x 7'7" x 9'8"	"	8.000	8,660	510	9,170

EQUIPMENT

ARCHITECTURAL EQUIPMENT

11500.10 INDUSTRIAL EQUIPMENT, Cont'd...	UNIT	HOURS	MAT.	INST.	TOTAL
20'4" x 7'7" x 10'8"	EA.	8.000	9,730	510	10,240
Air compressor, electric					
1 hp					
115 volt	EA.	5.333	1,110	340	1,450
7.5 hp					
115 volt	EA.	8.000	3,620	510	4,130
230 volt	"	8.000	3,710	510	4,220
Hydraulic lifts					
8,000 lb capacity	EA.	20.000	7,390	1,270	8,660
11,000 lb capacity	"	32.000	9,350	2,030	11,380
24,000 lb capacity	"	53.333	13,100	3,380	16,480
Power tools					
Band saws					
10"	EA.	0.667	850	42.25	892
14"	"	0.800	1,420	51.00	1,471
Motorized shaper	"	0.615	800	39.00	839
Motorized lathe	"	0.667	940	42.25	982
Bench saws					
9" saw	EA.	0.533	1,790	33.75	1,824
10" saw	"	0.571	2,910	36.25	2,946
12" saw	"	0.667	3,690	42.25	3,732
Electric grinders					
1/3 hp	EA.	0.320	350	20.25	370
1/2 hp	"	0.348	480	22.00	502
3/4 hp	"	0.348	590	22.00	612
11600.10 LABORATORY EQUIPMENT					
Cabinets, base					
Minimum	L.F.	0.667	350	42.25	392
Maximum	"	0.667	570	42.25	612
Full storage, 7' high					
Minimum	L.F.	0.667	440	42.25	482
Maximum	"	0.667	570	42.25	612
Wall					
Minimum	L.F.	0.800	130	51.00	181
Maximum	"	0.800	210	51.00	261
Counter tops					
Minimum	S.F.	0.100	27.00	6.33	33.33
Average	"	0.114	63.00	7.24	70.24
Maximum	"	0.133	100	8.44	108
Tables					
Open underneath	S.F.	0.400	170	25.25	195
Doors underneath	"	0.500	270	31.75	302
Medical laboratory equipment					
Analyzer					
Chloride	EA.	0.400	690	26.00	716
Blood	"	0.667	31,130	43.25	31,173
Bath, water, utility, countertop unit	"	0.800	750	52.00	802
Hot plate, lab, countertop	"	0.727	330	47.00	377
Stirrer	"	0.727	360	47.00	407
Incubator, anaerobic, 23x23x36"	"	4.000	8,080	260	8,340
Dry heat bath	"	1.333	590	86.00	676
Incinerator, for sterilizing	"	0.080	300	5.18	305
Meter, serum protein	"	0.100	1,140	6.48	1,146

ARCHITECTURAL EQUIPMENT

11600.10 LABORATORY EQUIPMENT, Cont'd...	UNIT	HOURS	MAT.	INST.	TOTAL
Ph analog, general purpose	EA.	0.114	830	7.40	837
Refrigerator, blood bank, undercounter type	"	1.333	5,730	86.00	5,816
5.4 cf, undercounter type	"	1.333	4,790	86.00	4,876
Refrigerator/freezer, 4.4 cf, undercounter type	"	1.333	740	86.00	826
Sealer, impulse, free standing, 20x12x4"	"	0.267	360	17.25	377
Timer, electric, 1-60 minutes, bench or wall	"	0.444	170	28.75	199
Glassware washer - dryer, undercounter	"	10.000	7,480	650	8,130
Balance, torsion suspension, tabletop, 4.5 lb	"	0.444	680	28.75	709
Binocular microscope, with in base illuminator	"	0.308	3,280	20.00	3,300
Centrifuge, table model, 19x16x13"	"	0.320	2,170	20.75	2,191
Clinical model, with four place head	"	0.178	990	11.50	1,002

11700.10 MEDICAL EQUIPMENT					
Hospital equipment, lights					
Examination, portable	EA.	0.667	1,650	43.25	1,693
Meters					
Air flow meter	EA.	0.444	70.00	28.75	98.75
Oxygen flow meters	"	0.333	58.00	21.50	79.50
Racks					
40 chart, revolving open frame; mobile	EA.	0.667	1,470	43.25	1,513
Scales.					
Clinical, metric with measure rod, 350 lb	EA.	0.727	470	47.00	517
Physical therapy					
Chair, hydrotherapy	EA.	0.133	500	8.44	508
Diathermy, shortwave, portable, on casters	"	0.320	3,700	20.25	3,720
Exercise bicycle, floor standing, 35" x 15"	"	0.267	890	17.00	907
Hydrocollator, 4 pack, portable, 129 x 90 x	"	0.114	400	7.24	407
Lamp, infrared, mobile with variable heat	"	0.615	480	39.00	519
Ultra violet, base mounted	"	0.615	530	39.00	569
Mirror, posture training, 27" wide and 72"	"	0.200	500	12.75	513
Parallel bars, adjustable	"	1.000	2,110	63.00	2,173
Platform mat 10'x6', 1" thick	"	0.200	600	12.75	613
Pulley, duplex, wall mounted	"	2.667	800	170	970
Rack, crutch, wall mounted, 66 x 16 x 13"	"	0.800	910	51.00	961
Stimulator, galvanic-faradic, hand held	"	0.053	110	3.37	113
Ultrasound, muscle stimulator, portable,	"	0.067	1,580	4.22	1,584
Sandbag set, velcro straps, saddle bag	"	0.114	130	7.24	137
Whirlpool, 85 gallon	"	4.000	3,620	250	3,870
65 gallon capacity	"	4.000	3,300	250	3,550
Radiology					
Radiographic table, motor driven tilting	EA.	80.000	38,060	5,070	43,130
Fluoroscope image/tv system	"	160.000	100,980	10,140	111,120
Processor for washing and drying					
Water filter unit, 30" x 48-1/2" x 37-1/2"	EA.	13.333	38.50	860	899
Cassette transfer cabinet	"	0.667	1,340	43.25	1,383
Base storage cabinets, sectional design					
With back splash, 24" deep and 35" high	L.F.	0.667	2,860	43.25	2,903
Wall storage cabinets	"	1.000	220	65.00	285
Steam sterilizers					
For heat and moisture stable materials	EA.	0.800	3,520	52.00	3,572
For fast drying after sterilization	"	1.000	4,040	65.00	4,105
Compact unit	"	1.000	1,970	65.00	2,035
Semi-automatic	"	4.000	7,240	260	7,500
Floor loading					

EQUIPMENT

ARCHITECTURAL EQUIPMENT

11700.10 MEDICAL EQUIPMENT, Cont'd...	UNIT	HOURS	MAT.	INST.	TOTAL
Single door	EA.	6.667	18,590	430	19,020
Double door	"	8.000	20,560	520	21,080
Utensil washer, sanitizer	"	6.154	12,090	400	12,490
Automatic washer/sterilizer	"	16.000	7,550	1,040	8,590
16 x 16 x 26", including generator &	"	26.667	8,690	1,730	10,420
Steam generator, elec., 10 kw to 180 kw	"	16.000	20,800	1,040	21,840
Surgical scrub					
Minimum	EA.	2.667	1,060	170	1,230
Maximum	"	2.667	7,040	170	7,210
Gas sterilizers					
Automatic, free standing, 21x19x29"	EA.	8.000	5,110	520	5,630
Surgical tables					
Minimum	EA.	11.429	20,460	740	21,200
Maximum	"	16.000	99,950	1,040	100,990
Surgical lights, ceiling mounted					
Minimum	EA.	13.333	7,150	860	8,010
Maximum	"	16.000	14,580	1,040	15,620
Water stills					
4 liters/hr	EA.	2.667	3,140	170	3,310
8 liters/hr	"	2.667	5,130	170	5,300
19 liters/hr	"	6.667	11,120	430	11,550
X-ray equipment					
Mobile unit					
Minimum	EA.	4.000	10,770	260	11,030
Maximum	"	8.000	20,790	520	21,310
Film viewers					
Minimum	EA.	1.333	190	86.00	276
Maximum	"	2.667	850	170	1,020
Autopsy table					
Minimum	EA.	8.000	15,560	520	16,080
Maximum	"	8.000	19,950	520	20,470
Incubators					
15 cf	EA.	4.000	5,340	260	5,600
29 cf	"	6.667	6,380	430	6,810
Infant transport, portable	"	4.211	5,060	270	5,330
Beds					
Stretcher, with pad, 30" x 78"	EA.	2.000	2,140	130	2,270
Transfer, for patient transport	"	2.000	4,550	130	4,680
Headwall					
Aluminum, with back frame and console	EA.	4.000	4,090	260	4,350
Hospital ground detection system					
Power ground module	EA.	2.286	900	150	1,050
Ground slave module	"	1.739	630	110	740
Master ground module	"	1.509	390	98.00	488
Remote indicator	"	1.600	430	100	530
X-ray indicator	"	1.739	1,320	110	1,430
Micro ammeter	"	2.000	1,610	130	1,740
Supervisory module	"	1.739	1,250	110	1,360
Ground cords	"	0.296	100	19.25	119
Hospital isolation monitors, 5 ma					
120v	EA.	3.478	2,470	230	2,700
208v	"	3.478	2,370	230	2,600
240v	"	3.478	2,370	230	2,600

ARCHITECTURAL EQUIPMENT

11700.10 MEDICAL EQUIPMENT, Cont'd...	UNIT	HOURS	MAT.	INST.	TOTAL
Digital clock-timers separate display	EA.	1.600	970	100	1,070
One display	"	1.600	920	100	1,020
Remote control	"	1.250	550	81.00	631
Battery pack	"	1.250	130	81.00	211
Surgical chronometer clock and 3 timers	"	2.500	2,050	160	2,210
Auxilary control	"	1.159	740	75.00	815
11700.20 DENTAL EQUIPMENT					
Dental care equipment					
Drill console with accessories	EA.	13.333	3,710	860	4,570
Amalgamator	"	0.400	350	26.00	376
Lathe	"	0.267	930	17.25	947
Finish polisher	"	0.533	3,650	34.50	3,685
Model trimmer	"	0.364	720	23.50	744
Motor, wall mounted	"	0.364	600	23.50	624
Cleaner, ultrasonic	"	0.800	2,270	52.00	2,322
Curing unit, bench mounted	"	1.333	2,930	86.00	3,016
Oral evacuation system, dual pump	"	1.000	11,920	65.00	11,985
Sterilizer, table top, self contained	"	0.444	1,010	28.75	1,039
Dental lights					
Light, floor or ceiling mounted	EA.	4.000	1,920	260	2,180
X-ray unit					
Portable	EA.	2.000	3,900	130	4,030
Wall mounted with remote control	"	6.667	5,370	430	5,800
Illuminator, single panel	"	11.429	520	740	1,260
X-ray film processor	"	6.667	1,940	430	2,370
Shield, portable x-ray, lead lined	"	0.533	590	34.50	625

FURNISHINGS

INTERIOR

12100.00 CASEWORK	UNIT	HOURS	MAT.	INST.	TOTAL
Kitchen base cabinet, prefinished, 24" deep,					
12"wide	EA.	0.800	200	51.00	251
18" wide	"	0.800	240	51.00	291
24" wide	"	0.889	260	56.00	316
27" wide	"	0.889	310	56.00	366
36" wide	"	1.000	350	63.00	413
48" wide	"	1.000	400	63.00	463
Corner cabinet, 36" wide	"	1.000	270	63.00	333
Wall cabinet, 12" deep, 12" high					
30" wide	EA.	0.800	150	51.00	201
36" wide	"	0.800	160	51.00	211
15" high					
30" wide	EA.	0.889	160	56.00	216
36" wide	"	0.889	170	56.00	226
24" high					
30" wide	EA.	0.889	190	56.00	246
36" wide	"	0.889	230	56.00	286
30" high					
12" wide	EA.	1.000	140	63.00	203
18" wide	"	1.000	160	63.00	223
24" wide	"	1.000	180	63.00	243
27" wide	"	1.000	210	63.00	273
30" wide	"	1.143	240	72.00	312
36" wide	"	1.143	240	72.00	312
Corner cabinet, 30" high					
24" wide	EA.	1.333	230	84.00	314
30" wide	"	1.333	280	84.00	364
36" wide	"	1.333	310	84.00	394
Wardrobe	"	2.000	720	130	850
Vanity with top, laminated plastic					
24" wide	EA.	2.000	450	130	580
30" wide	"	2.000	550	130	680
36" wide	"	2.667	580	170	750
48" wide	"	3.200	660	200	860
12390.10 COUNTER TOPS					
Stainless steel, counter top, with backsplash	S.F.	0.200	140	12.75	153
Acid-proof, kemrock surface	"	0.133	46.25	8.44	54.69

BNi. Building News

CONSTRUCTION

13050.00 SWIMMING POOL EQUIPMENT	UNIT	HOURS	MAT.	INST.	TOTAL
Lights, underwater					
12 volt, with transformer	EA.	2.000	500	99.00	599
110 volt					
Minimum	EA.	2.000	600	99.00	699
Maximum	"	2.000	1,370	99.00	1,469
Ground fault interrupter for 110 volt, each	"	0.667	180	32.75	213

HAZARDOUS WASTE

13280.10 ASBESTOS REMOVAL	UNIT	HOURS	MAT.	INST.	TOTAL
Enclosure using wood studs & poly, install &	S.F.	0.020	460	0.98	461
Trailer (change room)	DAY				110
Disposal suits (4 suits per man day)	"				45.00
Type C respirator mask, includes hose &	"				22.00
Respirator mask & filter, light contamination	"				8.80
Air monitoring test, 12 tests per day					
Off job testing	DAY				1,160
On the job testing	"				1,540
Asbestos vacuum with attachments	EA.				670
Hydraspray piston pump	"				860
Negative air pressure system	"				790
Grade D breathing air equipment	"				1,980
Glove bag, 44" x 60" x 6 mil plastic	"				5.50
40 CY asbestos dumpster					
Weekly rental	EA.				750
Pick up/delivery	"				350
Asbestos dump fee	"				190
13280.12 DUCT INSULATION REMOVAL					
Remove duct insulation, duct size					
6" x 12"	L.F.	0.044	210	2.18	212
x 18"	"	0.062	150	3.03	153
x 24"	"	0.089	100	4.37	104
8" x 12"	"	0.067	140	3.28	143
x 18"	"	0.073	130	3.58	134
x 24"	"	0.100	92.00	4.92	96.92
12" x 12"	"	0.067	140	3.28	143
x 18"	"	0.089	100	4.37	104
x 24"	"	0.114	80.00	5.62	85.62
13280.15 PIPE INSULATION REMOVAL					
Removal, asbestos insulation					
2" thick, pipe					
1" to 3" dia.	L.F.	0.067	140	3.28	143
4" to 6" dia.	"	0.076	120	3.75	124
3" thick					
7" to 8" dia.	L.F.	0.080	110	3.94	114
9" to 10" dia.	"	0.084	110	4.14	114
11" to 12" dia.	"	0.089	100	4.37	104
13" to 14" dia.	"	0.094	97.00	4.63	102
15" to 18" dia.	"	0.100	92.00	4.92	96.92

CONVEYING

ELEVATORS

14200.00   ELEVATORS

	UNIT	HOURS	MAT.	INST.	TOTAL
Passenger elevators, electric, geared					
Based on a shaft of 6 stops and 6 openings					
50 fpm, 2000 lb	EA.	24.000	105,450	2,170	107,620
100 fpm, 2000 lb	"	26.667	109,350	2,410	111,760
150 fpm					
2000 lb	EA.	30.000	121,070	2,710	123,780
3000 lb	"	34.286	152,310	3,100	155,410
4000 lb	"	40.000	158,170	3,620	161,790
Based on a shaft of 8 stops and 8 openings					
300 fpm					
3000 lb	EA.	48.000	181,610	4,340	185,950
3500 lb	"	48.000	185,670	4,340	190,010
4000 lb	"	53.333	195,280	4,820	200,100
5000 lb	"	57.143	218,710	5,170	223,880
Freight elevators, electric					
Based on a shaft of 6 stops and 6 openings					
50 fpm					
3500 lb	EA.	26.667	190,130	2,410	192,540
4000 lb	"	26.667	190,850	2,410	193,260
5000 lb	"	30.000	192,660	2,710	195,370
100 fpm					
3500 lb	EA.	30.000	200,090	2,710	202,800
4000 lb	"	30.000	200,990	2,710	203,700
5000 lb	"	34.286	196,100	3,100	199,200
For variable voltage control, add 20%					

14300.10   ESCALATORS

	UNIT	HOURS	MAT.	INST.	TOTAL
Escalators					
32" wide, floor to floor					
12' high	EA.	40.000	137,320	3,620	140,940
15' high	"	48.000	148,930	4,340	153,270
18' high	"	60.000	160,540	5,430	165,970
22' high	"	80.000	174,070	7,230	181,300
25' high	"	96.000	193,420	8,680	202,100

LIFTS

14410.10   PERSONNEL LIFTS

	UNIT	HOURS	MAT.	INST.	TOTAL
Electrically operated, 1 or 2 person lift					
With attached foot platforms					
3 stops	EA.				24,840
5 stops	"				30,530
7 stops	"				35,380
For each additional stop, add $1250					
Residential stair climber, per story	EA.	6.667	6,490	430	6,920

14580.10   PNEUMATIC SYSTEMS

	UNIT	HOURS	MAT.	INST.	TOTAL
Pneumatic message tube system					
Average, 20 station job					
3" round system	E.A.	72.727	332,520	4,710	337,230
4" round system	"	80.000	415,640	5,180	420,820
6" round system	"	88.889	628,080	5,760	633,840
4" x 7" oval system	"	160.000	655,790	10,370	666,160
Trash and linen tube system					
10 stations	EA.	120.000	212,440	10,850	223,290

LIFTS

14580.10 PNEUMATIC SYSTEMS, Cont'd...	UNIT	HOURS	MAT.	INST.	TOTAL
15 stations	EA.	160.000	267,860	14,470	282,330
20 stations	"	184.615	359,330	16,690	376,020
30 stations	"	218.182	471,060	19,730	490,790

HOISTS AND CRANES

14600.10 INDUSTRIAL HOISTS	UNIT	HOURS	MAT.	INST.	TOTAL
Industrial hoists, electric, light to medium duty					
500 lb	EA.	4.000	6,490	260	6,750
1000 lb	"	4.211	6,670	270	6,940
2000 lb	"	4.444	6,880	290	7,170
3000 lb	"	4.706	7,280	300	7,580
4000 lb	"	5.000	7,750	320	8,070
5000 lb	"	5.333	9,760	350	10,110
6000 lb	"	5.517	10,660	360	11,020
7500 lb	"	5.714	11,960	370	12,330
10,000 lb	"	5.926	30,090	380	30,470
15,000 lb	"	6.154	38,230	400	38,630
20,000 lb	"	6.667	46,200	430	46,630
25,000 lb	"	7.273	47,350	470	47,820
30,000 lb	"	8.000	50,000	520	50,520
Heavy duty					
500 lb	EA.	4.000	10,340	260	10,600
1000 lb	"	4.211	15,300	270	15,570
2000 lb	"	4.444	15,520	290	15,810
3000 lb	"	4.706	16,070	300	16,370
4000 lb	"	5.000	16,390	320	16,710
5000 lb	"	5.333	16,610	350	16,960
6000 lb	"	5.517	21,890	360	22,250
7500 lb	"	5.714	23,380	370	23,750
10,000 lb	"	5.926	30,090	380	30,470
15,000 lb	"	6.154	32,370	400	32,770
20,000 lb	"	6.667	36,960	430	37,390
25,000 lb	"	7.273	39,930	470	40,400
30,000 lb	"	8.000	41,690	520	42,210

BASIC MATERIALS

15050.00 SPECIALTIES	UNIT	HOURS	MAT.	INST.	TOTAL
Wall penetration					
Concrete wall, 6" thick					
2" dia.	EA.	0.267		13.25	13.25
4" dia.	"	0.400		19.75	19.75
8" dia.	"	0.571		28.25	28.25
12" thick					
2" dia.	EA.	0.364		18.00	18.00
4" dia.	"	0.571		28.25	28.25
8" dia.	"	0.889		43.75	43.75
15120.10 BACKFLOW PREVENTERS					
Backflow preventer, flanged, cast iron, with					
3" pipe	EA.	4.000	2,760	280	3,040
4" pipe	"	4.444	3,540	310	3,850
Threaded					
3/4" pipe	EA.	0.500	570	35.00	605
2" pipe	"	0.800	1,000	56.00	1,056
15140.11 PIPE HANGERS, LIGHT					
A band, black iron					
1/2"	EA.	0.057	1.00	4.00	5.00
1"	"	0.059	1.07	4.14	5.21
1-1/4"	"	0.062	1.19	4.30	5.49
1-1/2"	"	0.067	1.25	4.66	5.91
2"	"	0.073	1.32	5.09	6.41
2-1/2"	"	0.080	1.98	5.60	7.58
3"	"	0.089	2.40	6.22	8.62
4"	"	0.100	3.16	7.00	10.16
Copper					
1/2"	EA.	0.057	1.62	4.00	5.62
3/4"	"	0.059	1.89	4.14	6.03
1"	"	0.059	1.89	4.14	6.03
1-1/4"	"	0.062	2.02	4.30	6.32
1-1/2"	"	0.067	2.17	4.66	6.83
2"	"	0.073	2.31	5.09	7.40
2-1/2"	"	0.080	4.65	5.60	10.25
3"	"	0.089	4.85	6.22	11.07
4"	"	0.100	5.34	7.00	12.34
2 hole clips, galvanized					
3/4"	EA.	0.053	0.26	3.73	3.99
1"	"	0.055	0.29	3.86	4.15
1-1/4"	"	0.057	0.38	4.00	4.38
1-1/2"	"	0.059	0.47	4.14	4.61
2"	"	0.062	0.61	4.30	4.91
2-1/2"	"	0.064	1.11	4.48	5.59
3"	"	0.067	1.61	4.66	6.27
4"	"	0.073	3.46	5.09	8.55
Perforated strap					
3/4"					
Galvanized, 20 ga.	L.F.	0.040	0.40	2.80	3.20
Copper, 22 ga.	"	0.040	0.63	2.80	3.43
J-Hooks					
1/2"	EA.	0.036	0.41	2.54	2.95
3/4"	"	0.036	0.45	2.54	2.99
1"	"	0.038	0.46	2.66	3.12

BASIC MATERIALS

15140.11 PIPE HANGERS, LIGHT, Cont'd...	UNIT	HOURS	MAT.	INST.	TOTAL
1-1/4"	EA.	0.039	0.48	2.73	3.21
1-1/2"	"	0.040	0.49	2.80	3.29
2"	"	0.040	0.51	2.80	3.31
3"	"	0.042	0.59	2.94	3.53
4"	"	0.042	0.63	2.94	3.57
PVC coated hangers, galvanized, 28 ga.					
1-1/2" x 12"	EA.	0.053	1.26	3.73	4.99
2" x 12"	"	0.057	1.37	4.00	5.37
3" x 12"	"	0.062	1.54	4.30	5.84
4" x 12"	"	0.067	1.70	4.66	6.36
Copper, 30 ga.					
1-1/2" x 12"	EA.	0.053	1.76	3.73	5.49
2" x 12"	"	0.057	2.09	4.00	6.09
3" x 12"	"	0.062	2.31	4.30	6.61
4" x 12"	"	0.067	2.53	4.66	7.19
Wire hook hangers					
Black wire, 1/2" x					
4"	EA.	0.040	0.42	2.80	3.22
6"	"	0.042	0.49	2.94	3.43
Copper wire hooks					
1/2" x					
4"	EA.	0.040	0.59	2.80	3.39
6"	"	0.042	0.67	2.94	3.61

15240.10 VIBRATION CONTROL	UNIT	HOURS	MAT.	INST.	TOTAL
Vibration isolator, in-line, stainless connector,					
1/2"	EA.	0.444	93.00	31.00	124
3/4"	"	0.471	110	33.00	143
1"	"	0.500	110	35.00	145
1-1/4"	"	0.533	150	37.25	187
1-1/2"	"	0.571	170	40.00	210
2"	"	0.615	200	43.00	243
2-1/2"	"	0.667	310	46.75	357
3"	"	0.727	360	51.00	411
4"	"	0.800	460	56.00	516

INSULATION

15260.10 FIBERGLASS PIPE INSULATION	UNIT	HOURS	MAT.	INST.	TOTAL
Fiberglass insulation on 1/2" pipe					
1" thick	L.F.	0.027	0.99	1.86	2.85
1-1/2" thick	"	0.033	2.09	2.33	4.42
3/4" pipe					
1" thick	L.F.	0.027	1.21	1.86	3.07
1-1/2" thick	"	0.033	2.20	2.33	4.53
1" pipe					
1" thick	L.F.	0.027	1.21	1.86	3.07
1-1/2" thick	"	0.033	2.31	2.33	4.64
1-1/4" pipe					
1" thick	L.F.	0.033	1.37	2.33	3.70
1-1/2" thick	"	0.036	2.53	2.54	5.07
1-1/2" pipe					
1" thick	L.F.	0.033	1.48	2.33	3.81
1-1/2" thick	"	0.036	2.58	2.54	5.12
2" pipe					

© 2009 BNI Publications Inc.

MECHANICAL

INSULATION

15260.10 FIBERGLASS PIPE INSULATION, Cont'd...	UNIT	HOURS	MAT.	INST.	TOTAL
1" thick	L.F.	0.033	1.65	2.33	3.98
1-1/2" thick	"	0.036	2.86	2.54	5.40
2-1/2" pipe					
1" thick	L.F.	0.033	1.76	2.33	4.09
1-1/2" thick	"	0.036	3.08	2.54	5.62
3" pipe					
1" thick	L.F.	0.038	1.98	2.66	4.64
1-1/2" thick	"	0.040	3.19	2.80	5.99
4" pipe					
1" thick	L.F.	0.038	2.53	2.66	5.19
1-1/2" thick	"	0.040	3.63	2.80	6.43
15260.60 EXTERIOR PIPE INSULATION					
Fiberglass insulation, aluminum jacket					
1/2" pipe					
1" thick	L.F.	0.062	1.49	4.30	5.79
1-1/2" thick	"	0.067	2.80	4.66	7.46
1" pipe					
1" thick	L.F.	0.062	1.81	4.30	6.11
1-1/2" thick	"	0.067	3.13	4.66	7.79
3" pipe					
1" thick	L.F.	0.080	2.97	5.60	8.57
1-1/2" thick	"	0.084	4.40	5.89	10.29
4" pipe					
1" thick	L.F.	0.080	3.74	5.60	9.34
1-1/2" thick	"	0.084	5.06	5.89	10.95
15290.10 DUCTWORK INSULATION					
Fiberglass duct insulation, plain blanket					
1-1/2" thick	S.F.	0.010	0.20	0.70	0.90
2" thick	"	0.013	0.27	0.93	1.20
With vapor barrier					
1-1/2" thick	S.F.	0.010	0.24	0.70	0.94
2" thick	"	0.013	0.30	0.93	1.23
Rigid with vapor barrier					
2" thick	S.F.	0.027	1.32	1.86	3.18

PLUMBING

15410.05 C.I. PIPE, ABOVE GROUND	UNIT	HOURS	MAT.	INST.	TOTAL
No hub pipe					
1-1/2" pipe	L.F.	0.057	5.94	4.00	9.94
2" pipe	"	0.067	6.05	4.66	10.71
3" pipe	"	0.080	8.36	5.60	13.96
4" pipe	"	0.133	11.00	9.33	20.33
No hub fittings, 1-1/2" pipe					
1/4 bend	EA.	0.267	8.08	18.75	26.83
1/8 bend	"	0.267	6.76	18.75	25.51
Sanitary tee	"	0.400	11.25	28.00	39.25
Wye	"	0.400	14.00	28.00	42.00
2" pipe					
1/4 bend	EA.	0.320	9.35	22.50	31.85
1/8 bend	"	0.320	7.53	22.50	30.03
Sanitary tee	"	0.533	12.75	37.25	50.00
Coupling	"				14.00

PLUMBING

15410.05 C.I. PIPE, ABOVE GROUND, Cont'd...	UNIT	HOURS	MAT.	INST.	TOTAL
Wye	EA.	0.667	12.00	46.75	58.75
3" pipe					
1/4 bend	EA.	0.400	12.75	28.00	40.75
1/8 bend	"	0.400	10.75	28.00	38.75
Sanitary tee	"	0.500	15.75	35.00	50.75
Coupling	"				16.00
Wye	"	0.667	17.00	46.75	63.75
4" pipe					
1/4 bend	EA.	0.400	18.50	28.00	46.50
1/8 bend	"	0.400	13.50	28.00	41.50
Sanitary tee	"	0.667	24.25	46.75	71.00
Coupling	"				15.75
Wye	"	0.667	27.75	46.75	74.50
15410.09 SERVICE WEIGHT PIPE					
Service weight pipe, single hub					
3" x 5'	EA.	0.170	45.00	12.00	57.00
4" x 5'	"	0.178	52.00	12.50	64.50
6" x 5'	"	0.200	99.00	14.00	113
1/8 bend					
3"	EA.	0.320	11.50	22.50	34.00
4"	"	0.364	16.75	25.50	42.25
6"	"	0.400	28.50	28.00	56.50
1/4 bend					
3"	EA.	0.320	13.75	22.50	36.25
4"	"	0.364	21.50	25.50	47.00
6"	"	0.400	37.50	28.00	65.50
Sweep					
3"	EA.	0.320	22.25	22.50	44.75
4"	"	0.364	32.75	25.50	58.25
6"	"	0.400	66.00	28.00	94.00
Sanitary T					
3"	EA.	0.571	23.25	40.00	63.25
4"	"	0.667	28.50	46.75	75.25
6"	"	0.727	64.00	51.00	115
Wye					
3"	EA.	0.444	24.25	31.00	55.25
4"	"	0.471	32.50	33.00	65.50
6"	"	0.571	75.00	40.00	115
15410.10 COPPER PIPE					
Type "K" copper					
1/2"	L.F.	0.025	3.76	1.75	5.51
3/4"	"	0.027	7.01	1.86	8.87
1"	"	0.029	9.18	2.00	11.18
DWV, copper					
1-1/4"	L.F.	0.033	9.24	2.33	11.57
1-1/2"	"	0.036	12.00	2.54	14.54
2"	"	0.040	15.25	2.80	18.05
3"	"	0.044	26.25	3.11	29.36
4"	"	0.050	45.75	3.50	49.25
6"	"	0.057	180	4.00	184
Refrigeration tubing, copper, sealed					
1/8"	L.F.	0.032	0.73	2.24	2.97
3/16"	"	0.033	0.85	2.33	3.18

© 2009 BNI Publications Inc.

PLUMBING

15410.10 COPPER PIPE, Cont'd...	UNIT	HOURS	MAT.	INST.	TOTAL
1/4"	L.F.	0.035	1.02	2.43	3.45
Type "L" copper					
1/4"	L.F.	0.024	1.51	1.64	3.15
3/8"	"	0.024	2.33	1.64	3.97
1/2"	"	0.025	2.70	1.75	4.45
3/4"	"	0.027	4.32	1.86	6.18
1"	"	0.029	6.50	2.00	8.50
Type "M" copper					
1/2"	L.F.	0.025	1.91	1.75	3.66
3/4"	"	0.027	3.11	1.86	4.97
1"	"	0.029	5.06	2.00	7.06
Type "K" tube, coil					
1/4" x 60'	EA.				110
1/2" x 60'	"				240
3/4" x 60'	"				440
1" x 60'	"				570
Type "L" tube, coil					
1/4" x 60'	EA.				94.00
3/8" x 60'	"				150
1/2" x 60'	"				190
3/4" x 60'	"				310
1" x 60'	"				450
15410.11 COPPER FITTINGS					
Copper pipe fittings					
1/2"					
90 deg ell	EA.	0.178	1.67	12.50	14.17
45 deg ell	"	0.178	2.12	12.50	14.62
Tee	"	0.229	2.80	16.00	18.80
Cap	"	0.089	1.14	6.22	7.36
Coupling	"	0.178	1.23	12.50	13.73
Union	"	0.200	8.49	14.00	22.49
3/4"					
90 deg ell	EA.	0.200	3.65	14.00	17.65
45 deg ell	"	0.200	4.26	14.00	18.26
Tee	"	0.267	6.11	18.75	24.86
Cap	"	0.094	2.23	6.58	8.81
Coupling	"	0.200	2.48	14.00	16.48
Union	"	0.229	12.50	16.00	28.50
1"					
90 deg ell	EA.	0.267	8.49	18.75	27.24
45 deg ell	"	0.267	11.00	18.75	29.75
Tee	"	0.320	14.00	22.50	36.50
Cap	"	0.133	4.13	9.33	13.46
Coupling	"	0.267	6.11	18.75	24.86
Union	"	0.267	16.25	18.75	35.00
1-1/4"					
90 deg ell	EA.	0.229	11.50	16.00	27.50
45 deg ell	"	0.229	14.25	16.00	30.25
Tee	"	0.400	18.75	28.00	46.75
Cap	"	0.133	3.31	9.33	12.64
Union	"	0.286	27.00	20.00	47.00
1-1/2"					
90 deg ell	EA.	0.286	15.00	20.00	35.00

PLUMBING

15410.11	COPPER FITTINGS, Cont'd...	UNIT	HOURS	MAT.	INST.	TOTAL
	45 deg ell	EA.	0.286	18.00	20.00	38.00
	Tee	"	0.444	24.75	31.00	55.75
	Cap	"	0.133	3.31	9.33	12.64
	Coupling	"	0.267	11.00	18.75	29.75
	Union	"	0.364	41.25	25.50	66.75
2"						
	90 deg ell	EA.	0.320	29.50	22.50	52.00
	45 deg ell	"	0.500	27.00	35.00	62.00
	Tee	"	0.500	42.25	35.00	77.25
	Cap	"	0.160	6.83	11.25	18.08
	Coupling	"	0.320	18.00	22.50	40.50
	Union	"	0.400	44.75	28.00	72.75
2-1/2"						
	90 deg ell	EA.	0.400	57.00	28.00	85.00
	45 deg ell	"	0.400	49.50	28.00	77.50
	Tee	"	0.571	57.00	40.00	97.00
	Cap	"	0.200	14.00	14.00	28.00
	Coupling	"	0.400	27.00	28.00	55.00
	Union	"	0.444	82.00	31.00	113
15410.18	**GLASS PIPE**					
Glass pipe						
	1-1/2" dia.	L.F.	0.160	11.50	11.25	22.75
	2" dia.	"	0.178	15.50	12.50	28.00
	3" dia.	"	0.200	20.75	14.00	34.75
	4" dia.	"	0.229	38.00	16.00	54.00
	6" dia.	"	0.267	69.00	18.75	87.75
15410.30	**PVC/CPVC PIPE**					
PVC schedule 40						
	1/2" pipe	L.F.	0.033	0.44	2.33	2.77
	3/4" pipe	"	0.036	0.60	2.54	3.14
	1" pipe	"	0.040	0.77	2.80	3.57
	1-1/4" pipe	"	0.044	0.99	3.11	4.10
	1-1/2" pipe	"	0.050	1.48	3.50	4.98
	2" pipe	"	0.057	1.87	4.00	5.87
	2-1/2" pipe	"	0.067	3.02	4.66	7.68
	3" pipe	"	0.080	3.85	5.60	9.45
	4" pipe	"	0.100	5.50	7.00	12.50
	6" pipe	"	0.200	9.90	14.00	23.90
	8" pipe	"	0.267	14.50	18.75	33.25
PVC schedule 80 pipe						
	1-1/2" pipe	L.F.	0.050	1.87	3.50	5.37
	2" pipe	"	0.057	2.53	4.00	6.53
	3" pipe	"	0.080	5.22	5.60	10.82
	4" pipe	"	0.100	6.82	7.00	13.82
Polypropylene, acid resistant, DWV pipe						
Schedule 40						
	1-1/2" pipe	L.F.	0.057	5.50	4.00	9.50
	2" pipe	"	0.067	7.42	4.66	12.08
	3" pipe	"	0.080	15.25	5.60	20.85
	4" pipe	"	0.100	19.25	7.00	26.25
	6" pipe	"	0.200	38.50	14.00	52.50

PLUMBING

15410.33 ABS DWV PIPE	UNIT	HOURS	MAT.	INST.	TOTAL
Schedule 40 ABS					
1-1/2" pipe	L.F.	0.040	0.82	2.80	3.62
2" pipe	"	0.044	1.10	3.11	4.21
3" pipe	"	0.057	2.25	4.00	6.25
4" pipe	"	0.080	3.19	5.60	8.79
6" pipe	"	0.100	6.54	7.00	13.54
15410.35 PLASTIC PIPE					
Fiberglass reinforced pipe					
2" pipe	L.F.	0.062	2.80	4.30	7.10
3" pipe	"	0.067	3.99	4.66	8.65
4" pipe	"	0.073	5.21	5.09	10.30
6" pipe	"	0.080	9.99	5.60	15.59
15410.70 STAINLESS STEEL PIPE					
Stainless steel, schedule 40, threaded					
1/2" pipe	L.F.	0.114	9.35	8.00	17.35
1" pipe	"	0.123	15.25	8.61	23.86
1-1/2" pipe	"	0.133	20.75	9.33	30.08
2" pipe	"	0.145	31.00	10.25	41.25
2-1/2" pipe	"	0.160	43.50	11.25	54.75
3" pipe	"	0.178	61.00	12.50	73.50
4" pipe	"	0.200	79.00	14.00	93.00
15410.80 STEEL PIPE					
Black steel, extra heavy pipe, threaded					
1/2" pipe	L.F.	0.032	2.25	2.24	4.49
3/4" pipe	"	0.032	2.91	2.24	5.15
1" pipe	"	0.040	3.74	2.80	6.54
Fittings, malleable iron, threaded, 1/2" pipe					
90 deg ell	EA.	0.267	2.72	18.75	21.47
45 deg ell	"	0.267	3.68	18.75	22.43
Tee	"	0.400	2.97	28.00	30.97
Reducing tee	"	0.400	6.65	28.00	34.65
Cap	"	0.160	2.31	11.25	13.56
Coupling	"	0.320	3.08	22.50	25.58
Union	"	0.267	13.00	18.75	31.75
Nipple, 4" long	"	0.267	2.42	18.75	21.17
3/4" pipe					
90 deg ell	EA.	0.267	3.19	18.75	21.94
45 deg ell	"	0.400	5.06	28.00	33.06
Tee	"	0.400	4.29	28.00	32.29
Reducing tee	"	0.267	7.42	18.75	26.17
Cap	"	0.160	3.08	11.25	14.33
Coupling	"	0.267	3.63	18.75	22.38
Union	"	0.267	14.75	18.75	33.50
Nipple, 4" long	"	0.267	2.80	18.75	21.55
1" pipe					
90 deg ell	EA.	0.320	4.95	22.50	27.45
45 deg ell	"	0.320	6.54	22.50	29.04
Tee	"	0.444	7.42	31.00	38.42
Reducing tee	"	0.444	10.00	31.00	41.00
Cap	"	0.160	4.18	11.25	15.43
Coupling	"	0.320	5.39	22.50	27.89
Union	"	0.320	17.50	22.50	40.00
Nipple, 4" long	"	0.320	3.96	22.50	26.46

PLUMBING

15410.82 GALVANIZED STEEL PIPE	UNIT	HOURS	MAT.	INST.	TOTAL
Galvanized pipe					
1/2" pipe	L.F.	0.080	2.53	5.60	8.13
3/4" pipe	"	0.100	3.30	7.00	10.30
1" pipe	"	0.114	5.06	8.00	13.06
90 degree ell, 150 lb malleable iron,					
1/2"	EA.	0.160	2.69	11.25	13.94
3/4"	"	0.200	3.57	14.00	17.57
1"	"	0.211	5.83	14.75	20.58
45 degree ell, 150 lb m.i., galv.					
1/2"	EA.	0.160	4.29	11.25	15.54
3/4"	"	0.200	5.83	14.00	19.83
1"	"	0.211	6.54	14.75	21.29
Tees, straight, 150 lb m.i., galv.					
1/2"	EA.	0.200	3.57	14.00	17.57
3/4"	"	0.229	5.94	16.00	21.94
1"	"	0.267	8.74	18.75	27.49
Tees, reducing, out, 150 lb m.i., galv.					
1/2"	EA.	0.200	6.16	14.00	20.16
3/4"	"	0.229	7.15	16.00	23.15
1"	"	0.267	10.50	18.75	29.25
Couplings, straight, 150 lb m.i., galv.					
1/2"	EA.	0.160	3.30	11.25	14.55
3/4"	"	0.178	3.96	12.50	16.46
1"	"	0.200	6.76	14.00	20.76
Couplings, reducing, 150 lb m.i., galv					
1/2"	EA.	0.160	3.85	11.25	15.10
3/4"	"	0.178	4.29	12.50	16.79
1"	"	0.200	7.86	14.00	21.86
Caps, 150 lb m.i., galv.					
1/2"	EA.	0.080	2.75	5.60	8.35
3/4"	"	0.084	3.63	5.89	9.52
1"	"	0.089	4.95	6.22	11.17
Unions, 150 lb m.i., galv.					
1/2"	EA.	0.200	15.25	14.00	29.25
3/4"	"	0.229	17.25	16.00	33.25
1"	"	0.267	20.50	18.75	39.25
Nipples, galvanized steel, 4" long					
1/2"	EA.	0.100	2.64	7.00	9.64
3/4"	"	0.107	3.52	7.46	10.98
1"	"	0.114	4.84	8.00	12.84
90 degree reducing ell, 150 lb m.i., galv.					
3/4" x 1/2"	EA.	0.160	4.29	11.25	15.54
1" x 3/4"	"	0.178	5.83	12.50	18.33
Square head plug (C.I.)					
1/2"	EA.	0.089	1.98	6.22	8.20
3/4"	"	0.100	4.40	7.00	11.40
1"	"	0.107	4.62	7.46	12.08

PLUMBING

15430.23 CLEANOUTS	UNIT	HOURS	MAT.	INST.	TOTAL
Cleanout, wall					
2"	EA.	0.533	160	37.25	197
3"	"	0.533	230	37.25	267
4"	"	0.667	240	46.75	287
Floor					
2"	EA.	0.667	150	46.75	197
3"	"	0.667	200	46.75	247
4"	"	0.800	200	56.00	256
15430.25 HOSE BIBBS					
Hose bibb					
1/2"	EA.	0.267	9.07	18.75	27.82
3/4"	"	0.267	9.62	18.75	28.37
15430.60 VALVES					
Gate valve, 125 lb, bronze, soldered					
1/2"	EA.	0.200	25.75	14.00	39.75
3/4"	"	0.200	31.00	14.00	45.00
1"	"	0.267	38.00	18.75	56.75
Threaded					
1/4", 125 lb	EA.	0.320	29.75	22.50	52.25
1/2"					
125 lb	EA.	0.320	28.50	22.50	51.00
300 lb	"	0.320	72.00	22.50	94.50
3/4"					
125 lb	EA.	0.320	33.25	22.50	55.75
300 lb	"	0.320	86.00	22.50	109
1"					
125 lb	EA.	0.320	43.25	22.50	65.75
300 lb	"	0.400	120	28.00	148
1-1/2"					
125 lb	EA.	0.400	75.00	28.00	103
300 lb	"	0.444	220	31.00	251
2"					
125 lb	EA.	0.571	100	40.00	140
300 lb	"	0.667	280	46.75	327
Cast iron, flanged					
2", 150 lb	EA.	0.667	350	46.75	397
2-1/2"					
125 lb	EA.	0.667	340	46.75	387
250 lb	"	0.667	930	46.75	977
3"					
125 lb	EA.	0.800	410	56.00	466
250 lb	"	0.800	860	56.00	916
4"					
125 lb	EA.	1.143	540	80.00	620
150 lb	"	1.143	890	80.00	970
250 lb	"	1.143	1,160	80.00	1,240
6"					
125 lb	EA.	1.600	990	110	1,100
250 lb	"	1.600	2,310	110	2,420
8"					
125 lb	EA.	2.000	1,570	140	1,710
250 lb	"	2.000	4,480	140	4,620
OS&Y, flanged					

PLUMBING

15430.60 VALVES, Cont'd...	UNIT	HOURS	MAT.	INST.	TOTAL
2"					
125 lb	EA.	0.667	310	46.75	357
250 lb	"	0.667	810	46.75	857
2-1/2"					
125 lb	EA.	0.667	320	46.75	367
250 lb	"	0.800	1,010	56.00	1,066
3"					
125 lb	EA.	0.800	360	56.00	416
250 lb	"	0.800	1,040	56.00	1,096
4"					
125 lb	EA.	1.333	470	93.00	563
250 lb	"	1.333	1,590	93.00	1,683
6"					
125 lb	EA.	1.600	790	110	900
250 lb	"	1.600	2,530	110	2,640
Ball valve, bronze, 250 lb, threaded					
1/2"	EA.	0.320	14.25	22.50	36.75
3/4"	"	0.320	21.25	22.50	43.75
1"	"	0.400	27.00	28.00	55.00
1-1/4"	"	0.444	39.50	31.00	70.50
1-1/2"	"	0.500	63.00	35.00	98.00
2"	"	0.571	71.00	40.00	111
Angle valve, bronze, 150 lb, threaded					
1/2"	EA.	0.286	87.00	20.00	107
3/4"	"	0.320	120	22.50	143
1"	"	0.320	170	22.50	193
1-1/4"	"	0.400	220	28.00	248
1-1/2"	"	0.444	290	31.00	321
Balancing valve, with meter connections,					
1/2"	EA.	0.320	82.00	22.50	105
3/4"	"	0.364	86.00	25.50	112
1"	"	0.400	110	28.00	138
1-1/4"	"	0.444	150	31.00	181
1-1/2"	"	0.533	190	37.25	227
2"	"	0.667	260	46.75	307
2-1/2"	"	0.800	520	56.00	576
3"	"	1.000	760	70.00	830
4"	"	1.333	1,070	93.00	1,163
Pressure reducing valve, bronze, threaded,					
1/2"	EA.	0.500	160	35.00	195
3/4"	"	0.500	160	35.00	195
1"	"	0.500	260	35.00	295
1-1/4"	"	0.571	370	40.00	410
1-1/2"	"	0.667	430	46.75	477
Pressure regulating valve, bronze, class 300					
1"	EA.	0.500	620	35.00	655
1-1/2"	"	0.615	830	43.00	873
2"	"	0.800	930	56.00	986
3"	"	1.143	1,060	80.00	1,140
4"	"	1.600	1,320	110	1,430
Solar water temperature regulating valve					
3/4"	EA.	0.667	640	46.75	687
1"	"	0.800	650	56.00	706

PLUMBING

15430.60 VALVES, Cont'd...	UNIT	HOURS	MAT.	INST.	TOTAL
1-1/4"	EA.	0.889	700	62.00	762
1-1/2"	"	1.000	780	70.00	850
2"	"	1.143	970	80.00	1,050
2-1/2"	"	2.000	1,830	140	1,970
Tempering valve, threaded					
3/4"	EA.	0.267	350	18.75	369
1"	"	0.320	440	22.50	463
1-1/4"	"	0.400	650	28.00	678
1-1/2"	"	0.400	740	28.00	768
2"	"	0.500	1,020	35.00	1,055
2-1/2"	"	0.667	1,720	46.75	1,767
3"	"	0.800	2,270	56.00	2,326
4"	"	1.143	4,540	80.00	4,620
Thermostatic mixing valve, threaded					
1/2"	EA.	0.286	120	20.00	140
3/4"	"	0.320	120	22.50	143
1"	"	0.348	440	24.25	464
1-1/2"	"	0.400	500	28.00	528
2"	"	0.500	620	35.00	655
Sweat connection					
1/2"	EA.	0.286	130	20.00	150
3/4"	"	0.320	160	22.50	183
Mixing valve, sweat connection					
1/2"	EA.	0.286	72.00	20.00	92.00
3/4"	"	0.320	72.00	22.50	94.50
Liquid level gauge, aluminum body					
3/4"	EA.	0.320	360	22.50	383
4125 psi, pvc body					
3/4"	EA.	0.320	430	22.50	453
150 psi, crs body					
3/4"	EA.	0.320	340	22.50	363
1"	"	0.320	370	22.50	393
175 psi, bronze body, 1/2"	"	0.286	690	20.00	710
15430.65 VACUUM BREAKERS					
Vacuum breaker, atmospheric, threaded					
3/4"	EA.	0.320	45.75	22.50	68.25
1"	"	0.320	67.00	22.50	89.50
Anti-siphon, brass					
3/4"	EA.	0.320	49.50	22.50	72.00
1"	"	0.320	77.00	22.50	99.50
1-1/4"	"	0.400	130	28.00	158
1-1/2"	"	0.444	160	31.00	191
2"	"	0.500	250	35.00	285
15430.68 STRAINERS					
Strainer, Y pattern, 125 psi, cast iron body,					
3/4"	EA.	0.286	11.50	20.00	31.50
1"	"	0.320	14.75	22.50	37.25
250 psi, brass body, threaded					
3/4"	EA.	0.320	29.75	22.50	52.25
1"	"	0.320	41.50	22.50	64.00
Cast iron body, threaded					
3/4"	EA.	0.320	17.50	22.50	40.00
1"	"	0.320	22.00	22.50	44.50

PLUMBING

15430.70 DRAINS, ROOF & FLOOR	UNIT	HOURS	MAT.	INST.	TOTAL
Floor drain, cast iron, with cast iron top					
2"	EA.	0.667	130	46.75	177
3"	"	0.667	140	46.75	187
4"	"	0.667	290	46.75	337
Roof drain, cast iron					
2"	EA.	0.667	210	46.75	257
3"	"	0.667	220	46.75	267
4"	"	0.667	280	46.75	327

15430.80 TRAPS	UNIT	HOURS	MAT.	INST.	TOTAL
Bucket trap, threaded					
3/4"	EA.	0.500	190	35.00	225
1"	"	0.533	540	37.25	577
Inverted bucket steam trap, threaded					
3/4"	EA.	0.500	230	35.00	265
1"	"	0.500	450	35.00	485
With stainless interior					
3/4"	EA.	0.500	160	35.00	195
1"	"	0.500	340	35.00	375
Brass interior					
3/4"	EA.	0.500	250	35.00	285
1"	"	0.533	510	37.25	547
Cast steel body, threaded, high temperature					
3/4"	EA.	0.500	660	35.00	695
1"	"	0.571	890	40.00	930
Float trap, 15 psi					
3/4"	EA.	0.500	160	35.00	195
1"	"	0.533	250	37.25	287
Float and thermostatic trap, 15 psi					
3/4"	EA.	0.500	180	35.00	215
1"	"	0.533	200	37.25	237
Steam trap, cast iron body, threaded, 125 psi					
3/4"	EA.	0.500	210	35.00	245
1"	"	0.533	240	37.25	277
Thermostatic trap, low pressure, angle type, 25					
3/4"	EA.	0.500	110	35.00	145
1"	"	0.533	140	37.25	177
Cast iron body, threaded, 125 psi					
3/4"	EA.	0.500	140	35.00	175
1"	"	0.571	180	40.00	220

PLUMBING FIXTURES

15440.12 DISPOSALS & ACCESSORIES	UNIT	HOURS	MAT.	INST.	TOTAL
Continuous feed					
Minimum	EA.	1.600	72.00	110	182
Average	"	2.000	200	140	340
Maximum	"	2.667	390	190	580
Batch feed, 1/2 hp					
Minimum	EA.	1.600	280	110	390
Average	"	2.000	550	140	690
Maximum	"	2.667	950	190	1,140
Hot water dispenser					
Minimum	EA.	1.600	200	110	310
Average	"	2.000	320	140	460

PLUMBING FIXTURES

15440.12 DISPOSALS & ACCESSORIES, Cont'd...	UNIT	HOURS	MAT.	INST.	TOTAL
Maximum	EA.	2.667	510	190	700
Epoxy finish faucet	"	1.600	290	110	400
Lock stop assembly	"	1.000	61.00	70.00	131
Mounting gasket	"	0.667	7.04	46.75	53.79
Tailpipe gasket	"	0.667	1.03	46.75	47.78
Stopper assembly	"	0.800	24.00	56.00	80.00
Switch assembly, on/off	"	1.333	27.50	93.00	121
Tailpipe gasket washer	"	0.400	1.10	28.00	29.10
Stop gasket	"	0.444	2.42	31.00	33.42
Tailpipe flange	"	0.400	0.27	28.00	28.27
Tailpipe	"	0.500	3.13	35.00	38.13
15440.18 HYDRANTS					
Wall hydrant					
8" thick	EA.	1.333	360	93.00	453
12" thick	"	1.600	430	110	540
15440.70 WATER HEATERS					
Water heater, electric					
6 gal	EA.	1.333	350	93.00	443
10 gal	"	1.333	360	93.00	453
15 gal	"	1.333	360	93.00	453
20 gal	"	1.600	500	110	610
30 gal	"	1.600	520	110	630
40 gal	"	1.600	560	110	670
52 gal	"	2.000	630	140	770
66 gal	"	2.000	760	140	900
80 gal	"	2.000	830	140	970
100 gal	"	2.667	1,030	190	1,220
120 gal	"	2.667	1,320	190	1,510
Oil fired					
20 gal	EA.	4.000	1,300	280	1,580
50 gal	"	5.714	2,020	400	2,420
15440.90 MISCELLANEOUS FIXTURES					
Electric water cooler					
Floor mounted	EA.	2.667	1,010	190	1,200
Wall mounted	"	2.667	950	190	1,140
15450.30 PUMPS					
In-line pump, bronze, centrifugal					
5 gpm, 20' head	EA.	0.500	560	35.00	595
20 gpm, 40' head	"	0.500	1,010	35.00	1,045
50 gpm					
50' head	EA.	1.000	1,150	70.00	1,220
Cast iron, centrifugal					
50 gpm, 200' head	EA.	1.000	1,090	70.00	1,160
100 gpm					
100' head	EA.	1.333	1,860	93.00	1,953
Centrifugal, close coupled, c.i., single stage					
50 gpm, 100' head	EA.	1.000	1,300	70.00	1,370
100 gpm, 100' head	"	1.333	1,580	93.00	1,673
Base mounted					
50 gpm, 100' head	EA.	1.000	2,660	70.00	2,730
100 gpm, 50' head	"	1.333	3,030	93.00	3,123
200 gpm, 100' head	"	2.000	3,870	140	4,010

PLUMBING FIXTURES

15450.30 PUMPS, Cont'd...	UNIT	HOURS	MAT.	INST.	TOTAL
300 gpm, 175' head	EA.	2.000	5,030	140	5,170
Condensate pump, simplex					
1000 sf EDR, 2 gpm	EA.	6.667	1,360	470	1,830
2000 sf EDR, 3 gpm	"	6.667	1,390	470	1,860
4000 sf EDR, 6 gpm	"	7.273	1,400	510	1,910
6000 sf EDR, 9 gpm	"	7.273	1,420	510	1,930
Duplex, bronze					
8000 sf EDR, 12 gpm	EA.	7.273	1,950	510	2,460
10,000 sf EDR, 15 gpm	"	10.000	2,020	700	2,720
15,000 sf EDR, 23 gpm	"	11.429	2,430	800	3,230
20,000 sf EDR, 30 gpm	"	16.000	2,830	1,120	3,950
25,000 sf EDR, 38 gpm	"	16.000	2,930	1,120	4,050
15480.10 SPECIAL SYSTEMS					
Air compressor, air cooled, two stage					
5.0 cfm, 175 psi	EA.	16.000	2,350	1,120	3,470
10 cfm, 175 psi	"	17.778	2,870	1,240	4,110
20 cfm, 175 psi	"	19.048	3,960	1,330	5,290
50 cfm, 125 psi	"	21.053	5,780	1,470	7,250
80 cfm, 125 psi	"	22.857	8,260	1,600	9,860
Single stage, 125 psi					
1.0 cfm	EA.	11.429	2,270	800	3,070
1.5 cfm	"	11.429	2,310	800	3,110
2.0 cfm	"	11.429	2,360	800	3,160
Automotive, hose reel, air and water, 50' hose	"	6.667	1,060	470	1,530
Lube equipment, 3 reel, with pumps	"	32.000	5,530	2,240	7,770
Tire changer					
Truck	EA.	11.429	14,430	800	15,230
Passenger car	"	6.154	3,410	430	3,840
Air hose reel, includes, 50' hose	"	6.154	900	430	1,330
Hose reel, 5 reel, motor oil, gear oil, lube, air &	"	32.000	8,420	2,240	10,660
Water hose reel, 50' hose	"	6.154	900	430	1,330
Pump, air operated, for motor or gear oil, fits	"	0.800	1,180	56.00	1,236
For chassis lube	"	0.800	1,930	56.00	1,986
Fuel dispensing pump, lighted dial, one					
One hose	EA.	6.667	4,200	470	4,670
Two hose	"	6.667	7,410	470	7,880
Two products, two hose	"	6.667	7,810	470	8,280

HEATING & VENTILATING

15555.10 BOILERS	UNIT	HOURS	MAT.	INST.	TOTAL
Electric, hot water					
115 mbh	EA.	12.000	3,880	1,080	4,960
175 mbh	"	12.000	4,290	1,080	5,370
235 mbh	"	12.000	4,900	1,080	5,980
940 mbh	"	24.000	11,910	2,170	14,080
1600 mbh	"	48.000	16,860	4,340	21,200
3000 mbh	"	60.000	25,190	5,430	30,620
6000 mbh	"	80.000	43,840	7,230	51,070

HEATING & VENTILATING

15610.10 FURNACES	UNIT	HOURS	MAT.	INST.	TOTAL
Electric, hot air					
40 mbh	EA.	4.000	810	280	1,090
60 mbh	"	4.211	880	290	1,170
80 mbh	"	4.444	960	310	1,270
100 mbh	"	4.706	1,080	330	1,410
125 mbh	"	4.848	1,320	340	1,660
160 mbh	"	5.000	1,810	350	2,160
200 mbh	"	5.161	2,640	360	3,000
400 mbh	"	5.333	4,680	370	5,050

REFRIGERATION

15670.10 CONDENSING UNITS	UNIT	HOURS	MAT.	INST.	TOTAL
Air cooled condenser, single circuit					
3 ton	EA.	1.333	1,430	93.00	1,523
5 ton	"	1.333	2,260	93.00	2,353
7.5 ton	"	3.810	3,690	270	3,960
20 ton	"	4.000	10,950	280	11,230
25 ton	"	4.000	16,500	280	16,780
30 ton	"	4.000	18,810	280	19,090
40 ton	"	5.714	24,320	400	24,720
50 ton	"	5.714	29,580	400	29,980
60 ton	"	5.000	34,060	350	34,410
With low ambient dampers					
3 ton	EA.	2.000	1,640	140	1,780
5 ton	"	2.000	2,590	140	2,730
7.5 ton	"	4.000	3,970	280	4,250
20 ton	"	5.333	10,980	370	11,350
25 ton	"	5.333	16,720	370	17,090
30 ton	"	5.333	19,210	370	19,580
40 ton	"	6.667	25,490	470	25,960
50 ton	"	7.273	30,740	510	31,250
60 ton	"	7.273	35,220	510	35,730
Dual circuit					
10 ton	EA.	4.000	3,510	280	3,790
15 ton	"	5.714	5,140	400	5,540
20 ton	"	5.714	10,500	400	10,900
25 ton	"	5.714	16,730	400	17,130
30 ton	"	5.714	19,460	400	19,860
40 ton	"	6.667	27,830	470	28,300
50 ton	"	6.667	30,740	470	31,210
60 ton	"	6.667	31,910	470	32,380
80 ton	"	8.889	39,900	620	40,520
100 ton	"	8.889	46,710	620	47,330
120 ton	"	8.889	55,460	620	56,080
With low ambient dampers					
15 ton	EA.	5.714	5,720	400	6,120
20 ton	"	5.714	11,170	400	11,570
25 ton	"	5.714	17,710	400	18,110
30 ton	"	5.714	19,970	400	20,370
40 ton	"	6.667	28,800	470	29,270
50 ton	"	6.667	31,720	470	32,190
60 ton	"	6.667	32,890	470	33,360
80 ton	"	8.889	41,830	620	42,450

REFRIGERATION

15670.10 CONDENSING UNITS, Cont'd...	UNIT	HOURS	MAT.	INST.	TOTAL
100 ton	EA.	8.889	48,650	620	49,270
120 ton	"	8.889	57,990	620	58,610
15680.10 CHILLERS					
Chiller, reciprocal					
Air cooled, remote condenser, starter					
20 ton	EA.	8.000	29,960	720	30,680
25 ton	"	8.000	33,810	720	34,530
30 ton	"	8.000	35,750	720	36,470
40 ton	"	12.000	52,870	1,080	53,950
50 ton	"	13.333	58,690	1,210	59,900
60 ton	"	14.118	65,930	1,280	67,210
80 ton	"	21.818	81,350	1,970	83,320
100 ton	"	24.000	96,330	2,170	98,500
120 ton	"	26.667	109,180	2,410	111,590
150 ton	"	30.000	139,140	2,710	141,850
180 ton	"	34.286	159,480	3,100	162,580
200 ton	"	40.000	175,530	3,620	179,150
Water cooled, with starter					
20 ton	EA.	8.000	25,690	720	26,410
25 ton	"	8.000	28,470	720	29,190
30 ton	"	12.000	34,240	1,080	35,320
40 ton	"	12.000	47,090	1,080	48,170
50 ton	"	13.333	51,370	1,210	52,580
60 ton	"	14.118	55,650	1,280	56,930
80 ton	"	21.818	64,220	1,970	66,190
100 ton	"	24.000	74,920	2,170	77,090
120 ton	"	26.667	87,770	2,410	90,180
150 ton	"	30.000	109,180	2,710	111,890
180 ton	"	34.286	113,450	3,100	116,550
200 ton	"	40.000	119,870	3,620	123,490
Packaged, air cooled, with starter					
20 ton	EA.	6.000	28,690	540	29,230
25 ton	"	6.000	31,040	540	31,580
30 ton	"	6.000	36,180	540	36,720
40 ton	"	6.000	41,530	540	42,070
50 ton	"	8.000	46,880	720	47,600
60 ton	"	8.000	55,230	720	55,950
80 ton	"	12.000	64,430	1,080	65,510
100 ton	"	12.000	75,550	1,080	76,630
120 ton	"	12.000	85,830	1,080	86,910
Heat recovery, air cooled, with starter					
40 ton	EA.	12.000	48,160	1,080	49,240
50 ton	"	12.000	55,650	1,080	56,730
60 ton	"	16.000	61,010	1,450	62,460
75 ton	"	24.000	69,780	2,170	71,950
100 ton	"	24.000	79,630	2,170	81,800
Water cooled, with starter					
40 ton	EA.	12.000	47,520	1,080	48,600
50 ton	"	12.000	56,730	1,080	57,810
60 ton	"	16.000	62,500	1,450	63,950
75 ton	"	24.000	75,990	2,170	78,160
100 ton	"	26.667	85,830	2,410	88,240
Centrifugal, single bundle condenser, with					

REFRIGERATION

15680.10 CHILLERS, Cont'd...	UNIT	HOURS	MAT.	INST.	TOTAL
80 ton	EA.	34.286	112,380	3,100	115,480
130 ton	"	40.000	113,820	3,620	117,440
160 ton	"	43.636	115,680	3,950	119,630
180 ton	"	48.000	123,900	4,340	128,240
230 ton	"	53.333	129,460	4,820	134,280
280 ton	"	60.000	142,640	5,430	148,070
360 ton	"	60.000	159,100	5,430	164,530
460 ton	"	80.000	196,150	7,230	203,380
560 ton	"	85.714	214,610	7,750	222,360
670 ton	"	96.000	261,580	8,680	270,260
15710.10 COOLING TOWERS					
Cooling tower, propeller type					
100 ton	EA.	8.000	11,660	720	12,380
200 ton	"	12.000	19,360	1,080	20,440
300 ton	"	20.000	29,260	1,810	31,070
400 ton	"	24.000	38,940	2,170	41,110
600 ton	"	34.286	58,410	3,100	61,510
800 ton	"	48.000	77,880	4,340	82,220
1000 ton	"	60.000	93,500	5,430	98,930
Centrifugal					
100 ton	EA.	8.000	16,170	720	16,890
200 ton	"	12.000	24,750	1,080	25,830
300 ton	"	20.000	34,980	1,810	36,790
400 ton	"	24.000	46,640	2,170	48,810
600 ton	"	34.286	66,760	3,100	69,860
800 ton	"	48.000	88,990	4,340	93,330
1000 ton	"	60.000	109,120	5,430	114,550

HEAT TRANSFER

15780.10 COMPUTER ROOM A/C	UNIT	HOURS	MAT.	INST.	TOTAL
Air cooled, alarm, high efficiency filter, elec.					
3 ton	EA.	6.154	16,140	430	16,570
5 ton	"	6.667	17,230	470	17,700
7.5 ton	"	8.000	31,220	560	31,780
10 ton	"	10.000	32,630	700	33,330
15 ton	"	11.429	35,850	800	36,650
Steam heat					
3 ton	EA.	6.154	17,270	430	17,700
5 ton	"	6.667	18,370	470	18,840
7.5 ton	"	8.000	29,260	560	29,820
10 ton	"	10.000	30,140	700	30,840
15 ton	"	11.429	33,330	800	34,130
Hot water heat					
3 ton	EA.	6.154	17,270	430	17,700
5 ton	"	6.667	18,370	470	18,840
7.5 ton	"	8.000	29,260	560	29,820
10 ton	"	10.000	30,140	700	30,840
15 ton	"	11.429	33,440	800	34,240
Air cooled condenser, low ambient damper					
3 ton	EA.	1.600	1,640	110	1,750
5 ton	"	2.000	2,590	140	2,730
7.5 ton	"	4.000	3,970	280	4,250
10 ton	"	5.714	5,810	400	6,210

HEAT TRANSFER

15780.10	COMPUTER ROOM A/C, Cont'd...	UNIT	HOURS	MAT.	INST.	TOTAL
	15 ton	EA.	4.706	6,410	330	6,740
Water cooled, high efficiency filter, alarm, elec.						
	3 ton	EA.	5.714	17,050	400	17,450
	5 ton	"	6.667	18,370	470	18,840
	7.5 ton	"	10.000	29,260	700	29,960
	10 ton	"	11.429	30,360	800	31,160
	15 ton	"	13.333	35,530	930	36,460
Steam heat						
	3 ton	EA.	5.714	19,470	400	19,870
	5 ton	"	6.667	22,220	470	22,690
	7.5 ton	"	10.000	31,350	700	32,050
	10 ton	"	11.429	32,450	800	33,250
	15 ton	"	13.333	37,730	930	38,660
Hot water heat						
	3 ton	EA.	5.714	19,470	400	19,870
	5 ton	"	6.667	20,790	470	21,260
	7.5 ton	"	10.000	31,350	700	32,050
	10 ton	"	11.429	32,450	800	33,250
	15 ton	"	13.333	37,730	930	38,660
Chilled water, alarm, high eff. filter, elec. heat						
	7.5 ton	EA.	7.273	13,640	510	14,150
	10 ton	"	8.889	14,300	620	14,920
	15 ton	"	10.000	16,280	700	16,980
Steam heat						
	7.5 ton	EA.	7.273	15,620	510	16,130
	10 ton	"	8.889	16,280	620	16,900
	15 ton	"	10.000	18,260	700	18,960
Hot water heat						
	7.5 ton	EA.	7.273	15,620	510	16,130
	10 ton	"	8.889	16,280	620	16,900
	15 ton	"	10.000	18,260	700	18,960
15780.20	**ROOFTOP UNITS**					
Packaged, single zone rooftop unit, with roof						
	2 ton	EA.	8.000	3,400	560	3,960
	3 ton	"	8.000	3,580	560	4,140
	4 ton	"	10.000	3,900	700	4,600
	5 ton	"	13.333	4,240	930	5,170
	7.5 ton	"	16.000	6,160	1,120	7,280
15820.10	**DEHUMIDIFIERS**					
Dessicant dehumidifier, 1125 cfm		EA.				27,850
15830.20	**FAN COIL UNITS**					
Fan coil unit, 2 pipe, complete						
	200 cfm ceiling hung	EA.	2.667	920	190	1,110
	Floor mounted	"	2.000	870	140	1,010
	300 cfm, ceiling hung	"	3.200	980	220	1,200
	Floor mounted	"	2.667	930	190	1,120
	400 cfm, ceiling hung	"	3.810	1,030	270	1,300
	Floor mounted	"	2.667	990	190	1,180
	500 cfm, ceiling hung	"	4.000	1,200	280	1,480
	Floor mounted	"	3.077	1,160	220	1,380
	600 cfm, ceiling hung	"	4.420	1,520	310	1,830
	Floor mounted	"	3.636	1,410	250	1,660
	800 cfm, ceiling hung	"	5.000	1,770	350	2,120

HEAT TRANSFER

15830.20 FAN COIL UNITS, Cont'd...	UNIT	HOURS	MAT.	INST.	TOTAL
Floor mounted	EA.	3.810	1,410	270	1,680
1000 cfm, ceiling hung	"	5.714	2,020	400	2,420
Floor mounted	"	4.211	2,220	290	2,510
1200 cfm ceiling hung	"	6.667	2,300	470	2,770
Floor mounted	"	5.000	2,410	350	2,760
15830.70 UNIT HEATERS					
Steam unit heater, horizontal					
12,500 btuh, 200 cfm	EA.	1.333	430	93.00	523
17,000 btuh, 300 cfm	"	1.333	570	93.00	663
40,000 btuh, 500 cfm	"	1.333	690	93.00	783
60,000 btuh, 700 cfm	"	1.333	730	93.00	823
70,000 btuh, 1000 cfm	"	2.000	750	140	890
Vertical					
12,500 btuh, 200 cfm	EA.	1.333	430	93.00	523
17,000 btuh, 300 cfm	"	1.333	720	93.00	813
40,000 btuh, 500 cfm	"	1.333	690	93.00	783
60,000 btuh, 700 cfm	"	1.333	730	93.00	823
70,000 btuh, 1000 cfm	"	1.333	750	93.00	843
Gas unit heater, horizontal					
27,400 btuh	EA.	3.200	660	220	880
38,000 btuh	"	3.200	690	220	910
56,000 btuh	"	3.200	730	220	950
82,200 btuh	"	3.200	750	220	970
103,900 btuh	"	5.000	840	350	1,190
125,700 btuh	"	5.000	990	350	1,340
133,200 btuh	"	5.000	1,070	350	1,420
149,000 btuh	"	5.000	1,250	350	1,600
172,000 btuh	"	5.000	1,350	350	1,700
190,000 btuh	"	5.000	1,420	350	1,770
225,000 btuh	"	5.000	1,570	350	1,920
Hot water unit heater, horizontal					
12,500 btuh, 200 cfm	EA.	1.333	350	93.00	443
17,000 btuh, 300 cfm	"	1.333	390	93.00	483
25,000 btuh, 500 cfm	"	1.333	450	93.00	543
30,000 btuh, 700 cfm	"	1.333	520	93.00	613
50,000 btuh, 1000 cfm	"	2.000	570	140	710
60,000 btuh, 1300 cfm	"	2.000	600	140	740
Vertical					
12,500 btuh, 200 cfm	EA.	1.333	510	93.00	603
17,000 btuh, 300 cfm	"	1.333	510	93.00	603
25,000 btuh, 500 cfm	"	1.333	510	93.00	603
30,000 btuh, 700 cfm	"	1.333	510	93.00	603
50,000 btuh, 1000 cfm	"	1.333	530	93.00	623
60,000 btuh, 1300 cfm	"	1.333	650	93.00	743
Cabinet unit heaters, ceiling, exposed, hot					
200 cfm	EA.	2.667	1,000	190	1,190
300 cfm	"	3.200	1,070	220	1,290
400 cfm	"	3.810	1,110	270	1,380
600 cfm	"	4.211	1,140	290	1,430
800 cfm	"	5.000	1,420	350	1,770
1000 cfm	"	5.714	1,860	400	2,260
1200 cfm	"	6.667	2,000	470	2,470
2000 cfm	"	8.889	3,420	620	4,040

AIR HANDLING

15855.10 AIR HANDLING UNITS	UNIT	HOURS	MAT.	INST.	TOTAL
Air handling unit, medium pressure, single					
1500 cfm	EA.	5.000	4,000	350	4,350
3000 cfm	"	8.889	5,260	620	5,880
4000 cfm	"	10.000	6,730	700	7,430
5000 cfm	"	10.667	8,490	750	9,240
6000 cfm	"	11.429	10,910	800	11,710
7000 cfm	"	12.308	12,520	860	13,380
8500 cfm	"	13.333	15,390	930	16,320
10,500 cfm	"	16.000	16,910	1,120	18,030
12,500 cfm	"	17.778	19,460	1,240	20,700
15,500 cfm	"	22.857	25,160	1,600	26,760
17,500 cfm	"	26.667	27,920	1,870	29,790
20,500 cfm	"	32.000	31,560	2,240	33,800
25,000 cfm	"	40.000	35,770	2,800	38,570
31,500 cfm	"	53.333	44,250	3,730	47,980
Rooftop air handling units					
4950 cfm	EA.	8.889	11,500	620	12,120
7370 cfm	"	11.429	14,580	800	15,380
9790 cfm	"	13.333	15,510	930	16,440
14,300 cfm	"	11.429	21,910	800	22,710
21,725 cfm	"	11.429	31,040	800	31,840
33,000 cfm	"	13.333	43,820	930	44,750

15870.20 EXHAUST FANS					
Belt drive roof exhaust fans					
640 cfm, 2618 fpm	EA.	1.000	1,030	70.00	1,100
940 cfm, 2604 fpm	"	1.000	1,340	70.00	1,410
1050 cfm, 3325 fpm	"	1.000	1,200	70.00	1,270
1170 cfm, 2373 fpm	"	1.000	1,740	70.00	1,810
2440 cfm, 4501 fpm	"	1.000	1,360	70.00	1,430
2760 cfm, 4950 fpm	"	1.000	1,510	70.00	1,580
3890 cfm, 6769 fpm	"	1.000	1,720	70.00	1,790
2380 cfm, 3382 fpm	"	1.000	1,900	70.00	1,970
2880 cfm, 3859 fpm	"	1.000	1,990	70.00	2,060
3200 cfm, 4173 fpm	"	1.333	2,010	93.00	2,103
3660 cfm, 3437 fpm	"	1.333	2,050	93.00	2,143
4070 cfm, 3694 fpm	"	1.333	2,600	93.00	2,693
5030 cfm, 3251 fpm	"	1.333	1,810	93.00	1,903
5830 cfm, 6932 fpm	"	1.600	2,520	110	2,630
6380 cfm, 3817 fpm	"	1.600	2,520	110	2,630
8460 cfm, 6721 fpm	"	1.600	2,430	110	2,540
10,970 cfm, 5906 fpm	"	2.000	2,980	140	3,120
12,470 cfm, 6620 fpm	"	2.667	3,400	190	3,590
7000 cfm, 3449 fpm	"	2.000	2,430	140	2,570
13,000 cfm, 5456 fpm	"	2.000	3,600	140	3,740
11,250 cfm, 4854 fpm	"	2.000	3,290	140	3,430
18,490 cfm, 7405 fpm	"	3.636	4,810	250	5,060
11,300 cfm, 3232 fpm	"	3.478	3,120	240	3,360
18,330 cfm, 4488 fpm	"	3.478	5,200	240	5,440
21,720 cfm, 5131 fpm	"	3.478	5,470	240	5,710
31,110 cfm, 6965 fpm	"	4.000	6,020	280	6,300
Direct drive fans					
60 to 390 cfm	EA.	1.000	850	70.00	920
145 to 590 cfm	"	1.000	1,020	70.00	1,090

AIR HANDLING

15870.20 EXHAUST FANS, Cont'd...	UNIT	HOURS	MAT.	INST.	TOTAL
295 to 860 cfm	EA.	1.000	1,240	70.00	1,310
235 to 1300 cfm	"	1.000	1,330	70.00	1,400
415 to 1630 cfm	"	1.000	1,510	70.00	1,580
590 to 2045 cfm	"	1.000	1,740	70.00	1,810
805 cfm, 3235 fpm	"	1.000	1,140	70.00	1,210
1455 cfm, 4360 fpm	"	1.000	1,230	70.00	1,300
1385 cfm, 3655 fpm	"	1.000	1,270	70.00	1,340
2260 cfm, 4930 fpm	"	1.000	1,330	70.00	1,400
1720 cfm, 3870 fpm	"	1.000	1,450	70.00	1,520
2700 cfm, 5220 fpm	"	1.000	1,350	70.00	1,420
Terminal blenders and cooling					
400 cfm	EA.	1.600	460	110	570
800 cfm	"	1.600	510	110	620
1200 cfm	"	2.000	600	140	740
2000 cfm	"	2.000	690	140	830

AIR DISTRIBUTION

15890.10 METAL DUCTWORK	UNIT	HOURS	MAT.	INST.	TOTAL
Rectangular duct					
Galvanized steel					
Minimum	Lb.	0.073	0.88	5.09	5.97
Average	"	0.089	1.10	6.22	7.32
Maximum	"	0.133	1.68	9.33	11.01
Aluminum					
Minimum	Lb.	0.160	2.29	11.25	13.54
Average	"	0.200	3.05	14.00	17.05
Maximum	"	0.267	3.79	18.75	22.54
Fittings					
Minimum	EA.	0.267	7.26	18.75	26.01
Average	"	0.400	11.00	28.00	39.00
Maximum	"	0.800	16.00	56.00	72.00
For work					
10-20' high, add per pound, $.30					
30-50', add per pound, $.50					
15890.30 FLEXIBLE DUCTWORK					
Flexible duct, 1.25" fiberglass					
5" dia.	L.F.	0.040	3.31	2.80	6.11
6" dia.	"	0.044	3.68	3.11	6.79
7" dia.	"	0.047	4.54	3.29	7.83
8" dia.	"	0.050	4.76	3.50	8.26
10" dia.	"	0.057	6.34	4.00	10.34
12" dia.	"	0.062	6.93	4.30	11.23
14" dia.	"	0.067	8.69	4.66	13.35
16" dia.	"	0.073	13.00	5.09	18.09
Flexible duct connector, 3" wide fabric	"	0.133	2.31	9.33	11.64
15895.10 ROOF CURBS					
8" high, insulated, with liner and raised can					
15" x 15"	EA.	0.400	110	28.00	138
17" x 17"	"	0.400	110	28.00	138
19" x 19"	"	0.400	120	28.00	148
21" x 21"	"	0.400	130	28.00	158
25" x 25"	"	0.500	150	35.00	185

AIR DISTRIBUTION

15895.10 ROOF CURBS, Cont'd...	UNIT	HOURS	MAT.	INST.	TOTAL
28" x 28"	EA.	0.533	160	37.25	197
32" x 32"	"	0.571	170	40.00	210
36" x 36"	"	0.571	190	40.00	230
40" x 40"	"	0.571	220	40.00	260
44" x 44"	"	0.615	240	43.00	283
48" x 48"	"	0.615	540	43.00	583
15910.10 DAMPERS					
Horizontal parallel aluminum backdraft damper					
12" x 12"	EA.	0.200	69.00	14.00	83.00
16" x 16"	"	0.229	71.00	16.00	87.00
20" x 20"	"	0.286	91.00	20.00	111
24" x 24"	"	0.400	110	28.00	138
28" x 28"	"	0.444	150	31.00	181
32" x 32"	"	0.500	210	35.00	245
36" x 36"	"	0.571	250	40.00	290
40" x 40"	"	0.667	320	46.75	367
44" x 44"	"	0.727	370	51.00	421
48" x 48"	"	0.800	450	56.00	506
"Up", parallel dampers					
12" x 12"	EA.	0.200	89.00	14.00	103
16" x 16"	"	0.229	120	16.00	136
20" x 20"	"	0.286	140	20.00	160
24" x 24"	"	0.400	150	28.00	178
28" x 28"	"	0.444	220	31.00	251
32" x 32"	"	0.500	250	35.00	285
36" x 36"	"	0.571	260	40.00	300
40" x 40"	"	0.667	350	46.75	397
44" x 44"	"	0.727	420	51.00	471
48" x 48"	"	0.800	520	56.00	576
"Down", parallel dampers					
12" x 12"	EA.	0.200	89.00	14.00	103
16" x 16"	"	0.229	120	16.00	136
20" x 20"	"	0.286	140	20.00	160
24" x 24"	"	0.400	150	28.00	178
28" x 28"	"	0.444	220	31.00	251
32" x 32"	"	0.500	250	35.00	285
36" x 36"	"	0.571	260	40.00	300
40" x 40"	"	0.667	350	46.75	397
44" x 44"	"	0.727	420	51.00	471
48" x 48"	"	0.800	520	56.00	576
Fire damper, 1.5 hr rating					
12" x 12"	EA.	0.400	30.25	28.00	58.25
16" x 16"	"	0.400	48.50	28.00	76.50
20" x 20"	"	0.400	53.00	28.00	81.00
24" x 24"	"	0.400	61.00	28.00	89.00
28" x 28"	"	0.571	73.00	40.00	113
32" x 32"	"	0.667	85.00	46.75	132
36" x 36"	"	0.800	100	56.00	156
40" x 40"	"	0.889	120	62.00	182
44" x 44"	"	1.000	140	70.00	210
48" x 48"	"	1.143	200	80.00	280

MECHANICAL

AIR DISTRIBUTION

15940.10 DIFFUSERS	UNIT	HOURS	MAT.	INST.	TOTAL
Ceiling diffusers, round, baked enamel finish					
6" dia.	EA.	0.267	54.00	18.75	72.75
8" dia.	"	0.333	65.00	23.25	88.25
10" dia.	"	0.333	72.00	23.25	95.25
12" dia.	"	0.333	92.00	23.25	115
14" dia.	"	0.364	110	25.50	136
16" dia.	"	0.364	140	25.50	166
18" dia.	"	0.400	160	28.00	188
20" dia.	"	0.400	190	28.00	218
Rectangular					
6x6"	EA.	0.267	58.00	18.75	76.75
9x9"	"	0.400	70.00	28.00	98.00
12x12"	"	0.400	100	28.00	128
15x15"	"	0.400	130	28.00	158
18x18"	"	0.400	160	28.00	188
21x21"	"	0.500	200	35.00	235
24x24"	"	0.500	230	35.00	265
Lay in, flush mounted, perforated face, with					
6x6/24x24	EA.	0.320	83.00	22.50	106
8x8/24x24	"	0.320	83.00	22.50	106
9x9/24x24	"	0.320	83.00	22.50	106
10x10/24x24	"	0.320	90.00	22.50	113
12x12/24x24	"	0.320	96.00	22.50	119
15x15/24x24	"	0.320	130	22.50	153
18x6/24x24	"	0.320	96.00	22.50	119
18x18/24x24	"	0.320	150	22.50	173
Two-way slot diffuser with balancing damper,	"	0.800	92.00	56.00	148
15940.20 RELIEF VENTILATORS					
Intake ventilator, aluminum, with screen, no					
12" x 12"	EA.	0.667	200	46.75	247
16" x 16"	"	0.800	270	56.00	326
20" x 20"	"	0.800	440	56.00	496
30" x 30"	"	1.143	690	80.00	770
36" x 36"	"	1.333	1,050	93.00	1,143
42" x 42"	"	1.333	1,430	93.00	1,523
48" x 48"	"	1.600	1,720	110	1,830
15940.40 REGISTERS AND GRILLES					
Lay in flush mounted, perforated face, return					
6x6/24x24	EA.	0.320	48.50	22.50	71.00
8x8/24x24	"	0.320	48.50	22.50	71.00
9x9/24x24	"	0.320	53.00	22.50	75.50
10x10/24x24	"	0.320	57.00	22.50	79.50
12x12/24x24	"	0.320	57.00	22.50	79.50
Rectangular, ceiling return, single deflection					
10x10	EA.	0.400	29.25	28.00	57.25
12x12	"	0.400	34.00	28.00	62.00
14x14	"	0.400	41.50	28.00	69.50
16x8	"	0.400	34.00	28.00	62.00
16x16	"	0.400	34.00	28.00	62.00
18x8	"	0.400	39.00	28.00	67.00
20x20	"	0.400	63.00	28.00	91.00
24x12	"	0.400	92.00	28.00	120
24x18	"	0.400	120	28.00	148

AIR DISTRIBUTION

15940.40 REGISTERS AND GRILLES, Cont'd...	UNIT	HOURS	MAT.	INST.	TOTAL
36x24	EA.	0.444	220	31.00	251
36x30	"	0.444	330	31.00	361
Wall, return air register					
12x12	EA.	0.200	48.50	14.00	62.50
16x16	"	0.200	71.00	14.00	85.00
18x18	"	0.200	85.00	14.00	99.00
20x20	"	0.200	100	14.00	114
24x24	"	0.200	140	14.00	154
Ceiling, return air grille					
6x6	EA.	0.267	28.00	18.75	46.75
8x8	"	0.320	35.00	22.50	57.50
10x10	"	0.320	43.25	22.50	65.75
Ceiling, exhaust grille, aluminum egg crate					
6x6	EA.	0.267	19.25	18.75	38.00
8x8	"	0.320	19.25	22.50	41.75
10x10	"	0.320	21.25	22.50	43.75
12x12	"	0.400	26.25	28.00	54.25
14x14	"	0.400	34.50	28.00	62.50
16x16	"	0.400	40.50	28.00	68.50
18x18	"	0.400	48.50	28.00	76.50

CONTROLS

15950.10 HVAC CONTROLS	UNIT	HOURS	MAT.	INST.	TOTAL
Pressure gauge, direct reading gage cock and	EA.	0.500	120	35.00	155
Control valve, 1", modulating					
2-way	EA.	0.667	910	46.75	957
3-way	"	1.000	1,030	70.00	1,100
Self contained control valve w/ sensing elmnt,	"	0.500	180	35.00	215
Inst air syst 2-1/2 hp comp, rcvr refrg dryer	"				7,700
Thermostat primary control device	"				170
Humidistat primary control device	"				140
Timers primary control device, indoor/outdoor,	"				270
Thermometer, dir. reading, 3 dial	"				140
Control dampers, round					
6" dia.	EA.	0.320	93.00	22.50	116
8" dia	"	0.320	130	22.50	153
10" dia	"	0.320	180	22.50	203
12" dia	"	0.320	230	22.50	253
12" dia	"	0.400	340	28.00	368
18" dia	"	0.400	360	28.00	388
20" dia	"	0.400	480	28.00	508
Rectangular, parallel blade standard leakage					
12" x 12"	EA.	0.400	69.00	28.00	97.00
16" x 16"	"	0.400	100	28.00	128
20" x 20"	"	0.400	120	28.00	148
28" x 28"	"	0.500	150	35.00	185
32" x 32"	"	0.500	180	35.00	215
36" x 36"	"	0.667	260	46.75	307
40" x 40"	"	0.800	260	56.00	316
44" x 44"	"	1.000	320	70.00	390
48" x 48"	"	1.143	360	80.00	440
48" x 52"	"	1.333	390	93.00	483
48" x 56"	"	1.333	430	93.00	523

MECHANICAL

CONTROLS

15950.10 HVAC CONTROLS, Cont'd...	UNIT	HOURS	MAT.	INST.	TOTAL
48" x 60"	EA.	1.333	460	93.00	553
48" x 64"	"	1.333	470	93.00	563
48" x 68"	"	1.333	520	93.00	613
48" x 72"	"	1.333	560	93.00	653
Low leakage					
12" x 12"	EA.	0.400	130	28.00	158
16" x 16"	"	0.400	160	28.00	188
20" x 20"	"	0.400	220	28.00	248
24" x 24"	"	0.400	300	28.00	328
28" x 28"	"	0.500	340	35.00	375
32" x 32"	"	0.571	390	40.00	430
36" x 36"	"	0.667	430	46.75	477
40" x 40"	"	0.800	690	56.00	746
44" x 44"	"	1.000	730	70.00	800
48" x 48"	"	1.143	770	80.00	850
48" x 56"	"	1.333	890	93.00	983
48" x 60"	"	1.333	930	93.00	1,023
48" x 64"	"	1.333	970	93.00	1,063
48" x 68"	"	1.333	1,010	93.00	1,103
48" x 72"	"	1.333	1,200	93.00	1,293
Rectangular, opposed horizontal blade					
12" x 12"	EA.	0.400	89.00	28.00	117
16" x 16"	"	0.400	120	28.00	148
20" x 20"	"	0.400	140	28.00	168
24" x 24"	"	0.400	160	28.00	188
28" x 28"	"	0.500	230	35.00	265
32" x 32"	"	0.533	250	37.25	287
36" x 36"	"	0.667	280	46.75	327
40" x 40"	"	0.800	350	56.00	406
44" x 44"	"	1.000	440	70.00	510
48" x 48"	"	1.143	550	80.00	630
48" x 52"	"	1.143	560	80.00	640
48" x 56"	"	1.333	580	93.00	673
48" x 60"	"	1.333	620	93.00	713
48" x 64"	"	1.333	650	93.00	743
48" x 68"	"	1.333	720	93.00	813
48" x 72"	"	1.333	770	93.00	863

BASIC MATERIALS

16050.00 BUS DUCT	UNIT	HOURS	MAT.	INST.	TOTAL
Bus duct, 100a, plug-in					
10', 600v	EA.	2.759	230	180	410
With ground	"	4.211	310	270	580
10', 277/480v	"	2.759	300	180	480
With ground	"	4.211	370	270	640
Cable tap box	"	2.500	130	160	290
End closure	"	0.400	160	26.00	186
Edgewise hanger	"	0.727	19.75	47.00	66.75
Flatwise hanger	"	0.727	19.75	47.00	66.75
Outside elbow	"	0.800	180	52.00	232
Inside elbow	"	0.800	180	52.00	232
Outside tee	"	1.100	240	71.00	311
Inside tee	"	1.100	240	71.00	311
Outlet cover	"	0.400	13.75	26.00	39.75
Wall flange	"	0.400	38.50	26.00	64.50
Circuit breakers, with enclosure					
1 pole					
15a-60a	EA.	1.000	230	65.00	295
70a-100a	"	1.250	260	81.00	341
2 pole					
15a-60a	EA.	1.100	340	71.00	411
70a-100a	"	1.301	410	84.00	494
3 pole					
15a-60a	EA.	1.159	390	75.00	465
70a-100a	"	1.509	450	98.00	548
Bus duct, copper feeder duct, 277/480v, 4 wire					
800a	L.F.	0.400	250	26.00	276
1000a	"	0.500	280	32.50	313
1200a	"	0.533	320	34.50	355
1350a	"	0.615	390	39.75	430
1600a	"	0.727	470	47.00	517
2000a	"	0.800	580	52.00	632
2500a	"	0.851	720	55.00	775
3000a	"	0.952	910	62.00	972
Weatherproof					
800a	L.F.	0.444	300	28.75	329
1000a	"	0.533	350	34.50	385
1350a	"	0.667	470	43.25	513
1600a	"	0.727	560	47.00	607
2000a	"	0.833	690	54.00	744
2500a	"	0.899	850	58.00	908
3000a	"	0.976	1,090	63.00	1,153
4000a	"	1.509	1,390	98.00	1,488
5000a	"	1.818	1,670	120	1,790
Plug-in feeder duct, 277/480v, 4 wire					
400a	L.F.	0.400	170	26.00	196
600a	"	0.444	180	28.75	209
800a	"	0.500	280	32.50	313
1000a	"	0.500	310	32.50	343
1200a	"	0.533	370	34.50	405
1350a	"	0.615	410	39.75	450
1600a	"	0.727	500	47.00	547
2000a	"	0.800	600	52.00	652

BASIC MATERIALS

16050.30 BUS DUCT	UNIT	HOURS	MAT.	INST.	TOTAL
2500a	L.F.	0.851	730	55.00	785
3000a	"	0.952	920	62.00	982
Ground bus					
225a	L.F.				39.50
400a	"				40.75
600a	"				41.75
800a	"				45.00
1000a	"				47.25
1200a	"				58.00
1350a	"				62.00
1600a	"				81.00
2000a	"				99.00
2500a	"				130
3000a	"				180
4000a	"				220
5000a	"				280
Copper flanged ends, 277/480v, 4 wire					
225a	EA.	2.500	280	160	440
400a	"	2.759	340	180	520
600a	"	2.963	440	190	630
800a	"	3.077	510	200	710
1000a	"	3.200	580	210	790
1200a	"	3.265	630	210	840
1350a	"	3.333	650	220	870
1600a	"	3.478	760	230	990
2000a	"	3.478	870	230	1,100
2500a	"	3.636	880	240	1,120
3000a	"	3.810	1,260	250	1,510
4000a	"	4.444	1,690	290	1,980
5000a	"	4.706	1,960	300	2,260
Bus duct, copper elbows, 277/480v-4w					
225a-1000a	EA.	2.105	1,100	140	1,240
1200a-3000a	"	2.500	1,890	160	2,050
4000a-5000a	"	2.963	4,690	190	4,880
Tees, 277/480v-4w					
225a-1000a	EA.	2.222	1,740	140	1,880
1200a-3000a	"	2.581	2,450	170	2,620
4000a-5000a	"	2.963	6,710	190	6,900
Crosses, 277/480v-4w					
225a-1000a	EA.	2.222	1,850	140	1,990
1200a-3000a	"	2.581	2,860	170	3,030
4000a-5000a	"	2.963	4,510	190	4,700
Copper end closures, 277/480v-4w					
225a-1000a	EA.	0.899	160	58.00	218
1200a-3000a	"	1.194	220	77.00	297
4000a-5000a	"	1.667	280	110	390
Tap boxes, 277/480v-4w					
225a	EA.	3.478	1,230	230	1,460
400a	"	4.444	1,230	290	1,520
600a	"	7.273	1,340	470	1,810
800a	"	8.000	1,470	520	1,990
1000a	"	10.000	1,640	650	2,290
1200a	"	11.004	1,670	710	2,380

BASIC MATERIALS

16050.30 BUS DUCT	UNIT	HOURS	MAT.	INST.	TOTAL
1350a	EA.	13.008	2,040	840	2,880
1600a	"	14.011	2,270	910	3,180
2000a	"	16.985	2,670	1,100	3,770
2500a	"	22.989	3,230	1,490	4,720
3000a	"	27.972	4,010	1,810	5,820
4000a	"	37.915	3,520	2,460	5,980
5000a	"	44.944	3,520	2,910	6,430
Circuit breaker, adapter cubicle					
225a	EA.	1.509	3,710	98.00	3,808
400a	"	1.600	4,380	100	4,480
600a	"	1.702	6,490	110	6,600
800a	"	1.818	7,410	120	7,530
1000a	"	1.905	8,590	120	8,710
1200a	"	2.000	10,300	130	10,430
1600a	"	2.105	12,530	140	12,670
2000a	"	2.222	14,660	140	14,800
Transformer taps, 1 phase 277/480v					
600a	EA.	7.273	640	470	1,110
800a	"	8.000	670	520	1,190
1000a	"	10.000	810	650	1,460
1200a	"	11.004	890	710	1,600
1350a	"	13.008	930	840	1,770
1600a	"	14.011	1,070	910	1,980
2000a	"	16.985	1,220	1,100	2,320
2500a	"	22.989	1,480	1,490	2,970
3000a	"	27.972	1,750	1,810	3,560
4000a	"	37.915	2,060	2,460	4,520
5000a	"	45.977	2,590	2,980	5,570
3 phase, 480v, 3 wire					
600a	EA.	7.273	1,440	470	1,910
800a	"	8.000	1,560	520	2,080
1000a	"	10.000	1,780	650	2,430
1200a	"	11.004	1,930	710	2,640
1350a	"	13.008	2,040	840	2,880
1600a	"	14.011	2,450	910	3,360
2000a	"	16.985	2,750	1,100	3,850
2500a	"	22.989	3,190	1,490	4,680
3000a	"	27.972	3,720	1,810	5,530
4000a	"	37.915	4,280	2,460	6,740
5000a	"	45.977	4,940	2,980	7,920
3 phase, 4 wire, 277/480v					
600a	EA.	7.273	1,570	470	2,040
800a	"	8.000	1,680	520	2,200
1000a	"	10.000	1,940	650	2,590
1200a	"	11.004	2,120	710	2,830
1350a	"	13.008	2,230	840	3,070
1600a	"	14.011	2,620	910	3,530
2000a	"	16.985	2,980	1,100	4,080
2500a	"	22.989	3,490	1,490	4,980
3000a	"	27.972	4,080	1,810	5,890
4000a	"	40.816	4,730	2,640	7,370
5000a	"	45.977	5,360	2,980	8,340
Transformer connection, 4 wire, 277/480v					

BASIC MATERIALS

16050.30 BUS DUCT	UNIT	HOURS	MAT.	INST.	TOTAL
600a	EA.	2.759	3,270	180	3,450
800a	"	2.857	3,400	190	3,590
1000a	"	2.963	3,560	190	3,750
1200a	"	3.077	3,650	200	3,850
1350a	"	3.200	3,720	210	3,930
1600a	"	3.333	3,990	220	4,210
2000a	"	3.478	4,160	230	4,390
2500a	"	3.636	4,700	240	4,940
3000a	"	3.810	5,150	250	5,400
4000a	"	4.444	6,820	290	7,110
5000a	"	4.706	9,120	300	9,420
Unfused reducers, 3 wire, 480v, 3 phase					
400a	EA.	2.500	450	160	610
600a	"	3.810	480	250	730
800a	"	4.706	600	300	900
1000a	"	5.000	720	320	1,040
1200a	"	5.333	1,210	350	1,560
1350a	"	5.714	1,540	370	1,910
1600a	"	6.154	1,680	400	2,080
2000a	"	6.400	2,260	410	2,670
2500a	"	6.667	2,790	430	3,220
3000a	"	7.273	3,370	470	3,840
4000a	"	8.753	4,380	570	4,950
5000a	"	10.796	5,280	700	5,980
4 wire, 277/480v, 3 phase, 400a	"	2.759	690	180	870
600a	"	4.000	890	260	1,150
800a	"	5.000	1,100	320	1,420
1000a	"	5.333	1,290	350	1,640
1200a	"	5.714	2,210	370	2,580
1350a	"	6.154	2,810	400	3,210
1600a	"	6.667	3,060	430	3,490
2000a	"	6.957	4,120	450	4,570
2500a	"	7.273	5,080	470	5,550
3000a	"	8.247	6,140	530	6,670
4000a	"	9.744	7,980	630	8,610
5000a	"	11.994	9,610	780	10,390
Circuit breaker reducers, 4 wire, 277/480v					
400a	EA.	2.222	780	140	920
600a	"	3.478	850	230	1,080
800a	"	4.211	1,040	270	1,310
1000a	"	4.706	1,230	300	1,530
1350a	"	5.333	2,690	350	3,040
1600a	"	5.714	2,930	370	3,300
2000a	"	6.154	3,940	400	4,340
2500a	"	6.667	4,870	430	5,300
3000a	"	6.957	5,870	450	6,320
4000a	"	7.273	7,630	470	8,100
5000a	"	10.000	9,200	650	9,850
Expansion fittings, 4 wire, 277/480v					
225a	EA.	2.500	1,370	160	1,530
400a	"	3.810	1,440	250	1,690
600a	"	4.706	1,600	300	1,900
800a	"	5.000	1,880	320	2,200

BASIC MATERIALS

16050.30 BUS DUCT	UNIT	HOURS	MAT.	INST.	TOTAL
1000a	EA.	5.333	2,120	350	2,470
1200a	"	5.714	2,890	370	3,260
1350a	"	5.926	2,890	380	3,270
1600a	"	6.154	3,720	400	4,120
2000a	"	6.667	4,210	430	4,640
2500a	"	7.273	5,100	470	5,570
3000a	"	8.753	5,950	570	6,520
4000a	"	10.796	7,750	700	8,450
5000a	"	11.994	8,140	780	8,920
Wall flanges					
225a-2500a	EA.	4.000	190	260	450
3000a-5000a	"	6.154	290	400	690
Weather seals	"	1.000	360	65.00	425
Roof flanges	"	4.000	780	260	1,040
Fire barriers	"	1.509	370	98.00	468
Spring hangers	"	1.739	110	110	220
Sway brace collars	"	1.250	22.25	81.00	103
Hook sticks					
8'	EA.				200
14'	"				330
Fusible switches, 240v, 3 phase					
30a	EA.	1.000	590	65.00	655
60a	"	1.250	730	81.00	811
100a	"	1.509	970	98.00	1,068
200a	"	2.105	1,690	140	1,830
400a	"	4.000	2,740	260	3,000
600a	"	6.154	5,260	400	5,660
208v, 4 wire					
30a	EA.	1.194	730	77.00	807
60a	"	1.356	750	88.00	838
100a	"	1.818	1,080	120	1,200
200a	"	2.759	1,890	180	2,070
400a	"	5.000	2,950	320	3,270
600a	"	8.000	3,710	520	4,230
600v					
30a	EA.	1.000	660	65.00	725
60a	"	1.250	700	81.00	781
100a	"	1.509	1,010	98.00	1,108
200a	"	2.105	1,780	140	1,920
400a	"	4.000	2,750	260	3,010
600a	"	6.154	3,400	400	3,800
800a	"	6.667	5,870	430	6,300
1000a	"	8.000	6,940	520	7,460
1200a	"	11.004	11,030	710	11,740
1600a	"	11.994	11,170	780	11,950
480v, 4 wire					
30a	EA.	1.194	750	77.00	827
60a	"	1.356	790	88.00	878
100a	"	1.818	1,170	120	1,290
200a	"	2.759	2,000	180	2,180
400a	"	5.000	2,950	320	3,270
600a	"	8.000	3,710	520	4,230
800a	"	8.247	6,080	530	6,610

BASIC MATERIALS

16050.30 BUS DUCT	UNIT	HOURS	MAT.	INST.	TOTAL
1000a	EA.	11.004	7,180	710	7,890
1200a	"	11.994	11,200	780	11,980
1600a	"	14.011	11,700	910	12,610
Fusible combination starters, 600v, 3 phase					
Size 0	EA.	1.290	1,350	84.00	1,434
Size 1	"	1.600	1,520	100	1,620
Size 2	"	1.818	2,020	120	2,140
Size 3	"	2.581	3,340	170	3,510
Circuit breaker combination starters, 600v, 3					
Size 0	EA.	1.290	1,470	84.00	1,554
Size 1	"	1.600	1,680	100	1,780
Size 2	"	1.818	2,220	120	2,340
Size 3	"	2.581	3,320	170	3,490
Fusible combination contactors, 600v, 3 phase					
30a	EA.	1.290	1,160	84.00	1,244
60a	"	1.600	1,420	100	1,520
100a	"	1.818	2,130	120	2,250
200a	"	2.581	3,470	170	3,640
Circuit breaker, combination contactors, 600v,					
30a	EA.	1.290	1,190	84.00	1,274
60a	"	1.600	1,230	100	1,330
100a	"	1.818	1,730	120	1,850
200a	"	2.581	2,280	170	2,450
Fusible contactor electrically held, 480v, 4 wire					
30a	EA.	1.290	1,160	84.00	1,244
60a	"	1.600	1,470	100	1,570
100a	"	1.818	2,110	120	2,230
200a	"	2.759	4,420	180	4,600
Mechanically held					
30a	EA.	1.290	1,250	84.00	1,334
60a	"	1.600	1,790	100	1,890
100a	"	1.860	2,490	120	2,610
200a	"	2.759	5,100	180	5,280
Circuit breakers, 240v, 3 phase					
15a-60a	EA.	1.159	590	75.00	665
70a-100a	"	1.600	660	100	760
600v, 3 phase					
15a-60a	EA.	1.159	650	75.00	725
125a-225a	"	2.286	1,650	150	1,800
250a-400a	"	4.211	3,410	270	3,680
500a-600a	"	5.333	4,860	350	5,210
700a-800a	"	8.000	5,850	520	6,370
900a-1000a	"	10.000	6,960	650	7,610
1200a-1600a	"	11.004	11,030	710	11,740
120/208v, 4 wire					
15a-60a	EA.	1.290	550	84.00	634
70a-100a	"	1.860	640	120	760
277/480v, 4 wire					
15a-60a	EA.	1.290	670	84.00	754
70a-100a	"	1.905	730	120	850
125a-225a	"	2.759	1,770	180	1,950
250a-400a	"	5.000	3,580	320	3,900
500a-600a	"	8.000	5,090	520	5,610

ELECTRICAL

BASIC MATERIALS

16050.30 BUS DUCT	UNIT	HOURS	MAT.	INST.	TOTAL
700a-800a	EA.	8.000	6,080	520	6,600
900a-1000a	"	11.004	7,180	710	7,890
1200a-1600a	"	14.011	10,960	910	11,870
600v, 3 phase, 65,000 aic.					
60a	EA.	1.159	840	75.00	915
70a-100a	"	1.600	900	100	1,000
125a-225a	"	2.286	2,960	150	3,110
250a-400a	"	4.211	4,730	270	5,000
500a-600a	"	6.154	5,600	400	6,000
700a-800a	"	8.000	6,630	520	7,150
900a-1000a	"	10.000	7,520	650	8,170
277/480v, 4 wire, 65,000 aic.					
15a-60a	EA.	1.290	900	84.00	984
70a-100a	"	1.905	980	120	1,100
125a-225a	"	2.759	3,050	180	3,230
250a-400a	"	5.000	4,910	320	5,230
500a-600a	"	6.154	5,850	400	6,250
700a-800a	"	8.000	6,850	520	7,370
900a-1000a	"	10.349	11,200	670	11,870
600v, 3 phase, current limiting					
15a-60a	EA.	1.159	2,180	75.00	2,255
70a-100a	"	1.600	2,680	100	2,780
125a-225a	"	2.286	5,020	150	5,170
250a-400a	"	4.211	5,960	270	6,230
500a-600a	"	6.154	8,950	400	9,350
700a-800a	"	8.000	10,100	520	10,620
900a-1000a	"	10.000	11,240	650	11,890
277/480v, 4 wire, current limiting					
15a-60a	EA.	1.290	2,230	84.00	2,314
70a-100a	"	40.000	2,870	2,590	5,460
125a-225a	"	2.759	5,150	180	5,330
250a-400a	"	5.000	6,140	320	6,460
500a-600a	"	6.154	6,840	400	7,240
700a-800a	"	8.000	10,330	520	10,850
900a-1000a	"	11.004	11,470	710	12,180
Capacitors, 3 phase, 240v					
5 kvar	EA.	5.000	1,210	320	1,530
7.5 kvar	"	6.154	1,520	400	1,920
10 kvar	"	8.097	1,770	520	2,290
15 kvar	"	9.195	2,320	600	2,920
480v					
2.5 kvar	EA.	2.759	520	180	700
5 kvar	"	4.706	780	300	1,080
7.5 kvar	"	5.714	950	370	1,320
10 kvar	"	8.097	1,060	520	1,580
15 kvar	"	8.999	1,270	580	1,850
20 kvar	"	11.494	1,580	740	2,320
25 kvar	"	13.008	1,980	840	2,820
30 kvar	"	14.210	2,340	920	3,260
Transformers, 3 phase, 480v					
1.0 kva	EA.	1.739	690	110	800
1.5 kva	"	2.000	760	130	890
2 kva	"	2.500	820	160	980

BASIC MATERIALS

16050.30 BUS DUCT	UNIT	HOURS	MAT.	INST.	TOTAL
3 kva	EA.	2.759	980	180	1,160
5 kva	"	4.000	1,340	260	1,600
7.5 kva	"	5.000	1,620	320	1,940
10 kva	"	5.333	1,890	350	2,240
16110.12 CABLE TRAY					
Cable tray, 6"	L.F.	0.059	19.00	3.84	22.84
Ventilated cover	"	0.030	7.70	1.95	9.65
Solid cover	"	0.030	5.99	1.95	7.94
Flat 90	EA.	0.500	85.00	32.50	118
Outside 90	"	0.500	72.00	32.50	105
Inside 90	"	0.500	79.00	32.50	112
Flat 45	"	0.500	65.00	32.50	97.50
Outside 45	"	0.500	54.00	32.50	86.50
Inside 45	"	0.500	56.00	32.50	88.50
Adjustable elbow	"	0.500	81.00	32.50	114
Support riser	"	0.500	110	32.50	143
Adjustable riser	"	0.500	12.00	32.50	44.50
Tee	"	1.739	110	110	220
Cross	"	1.818	140	120	260
Blind end	"	0.296	8.80	19.25	28.05
Expansion joint	"	0.500	40.50	32.50	73.00
Box connector	"	2.500	27.00	160	187
Standard dropout	"	0.500	4.73	32.50	37.23
2"	"	0.615	23.00	39.75	62.75
3"	"	0.800	40.50	52.00	92.50
4"	"	1.000	65.00	65.00	130
Cable tray, 9"	L.F.	0.070	20.25	4.50	24.75
Ventilated cover	"	0.040	8.63	2.59	11.22
Solid cover	"	0.040	6.98	2.59	9.57
Flat 90	EA.	0.533	95.00	34.50	130
Outside 90	"	0.533	78.00	34.50	113
Inside 90	"	0.533	82.00	34.50	117
Flat 45	"	0.533	68.00	34.50	103
Outside 45	"	0.533	56.00	34.50	90.50
Inside 45	"	0.533	56.00	34.50	90.50
Adjustable elbow	"	0.533	86.00	34.50	121
Support riser	"	0.533	120	34.50	155
Adjustable riser	"	0.533	12.00	34.50	46.50
Tee	"	1.818	120	120	240
Cross	"	1.818	150	120	270
Blind end	"	0.320	9.51	20.75	30.26
Expansion joint	"	0.533	57.00	34.50	91.50
Box connector	"	2.581	27.25	170	197
Standard dropout	"	0.533	5.17	34.50	39.67
2"	"	0.667	23.25	43.25	66.50
3"	"	0.667	38.75	43.25	82.00
4"	"	1.096	65.00	71.00	136
Cable tray, 12"	L.F.	0.080	20.75	5.18	25.93
Ventilated cover	"	0.050	8.03	3.24	11.27
Solid cover	"	0.050	7.31	3.24	10.55
Flat 90	EA.	0.533	98.00	34.50	133
Outside 90	"	0.533	78.00	34.50	113
Inside 90	"	0.533	86.00	34.50	121

BASIC MATERIALS

16110.12 CABLE TRAY, Cont'd...	UNIT	HOURS	MAT.	INST.	TOTAL
Flat 45	EA.	0.533	72.00	34.50	107
Outside 45	"	0.533	110	34.50	145
Inside 45	"	0.533	92.00	34.50	127
Adjustable elbow	"	0.533	90.00	34.50	125
Support riser	"	0.533	120	34.50	155
Adjustable riser	"	0.533	13.50	34.50	48.00
Tee	"	2.000	130	130	260
Cross	"	2.000	160	130	290
Blind end	"	0.348	10.75	22.50	33.25
Expansion joint	"	0.615	62.00	39.75	102
Box connector	"	2.759	28.50	180	209
Standard dropout	"	0.615	5.61	39.75	45.36
2"	"	0.727	24.50	47.00	71.50
3"	"	0.899	40.50	58.00	98.50
4"	"	1.159	68.00	75.00	143
Cable tray, 18"	L.F.	0.100	21.75	6.48	28.23
Ventilated cover	"	0.059	11.25	3.84	15.09
Solid cover	"	0.059	9.40	3.84	13.24
Flat 90	EA.	0.727	110	47.00	157
Outside 90	"	0.727	120	47.00	167
Inside 90	"	0.727	94.00	47.00	141
Flat 45	"	0.727	82.00	47.00	129
Outside 45	"	0.727	110	47.00	157
Inside 45	"	0.727	95.00	47.00	142
Adjustable elbow	"	0.727	120	47.00	167
Support riser	"	0.727	140	47.00	187
Adjustable riser	"	0.727	12.00	47.00	59.00
Tee	"	2.105	150	140	290
Cross	"	2.105	230	140	370
Blind end	"	0.400	15.75	26.00	41.75
Expansion joint	"	0.727	80.00	47.00	127
Box connector	"	2.963	33.75	190	224
Standard dropout	"	0.667	8.52	43.25	51.77
2"	"	0.727	27.00	47.00	74.00
3"	"	0.952	42.75	62.00	105
4"	"	1.194	69.00	77.00	146
Cable tray, 24"	L.F.	0.123	21.00	7.97	28.97
Ventilated cover	"	0.070	15.50	4.50	20.00
Solid cover	"	0.070	10.50	4.50	15.00
Flat 90	EA.	0.727	140	47.00	187
Outside 90	"	0.727	120	47.00	167
Inside 90	"	0.727	99.00	47.00	146
Flat 45	"	0.727	94.00	47.00	141
Outside 45	"	0.727	120	47.00	167
Inside 45	"	0.727	99.00	47.00	146
Adjustable elbow	"	0.727	120	47.00	167
Support riser	"	0.727	150	47.00	197
Adjustable riser	"	0.727	13.25	47.00	60.25
Tee	"	2.222	180	140	320
Cross	"	2.222	260	140	400
Blind end	"	0.444	17.50	28.75	46.25
Expansion joint	"	0.727	82.00	47.00	129
Box connector	"	3.478	36.00	230	266

BASIC MATERIALS

16110.12 CABLE TRAY, Cont'd...	UNIT	HOURS	MAT.	INST.	TOTAL
Standard dropout	EA.	0.667	9.02	43.25	52.27
2"	"	0.800	28.00	52.00	80.00
3"	"	0.976	44.50	63.00	108
4"	"	1.250	72.00	81.00	153
Cable tray, 36"	L.F.	0.145	28.50	9.42	37.92
Ventilated cover	"	0.080	17.75	5.18	22.93
Solid cover	"	0.080	12.25	5.18	17.43
Flat 90	EA.	0.851	160	55.00	215
Outside 90	"	0.851	140	55.00	195
Inside 90	"	0.851	120	55.00	175
Flat 45	"	0.851	110	55.00	165
Outside 45	"	0.851	130	55.00	185
Inside 45	"	0.851	110	55.00	165
Adjustable elbow	"	0.851	130	55.00	185
Support riser	"	0.851	150	55.00	205
Adjustable riser	"	0.851	14.00	55.00	69.00
Tee	"	2.286	200	150	350
Cross	"	2.963	300	190	490
Blind end	"	0.471	18.00	30.50	48.50
Expansion joint	"	0.727	85.00	47.00	132
Box connector	"	3.810	42.00	250	292
Standard dropout	"	0.727	10.00	47.00	57.00
2"	"	0.800	29.75	52.00	81.75
3"	"	1.000	46.00	65.00	111
4"	"	1.290	72.00	84.00	156
Reducers					
9" - 6"	EA.	0.500	65.00	32.50	97.50
12" - 9"	"	0.500	68.00	32.50	101
18" - 12"	"	0.615	72.00	39.75	112
24" - 18"	"	0.727	80.00	47.00	127
36" - 18"	"	0.800	97.00	52.00	149
36" - 24"	"	0.899	99.00	58.00	157
Conduit dropouts					
3/4"	EA.	0.348	8.58	22.50	31.08
1"	"	0.348	8.85	22.50	31.35
1-1/4"	"	0.400	10.25	26.00	36.25
1-1/2"	"	0.500	12.00	32.50	44.50
2"	"	0.533	13.75	34.50	48.25
2-1/2"	"	0.727	15.50	47.00	62.50
3"	"	0.800	18.00	52.00	70.00
Wall brackets					
6"	EA.	0.145	33.75	9.42	43.17
9"	"	0.145	38.75	9.42	48.17
12"	"	0.200	41.00	13.00	54.00
18"	"	0.250	49.00	16.25	65.25
24"	"	0.296	57.00	19.25	76.25
36"	"	0.400	71.00	26.00	97.00

BASIC MATERIALS

16110.15 FIBERGLASS CABLE TRAY	UNIT	HOURS	MAT.	INST.	TOTAL
Fiberglass cable tray, 6"	L.F.	0.040	29.50	2.59	32.09
Tray cover	"	0.030	8.19	1.95	10.14
Horizontal					
90	EA.	0.276	320	17.75	338
45	"	0.276	130	17.75	148
30	"	0.276	140	17.75	158
Inside					
90	EA.	0.276	120	17.75	138
45	"	0.276	99.00	17.75	117
30	"	0.276	130	17.75	148
Horizontal tee	"	0.727	210	47.00	257
Horizontal cross	"	1.096	250	71.00	321
Splice plate	"	0.145	12.00	9.42	21.42
Floor flange	"	0.348	13.25	22.50	35.75
Panel flange	"	1.250	13.75	81.00	94.75
End plate	"	0.145	9.02	9.42	18.44
Nylon rivet	"	0.050	0.33	3.24	3.57
Barrier strip	"	0.050	4.51	3.24	7.75
Hold down clamp	"	0.050	1.98	3.24	5.22
Drop out	"	0.533	14.25	34.50	48.75
Cover stand off	"	0.050	3.79	3.24	7.03
Wall bracket	"	0.200	53.00	13.00	66.00
Sealer	"				19.50
Outside					
90	EA.	0.276	120	17.75	138
45	"	0.276	99.00	17.75	117
30	"	0.276	130	17.75	148
Fiberglass cable tray, 9"	L.F.	0.050	31.00	3.24	34.24
Tray cover	"	0.040	8.52	2.59	11.11
Horizontal					
90	EA.	0.276	330	17.75	348
45	"	0.276	140	17.75	158
30	"	0.276	140	17.75	158
Inside					
90	EA.	0.276	130	17.75	148
45	"	0.276	100	17.75	118
30	"	0.276	140	17.75	158
Horizontal tee	"	0.727	220	47.00	267
Horizontal cross	"	1.096	260	71.00	331
Splice plate	"	0.145	12.50	9.42	21.92
Floor flange	"	0.348	14.00	22.50	36.50
Panel flange	"	1.250	14.25	81.00	95.25
End plate	"	0.145	9.46	9.42	18.88
Nylon rivet	"	0.050	0.34	3.24	3.58
Barrier strap	"	0.050	4.73	3.24	7.97
Hold down clamp	"	0.050	2.09	3.24	5.33
Drop out	"	0.533	15.00	34.50	49.50
Cover stand off	"	0.050	3.96	3.24	7.20
Wall bracket	"	0.200	56.00	13.00	69.00
Sealer	"				19.50
Outside					
90	EA.	0.276	130	17.75	148
45	"	0.276	110	17.75	128

BASIC MATERIALS

16110.15 FIBERGLASS CABLE TRAY	UNIT	HOURS	MAT.	INST.	TOTAL
30	EA.	0.276	140	17.75	158
Fiberglass cable tray, 12"	L.F.	0.059	32.50	3.84	36.34
Tray cover	"	0.050	9.13	3.24	12.37
Horizontal					
90	EA.	0.348	350	22.50	373
45	"	0.348	150	22.50	173
30	"	0.348	150	22.50	173
Inside					
90	EA.	0.348	130	22.50	153
45	"	0.348	110	22.50	133
Inside 30	"	0.348	140	22.50	163
Horizontal tee	"	0.952	230	62.00	292
Horizontal cross	"	1.290	280	84.00	364
Splice plate	"	0.160	13.25	10.25	23.50
Floor flange	"	0.364	14.50	23.50	38.00
Panel flange	"	1.600	15.00	100	115
End plate	"	0.160	9.90	10.25	20.15
Nylon rivet	"	0.050	0.35	3.24	3.59
Barrier strip	"	0.050	4.95	3.24	8.19
Hold down clamp	"	0.050	2.20	3.24	5.44
Drop out	"	0.533	22.25	34.50	56.75
Cover stand off	"	0.050	4.12	3.24	7.36
Wall bracket	"	0.200	59.00	13.00	72.00
Sealer	"				19.50
Outside					
90	EA.	0.348	130	22.50	153
45	"	0.348	110	22.50	133
30	"	0.348	150	22.50	173
Fiberglass cable tray, 18"	L.F.	0.070	34.00	4.54	38.54
Tray cover	"	0.059	16.75	3.84	20.59
Horizontal					
90	EA.	0.400	370	26.00	396
45	"	0.400	150	26.00	176
30	"	0.400	160	26.00	186
Inside					
90	EA.	0.400	140	26.00	166
45	"	0.400	110	26.00	136
30	"	0.400	150	26.00	176
Horizontal tee	"	1.538	240	100	340
Horizontal cross	"	1.356	290	88.00	378
Splice plate	"	0.160	13.75	10.25	24.00
Floor flange	"	0.381	15.25	24.75	40.00
Panel flange	"	1.702	15.75	110	126
End plate	"	0.170	9.95	11.00	20.95
Nylon rivet	"	0.050	0.37	3.24	3.61
Barrier strip	"	0.050	5.22	3.24	8.46
Hold down clamp	"	0.050	2.31	3.24	5.55
Drop out	"	0.533	32.50	34.50	67.00
Cover stand off	"	0.050	4.40	3.24	7.64
Wall bracket	"	0.200	62.00	13.00	75.00
Sealer	"				19.50
Outside					
90	EA.	0.400	140	26.00	166

BASIC MATERIALS

16110.15 FIBERGLASS CABLE TRAY	UNIT	HOURS	MAT.	INST.	TOTAL
45	EA.	0.400	110	26.00	136
30	"	0.400	150	26.00	176
Fiberglass cable tray, 24"	L.F.	0.080	35.75	5.18	40.93
Tray cover	"	0.070	20.00	4.50	24.50
Horizontal					
90	EA.	0.500	370	32.50	403
45	"	0.500	160	32.50	193
30	"	0.500	160	32.50	193
Inside					
90	EA.	0.500	140	32.50	173
45	"	0.500	130	32.50	163
30	"	0.500	150	32.50	183
Horizontal tee	"	1.000	250	65.00	315
Horizontal cross	"	1.509	300	98.00	398
Splice plate	"	0.160	14.50	10.25	24.75
Floor flange	"	0.400	16.00	26.00	42.00
Panel flange	"	1.818	16.75	120	137
End plate	"	0.170	11.00	11.00	22.00
Nylon Rivet	"	0.050	0.38	3.24	3.62
Barrier strip	"	0.050	5.44	3.24	8.68
Hold down clamp	"	0.050	2.42	3.24	5.66
Drop out	"	0.533	42.50	34.50	77.00
Cover stand off	"	0.050	4.56	3.24	7.80
Wall bracket	"	0.200	68.00	13.00	81.00
Sealer	"				19.50
Outside					
90	EA.	0.500	140	32.50	173
45	"	0.500	120	32.50	153
30	"	0.500	150	32.50	183
Fiberglass cable tray, 30"	L.F.	0.089	41.00	5.76	46.76
Tray cover	"	0.080	28.25	5.18	33.43
Horizontal					
90	EA.	0.615	390	39.75	430
45	"	0.615	160	39.75	200
30	"	0.615	160	39.75	200
Inside					
90	EA.	0.615	150	39.75	190
45	"	0.615	120	39.75	160
30	"	0.615	160	39.75	200
Horizontal tee	"	1.096	290	71.00	361
Horizontal cross	"	1.600	340	100	440
Splice plate	"	0.160	15.25	10.25	25.50
Floor flange	"	0.400	16.75	26.00	42.75
Panel flange	"	1.905	17.50	120	138
End plate	"	0.200	11.50	13.00	24.50
Nylon rivet	"	0.050	0.41	3.24	3.65
Barrier strip	"	0.050	5.72	3.24	8.96
Hold down clamp	"	0.050	2.53	3.24	5.77
Dropout	"	0.615	48.75	39.75	88.50
Cover stand off	"	0.050	4.84	3.24	8.08
Wall bracket	"	0.200	76.00	13.00	89.00
Sealer	"				52.00
Outside					

BASIC MATERIALS

16110.15 FIBERGLASS CABLE TRAY	UNIT	HOURS	MAT.	INST.	TOTAL
90	EA.	0.615	150	39.75	190
45	"	0.615	120	39.75	160
30	"	0.615	160	39.75	200
Fiberglass cable tray, 36"	L.F.	0.100	47.00	6.48	53.48
Tray cover	"	0.089	37.50	5.76	43.26
Horizontal					
90	EA.	0.667	390	43.25	433
45	"	0.667	160	43.25	203
30	"	0.667	160	43.25	203
Inside					
90	EA.	0.667	150	43.25	193
45	"	0.667	120	43.25	163
30	"	0.667	160	43.25	203
Horizontal tee	"	1.194	320	77.00	397
horizontal cross	"	1.702	370	110	480
Splice plate	"	0.160	16.00	10.25	26.25
Floor flange	"	0.444	17.75	28.75	46.50
Panel flange	"	2.105	18.25	140	158
End plate	"	0.200	12.00	13.00	25.00
Nylon rivet	"	0.050	0.46	3.24	3.70
Barrier strip	"	0.050	6.05	3.24	9.29
Hold down clamp	"	0.050	2.64	3.24	5.88
Drop out	"	0.667	57.00	43.25	100
5Cover stand off	"	0.050	5.06	3.24	8.30
Wall bracket	"	0.200	84.00	13.00	97.00
Sealer	"				19.50
Outside					
90	EA.	0.667	150	43.25	193
45	"	0.667	130	43.25	173
30	"	0.667	160	43.25	203
Reducers					
12" - 6"	EA.	0.296	200	19.25	219
12" - 9"	"	0.296	200	19.25	219
18" - 6"	"	0.348	180	22.50	203
18" - 9"	"	0.348	180	22.50	203
18" - 12"	"	0.400	190	26.00	216
24" - 6"	"	0.400	210	26.00	236
24" - 9"	"	0.400	220	26.00	246
24" - 12"	"	0.400	220	26.00	246
24" - 18"	"	0.444	220	28.75	249
30" - 9"	"	0.400	220	26.00	246
30" - 12"	"	0.400	220	26.00	246
30" - 18"	"	0.444	220	28.75	249
30" - 24"	"	0.500	240	32.50	273
36" - 9"	"	0.500	230	32.50	263
36" - 12"	"	0.500	240	32.50	273
36" - 18"	"	0.533	240	34.50	275
36" - 24"	"	0.615	250	39.75	290
36" - 30"	"	0.727	250	47.00	297

BASIC MATERIALS

16110.20 CONDUIT SPECIALTIES	UNIT	HOURS	MAT.	INST.	TOTAL
Rod beam clamp, 1/2"	EA.	0.050	5.72	3.24	8.96
Hanger rod					
3/8"	L.F.	0.040	1.21	2.59	3.80
1/2"	"	0.050	3.01	3.24	6.25
All thread rod					
1/4"	L.F.	0.030	0.94	1.95	2.89
3/8"	"	0.040	1.47	2.59	4.06
1/2"	"	0.050	2.43	3.24	5.67
5/8"	"	0.080	3.13	5.18	8.31
Hanger channel, 1-1/2"					
No holes	EA.	0.030	3.80	1.95	5.75
Holes	"	0.030	4.70	1.95	6.65
Channel strap					
1/2"	EA.	0.050	1.03	3.24	4.27
3/4"	"	0.050	1.38	3.24	4.62
1"	"	0.050	1.77	3.24	5.01
1-1/4"	"	0.080	1.43	5.18	6.61
1-1/2"	"	0.080	1.71	5.18	6.89
2"	"	0.080	1.85	5.18	7.03
2-1/2"	"	0.123	2.97	7.97	10.94
3"	"	0.123	3.23	7.97	11.20
3-1/2"	"	0.123	4.02	7.97	11.99
4"	"	0.145	4.55	9.42	13.97
5"	"	0.145	8.85	9.42	18.27
6"	"	0.145	10.00	9.42	19.42
Conduit penetrations, roof and wall, 8" thick					
1/2"	EA.	0.615		39.75	39.75
3/4"	"	0.615		39.75	39.75
1"	"	0.800		52.00	52.00
1-1/4"	"	0.800		52.00	52.00
1-1/2"	"	0.800		52.00	52.00
2"	"	1.600		100	100
2-1/2"	"	1.600		100	100
3"	"	1.600		100	100
3-1/2"	"	2.000		130	130
4"	"	2.000		130	130
Plastic duct bank conduit spacer, 3" separation					
2"	EA.	0.050	1.54	3.24	4.78
3"	"	0.050	1.70	3.24	4.94
4"	"	0.050	1.91	3.24	5.15
5"	"	0.050	2.07	3.24	5.31
6"	"	0.050	3.36	3.24	6.60
Intermediate, 3" separation					
2"	EA.	0.050	1.59	3.24	4.83
3"	"	0.050	1.76	3.24	5.00
4"	"	0.050	1.96	3.24	5.20
5"	"	0.050	2.16	3.24	5.40
6"	"	0.050	3.42	3.24	6.66
Base with 1-1/2" separation					
2"	EA.	0.050	1.51	3.24	4.75
3"	"	0.160	1.66	10.25	11.91
4"	"	0.160	1.82	10.25	12.07
5"	"	0.160	1.96	10.25	12.21

BASIC MATERIALS

16110.20 CONDUIT SPECIALTIES	UNIT	HOURS	MAT.	INST.	TOTAL
6"	EA.	0.160	3.17	10.25	13.42
Intermediate, 1-1/2" separation					
2"	EA.	0.160	1.62	10.25	11.87
3"	"	0.160	1.74	10.25	11.99
3-1/2"	"	0.160	1.89	10.25	12.14
4"	"	0.160	1.92	10.25	12.17
5"	"	0.160	2.03	11.25	13.28
6"	"	0.160	3.22	10.25	13.47
OD beam clamp, 1/4"	"	0.200	0.69	13.00	13.69
Threaded rod couplings					
1/4"	EA.	0.050	0.84	3.24	4.08
3/8"	"	0.050	1.48	3.24	4.72
1/2"	"	0.050	1.84	3.24	5.08
5/8"	"	0.050	5.58	3.24	8.82
3/4"	"	0.050	7.09	3.24	10.33
Hex nuts					
1/4"	EA.	0.050	0.14	3.24	3.38
3/8"	"	0.050	0.27	3.24	3.51
1/2"	"	0.050	0.46	3.24	3.70
5/8"	"	0.050	1.10	3.24	4.34
3/4"	"	0.050	1.21	3.24	4.45
Square nuts					
1/4"	EA.	0.050	0.14	3.24	3.38
3/8"	"	0.050	0.27	3.24	3.51
3/8"	"	0.050	0.46	3.24	3.70
5/8"	"	0.050	1.10	3.24	4.34
3/4"	"	0.050	1.21	3.24	4.45
Flat washers					
1/4"	EA.				0.14
3/8"	"				0.19
1/2"	"				0.27
5/8"	"				0.55
3/4"	"				0.77
Lockwashers					
1/4"	EA.				0.08
3/8"	"				0.15
1/2"	"				0.18
5/8"	"				0.33
3/4"	"				0.55
Channel closure strip	L.F.	0.133	2.09	8.64	10.73
Channel end cap	EA.	0.133	0.95	8.64	9.59
Li-channel trapeze hangers					
12" long	EA.	0.145	16.00	9.42	25.42
18" long	"	0.145	18.25	9.42	27.67
24" long	"	0.145	22.50	9.42	31.92
30" long	"	0.250	25.75	16.25	42.00
36" long	"	0.250	29.75	16.25	46.00
42" long	"	0.296	35.75	19.25	55.00
Channel spring nuts					
1/4"	EA.	0.059	1.90	3.84	5.74
3/8"	"	0.080	2.59	5.18	7.77
1/2"	"	0.100	2.77	6.48	9.25
Fireproofing, for conduit penetrations					

BASIC MATERIALS

16110.20 CONDUIT SPECIALTIES	UNIT	HOURS	MAT.	INST.	TOTAL
1/2"	EA.	0.500	3.36	32.50	35.86
3/4"	"	0.500	3.49	32.50	35.99
1"	"	0.500	3.56	32.50	36.06
1-1/4"	"	0.727	8.38	51.00	59.38
1-1/2"	"	0.727	4.95	47.00	51.95
2"	"	0.727	5.08	47.00	52.08
2-1/2"	"	0.899	9.70	58.00	67.70
3"	"	0.899	10.00	63.00	73.00
3-1/2"	"	1.250	11.75	81.00	92.75
4"	"	1.509	14.25	98.00	112

16110.21 ALUMINUM CONDUIT					
Aluminum conduit					
1/2"	L.F.	0.030	1.32	1.95	3.27
3/4"	"	0.040	1.70	2.59	4.29
1"	"	0.050	2.38	3.24	5.62
1-1/4"	"	0.059	3.19	3.84	7.03
1-1/2"	"	0.080	3.96	5.18	9.14
2"	"	0.089	5.28	5.76	11.04
2-1/2"	"	0.100	8.36	6.48	14.84
3"	"	0.107	11.00	6.91	17.91
3-1/2"	"	0.123	13.25	7.97	21.22
4"	"	0.145	15.50	9.42	24.92
5"	"	0.182	22.25	11.75	34.00
6"	"	0.200	29.25	13.00	42.25
90 deg. elbow					
1/2"	EA.	0.190	12.75	12.25	25.00
3/4"	"	0.250	17.50	16.25	33.75
1"	"	0.308	24.25	20.00	44.25
1-1/4"	"	0.381	38.50	24.75	63.25
1-1/2"	"	0.400	51.00	26.00	77.00
2"	"	0.444	76.00	28.75	105
2-1/2"	"	0.571	130	37.00	167
3"	"	0.667	200	43.25	243
3-1/2"	"	0.800	300	52.00	352
4"	"	0.889	400	58.00	458
5"	"	1.143	1,000	74.00	1,074
6"	"	2.222	1,360	140	1,500
Coupling					
1/2"	EA.	0.050	4.23	3.24	7.47
3/4"	"	0.059	6.41	3.84	10.25
1"	"	0.080	8.47	5.18	13.65
1-1/4"	"	0.089	10.25	5.76	16.01
1-1/2"	"	0.100	12.00	6.48	18.48
2"	"	0.107	17.00	6.91	23.91
2-1/2"	"	0.123	38.25	7.97	46.22
3"	"	0.123	49.75	7.97	57.72
3-1/2"	"	0.145	68.00	9.42	77.42
4"	"	0.160	83.00	10.25	93.25
5"	"	0.160	250	10.25	260
6"	"	0.190	390	12.25	402

BASIC MATERIALS

16110.22 EMT CONDUIT	UNIT	HOURS	MAT.	INST.	TOTAL
EMT conduit					
1/2"	L.F.	0.030	0.56	1.95	2.51
3/4"	"	0.040	1.02	2.59	3.61
1"	"	0.050	1.70	3.24	4.94
1-1/4"	"	0.059	2.72	3.84	6.56
1-1/2"	"	0.080	3.45	5.18	8.63
2"	"	0.089	4.31	5.76	10.07
2-1/2"	"	0.100	8.61	6.48	15.09
3"	"	0.123	9.54	7.97	17.51
3-1/2"	"	0.145	13.50	9.42	22.92
4"	"	0.182	13.00	11.75	24.75
90 deg. elbow					
1/2"	EA.	0.089	5.26	5.76	11.02
3/4"	"	0.100	5.78	6.48	12.26
1"	"	0.107	8.92	6.91	15.83
1-1/4"	"	0.123	11.00	7.97	18.97
1-1/2"	"	0.145	12.75	9.42	22.17
2"	"	0.190	19.00	12.25	31.25
2-1/2"	"	0.211	46.00	13.75	59.75
3"	"	0.242	69.00	15.75	84.75
3-1/2"	"	0.258	92.00	18.00	110
4"	"	0.286	110	18.50	129
Connector, steel compression					
1/2"	EA.	0.089	1.17	5.76	6.93
3/4"	"	0.089	2.24	5.76	8.00
1"	"	0.089	3.38	5.76	9.14
1-1/4"	"	0.107	7.68	6.91	14.59
1-1/2"	"	0.145	11.25	9.42	20.67
2"	"	0.190	16.00	12.25	28.25
2-1/2"	"	0.250	45.25	16.25	61.50
3"	"	0.286	60.00	18.50	78.50
3-1/2"	"	0.308	87.00	20.00	107
4"	"	0.333	95.00	21.50	117
Coupling, steel, compression					
1/2"	EA.	0.059	1.99	3.84	5.83
3/4"	"	0.059	2.72	3.84	6.56
1"	"	0.059	4.11	3.84	7.95
1-1/4"	"	0.089	7.44	5.76	13.20
1-1/2"	"	0.107	11.75	6.91	18.66
2"	"	0.145	14.50	9.42	23.92
2-1/2"	"	0.222	53.00	14.50	67.50
3"	"	0.250	65.00	16.25	81.25
3-1/2"	"	0.286	100	18.50	119
4"	"	0.308	100	20.00	120
1 hole strap, steel					
1/2"	EA.	0.040	0.20	2.59	2.79
3/4"	"	0.040	0.26	2.59	2.85
1"	"	0.040	0.40	2.59	2.99
1-1/4"	"	0.050	0.62	3.24	3.86
1-1/2"	"	0.050	0.95	3.24	4.19
2"	"	0.050	1.51	3.24	4.75
2-1/2"	"	0.059	3.15	3.84	6.99
3"	"	0.059	3.52	3.84	7.36

BASIC MATERIALS

16110.22 EMT CONDUIT	UNIT	HOURS	MAT.	INST.	TOTAL
3-1/2"	EA.	0.059	5.32	3.84	9.16
4"	"	0.059	6.64	3.84	10.48
Connector, steel set screw					
1/2"	EA.	0.070	1.06	4.50	5.56
3/4"	"	0.070	1.71	4.50	6.21
1"	"	0.070	2.94	4.50	7.44
1-1/4"	"	0.107	6.28	6.91	13.19
1-1/2"	"	0.145	9.14	9.42	18.56
2"	"	0.182	13.00	11.75	24.75
2-1/2"	"	0.242	42.25	15.75	58.00
3"	"	0.267	50.00	17.25	67.25
3-1/2"	"	0.296	66.00	19.25	85.25
4"	"	0.348	76.00	22.50	98.50
Insulated throat					
1/2"	EA.	0.070	1.41	4.50	5.91
3/4"	"	0.070	2.29	4.50	6.79
1"	"	0.070	3.79	4.50	8.29
1-1/4"	"	0.107	7.57	6.91	14.48
1-1/2"	"	0.145	11.00	9.42	20.42
2"	"	0.182	16.00	11.75	27.75
2-1/2"	"	0.242	72.00	15.75	87.75
3"	"	0.267	90.00	17.25	107
3-1/2"	"	0.296	120	19.25	139
4"	"	0.348	130	22.50	153
Connector, die cast set screw					
1/2"	EA.	0.059	0.66	3.84	4.50
3/4"	"	0.059	1.12	3.84	4.96
1"	"	0.059	2.11	3.84	5.95
1-1/4"	"	0.089	3.69	5.76	9.45
1-1/2"	"	0.107	5.01	6.91	11.92
2"	"	0.145	5.88	9.42	15.30
2-1/2"	"	0.200	13.25	13.00	26.25
3"	"	0.222	16.00	14.50	30.50
3-1/2"	"	0.250	19.25	16.25	35.50
4"	"	0.286	24.25	18.50	42.75
Insulated throat					
1/2"	EA.	0.059	1.40	3.84	5.24
3/4"	"	0.059	2.26	3.84	6.10
1"	"	0.059	3.93	3.84	7.77
1-1/4"	"	0.089	7.53	5.76	13.29
1-1/2"	"	0.107	10.75	6.91	17.66
2"	"	0.145	15.75	9.42	25.17
2-1/2"	"	0.200	73.00	13.00	86.00
3"	"	0.222	88.00	14.50	103
3-1/2"	"	0.250	120	17.50	138
4"	"	0.286	130	18.50	149
Coupling, steel set screw					
1/2"	EA.	0.040	1.90	2.59	4.49
3/4"	"	0.040	2.87	2.59	5.46
1"	"	0.040	4.65	2.59	7.24
1-1/4"	"	0.050	9.99	3.24	13.23
1-1/2"	"	0.080	14.25	5.18	19.43
2"	"	0.107	19.00	6.91	25.91

BASIC MATERIALS

16110.22 EMT CONDUIT	UNIT	HOURS	MAT.	INST.	TOTAL
2-1/2"	EA.	0.160	53.00	10.25	63.25
3"	"	0.190	59.00	12.25	71.25
3-1/2"	"	0.222	67.00	14.50	81.50
4"	"	0.250	74.00	16.25	90.25
Diecast set screw					
1/2"	EA.	0.040	0.67	2.59	3.26
3/4"	"	0.040	1.07	2.59	3.66
1"	"	0.040	1.78	2.59	4.37
1-1/4"	"	0.050	3.10	3.24	6.34
1-1/2"	"	0.080	4.37	5.18	9.55
2"	"	0.107	5.87	6.91	12.78
2-1/2"	"	0.160	13.75	10.25	24.00
3"	"	0.186	16.00	12.00	28.00
3-1/2"	"	0.222	20.25	14.50	34.75
4"	"	0.250	24.00	16.25	40.25
1 hole malleable straps					
1/2"	EA.	0.040	0.37	2.59	2.96
3/4"	"	0.040	0.51	2.59	3.10
1"	"	0.040	0.84	2.59	3.43
1-1/4"	"	0.050	1.47	3.24	4.71
1-1/2"	"	0.050	1.79	3.24	5.03
2"	"	0.050	3.25	3.24	6.49
2-1/2"	"	0.059	7.31	3.84	11.15
3"	"	0.059	10.50	3.84	14.34
3-1/2"	"	0.059	15.75	3.84	19.59
4"	"	0.059	34.25	3.84	38.09
EMT to rigid compression coupling					
1/2"	EA.	0.100	3.94	6.48	10.42
3/4"	"	0.100	5.64	6.48	12.12
1"	"	0.150	8.59	9.72	18.31
Set screw couplings					
1/2"	EA.	0.100	1.03	6.48	7.51
3/4"	"	0.100	1.56	6.48	8.04
1"	"	0.145	2.60	9.42	12.02
Set screw offset connectors					
1/2"	EA.	0.100	2.32	6.48	8.80
3/4"	"	0.100	3.11	6.48	9.59
1"	"	0.145	5.65	9.42	15.07
Compression offset connectors					
1/2"	EA.	0.100	3.82	6.48	10.30
3/4"	"	0.100	4.84	6.48	11.32
1"	"	0.145	7.00	9.42	16.42
Type "LB" set screw condulets					
1/2"	EA.	0.229	9.04	14.75	23.79
3/4"	"	0.296	11.00	19.25	30.25
1"	"	0.381	16.75	24.75	41.50
1-1/4"	"	0.444	25.25	28.75	54.00
1-1/2"	"	0.533	33.50	34.50	68.00
2"	"	0.615	55.00	39.75	94.75
2-1/2"	"	0.727	87.00	47.00	134
3"	"	1.000	120	65.00	185
3-1/2"	"	1.333	180	86.00	266
4"	"	1.600	220	100	320

BASIC MATERIALS

16110.22 EMT CONDUIT	UNIT	HOURS	MAT.	INST.	TOTAL
Type "T" set screw condulets					
1/2"	EA.	0.296	11.25	19.25	30.50
3/4"	"	0.400	14.25	26.00	40.25
1"	"	0.444	20.50	28.75	49.25
1-1/4"	"	0.533	29.25	34.50	63.75
1-1/2"	"	0.615	36.25	39.75	76.00
2"	"	0.667	47.75	43.25	91.00
Type "C" set screw condulets					
1/2"	EA.	0.250	9.42	16.25	25.67
3/4"	"	0.296	11.75	19.25	31.00
1"	"	0.381	17.50	24.75	42.25
1-1/4"	"	0.444	30.50	28.75	59.25
1-1/2"	"	0.533	37.00	34.50	71.50
2"	"	0.381	63.00	24.75	87.75
Type "LL" set screw condulets					
1/2"	EA.	0.250	9.42	16.25	25.67
3/4"	"	0.296	11.50	19.25	30.75
1"	"	0.381	17.50	24.75	42.25
1-1/4"	"	0.444	22.25	28.75	51.00
1-1/2"	"	0.533	28.00	34.50	62.50
2"	"	0.615	48.00	39.75	87.75
Type "LR" set screw condulets					
1/2"	EA.	0.250	9.42	16.25	25.67
3/4"	"	0.296	11.50	19.25	30.75
1"	"	0.381	17.50	24.75	42.25
1-1/4"	"	0.444	21.50	28.75	50.25
1-1/2"	"	0.533	35.25	34.50	69.75
2"	"	0.615	46.75	39.75	86.50
Type "LB" compression condulets					
1/2"	EA.	0.296	21.25	19.25	40.50
3/4"	"	0.500	31.50	32.50	64.00
1"	"	0.500	40.25	32.50	72.75
Type "T" compression condulets					
1/2"	EA.	0.400	28.50	26.00	54.50
3/4"	"	0.444	37.50	28.75	66.25
1"	"	0.615	58.00	39.75	97.75
Condulet covers					
1/2"	EA.	0.123	1.44	7.97	9.41
3/4"	"	0.123	1.74	7.97	9.71
1"	"	0.123	2.38	7.97	10.35
1-1/4"	"	0.123	2.75	7.97	10.72
1-1/2"	"	0.145	2.88	9.42	12.30
2"	"	0.145	5.07	9.42	14.49
2-1/2"	"	0.145	6.21	9.42	15.63
3"	"	0.182	8.06	11.75	19.81
3-1/2"	"	0.182	9.07	11.75	20.82
4"	"	0.182	9.51	11.75	21.26
Clamp type entrance caps					
1/2"	EA.	0.250	6.71	16.25	22.96
3/4"	"	0.296	7.86	19.25	27.11
1"	"	0.400	9.29	26.00	35.29
1-1/4"	"	0.533	10.50	34.50	45.00
1-1/2"	"	0.615	17.75	39.75	57.50

BASIC MATERIALS

16110.22 EMT CONDUIT	UNIT	HOURS	MAT.	INST.	TOTAL
2"	EA.	0.899	24.25	58.00	82.25
2-1/2"	"	1.000	41.00	65.00	106
3"	"	1.509	62.00	98.00	160
3-1/2"	"	1.739	92.00	110	202
4"	"	2.222	140	140	280
Slip fitter type entrance caps					
1/2"	EA.	0.250	5.39	16.25	21.64
3/4"	"	0.296	6.43	19.25	25.68
1"	"	0.400	7.75	26.00	33.75
1-1/4"	"	0.533	8.80	34.50	43.30
1-1/2"	"	0.615	15.00	39.75	54.75
2"	"	0.899	22.50	58.00	80.50
2-1/2"	"	1.000	37.00	65.00	102
3"	"	1.509	57.00	98.00	155
3-1/2"	"	1.739	86.00	120	206
4"	"	2.222	130	140	270

16110.23 FLEXIBLE CONDUIT	UNIT	HOURS	MAT.	INST.	TOTAL
Flexible conduit, steel					
3/8"	L.F.	0.030	0.47	1.95	2.42
1/2	"	0.030	0.53	1.95	2.48
3/4"	"	0.040	0.73	2.59	3.32
1"	"	0.040	1.39	2.59	3.98
1-1/4"	"	0.050	1.74	3.24	4.98
1-1/2"	"	0.059	2.89	3.84	6.73
2"	"	0.080	3.56	5.18	8.74
2-1/2"	"	0.089	4.33	5.76	10.09
3"	"	0.107	7.54	6.91	14.45
Flexible conduit, liquid tight					
3/8"	L.F.	0.030	1.50	1.95	3.45
1/2"	"	0.030	1.70	1.95	3.65
3/4"	"	0.040	2.32	2.59	4.91
1"	"	0.040	3.49	2.59	6.08
1-1/4"	"	0.050	4.81	3.24	8.05
1-1/2"	"	0.059	6.02	3.84	9.86
2"	EA.	0.080	7.71	5.18	12.89
2-1/2"	"	0.089	13.75	5.76	19.51
3"	"	0.107	19.00	6.91	25.91
4"	"	0.145	28.75	9.42	38.17
Connector, straight					
3/8"	EA.	0.080	3.22	5.18	8.40
1/2"	"	0.080	3.45	5.18	8.63
3/4"	"	0.089	4.38	5.76	10.14
1"	"	0.100	7.82	6.48	14.30
1-1/4"	"	0.107	11.25	6.91	18.16
1-1/2"	"	0.123	16.25	7.97	24.22
2"	"	0.145	27.00	9.42	36.42
2-1/2"	"	0.182	39.75	11.75	51.50
3"	"	0.190	59.00	12.25	71.25
Straight insulated throat connectors					
3/8"	EA.	0.123	3.90	7.97	11.87
1/2"	"	0.123	3.90	7.97	11.87
3/4"	"	0.145	5.72	9.42	15.14
1"	"	0.145	8.84	9.42	18.26

BASIC MATERIALS

16110.23 FLEXIBLE CONDUIT, Cont'd...	UNIT	HOURS	MAT.	INST.	TOTAL
1-1/4"	EA.	0.182	13.50	11.75	25.25
1-1/2"	"	0.211	19.25	13.75	33.00
2"	"	0.229	36.25	14.75	51.00
2-1/2"	"	0.267	200	17.25	217
3"	"	0.333	220	21.50	242
4"	"	0.421	270	27.25	297
90 deg connectors					
3/8"	EA.	0.148	4.96	9.60	14.56
1/2"	"	0.148	4.96	9.60	14.56
3/4"	"	0.170	7.97	11.00	18.97
1"	"	0.182	15.25	11.75	27.00
1-1/4"	"	0.229	23.75	14.75	38.50
1-1/2"	"	0.250	28.50	16.25	44.75
2"	"	0.267	43.00	17.25	60.25
2-1/2"	"	0.333	190	21.50	212
3"	"	0.381	230	24.75	255
4"	"	0.444	290	28.75	319
90 degree insulated throat connectors					
3/8"	EA.	0.145	6.13	9.42	15.55
1/2"	"	0.145	6.13	9.42	15.55
3/4"	"	0.170	9.25	11.00	20.25
1"	"	0.178	17.50	11.50	29.00
1-1/4"	"	0.229	26.75	14.75	41.50
1-1/2"	"	0.250	32.75	16.25	49.00
2"	"	0.267	49.00	17.25	66.25
2-1/2"	"	0.333	250	21.50	272
3"	"	0.381	300	24.75	325
4"	"	0.444	390	28.75	419
Flexible aluminum conduit					
3/8"	L.F.	0.030	0.35	1.95	2.30
1/2"	"	0.030	0.41	1.95	2.36
3/4"	"	0.040	0.57	2.59	3.16
1"	"	0.040	1.07	2.59	3.66
1-1/4"	"	0.050	1.46	3.24	4.70
1-1/2"	"	0.059	2.40	3.84	6.24
2"	"	0.080	2.92	5.18	8.10
2-1/2"	"	0.089	3.86	5.76	9.62
3"	"	0.107	6.57	6.91	13.48
3-1/2"	"	0.123	7.55	7.97	15.52
4"	"	0.145	8.31	9.42	17.73
Connector, straight					
3/8"	EA.	0.100	1.23	6.48	7.71
1/2"	"	0.100	1.70	6.48	8.18
3/4"	"	0.107	1.87	6.91	8.78
1"	"	0.123	6.84	7.97	14.81
1-1/4"	"	0.145	9.47	9.42	18.89
1-1/2"	"	0.182	18.50	11.75	30.25
2"	"	0.190	25.75	12.25	38.00
2-1/2"	"	0.222	36.50	14.50	51.00
3"	"	0.276	61.00	17.75	78.75
4"	"	0.348	200	22.50	223
Straight insulated throat connectors					
3/8"	EA.	0.089	1.19	5.76	6.95

BASIC MATERIALS

16110.23 FLEXIBLE CONDUIT, Cont'd...	UNIT	HOURS	MAT.	INST.	TOTAL
1/2"	EA.	0.089	2.40	5.76	8.16
3/4"	"	0.089	2.56	5.76	8.32
1"	"	0.100	6.21	6.48	12.69
1-1/4"	"	0.107	9.98	6.91	16.89
1-1/2"	"	0.123	14.00	7.97	21.97
2"	"	0.145	22.50	9.42	31.92
2-1/2"	"	0.182	41.25	11.75	53.00
3"	"	0.190	54.00	12.25	66.25
3-1/2"	"	0.222	190	14.50	205
4"	"	0.276	230	17.75	248
90 deg connectors					
3/8"	EA.	0.145	1.96	9.42	11.38
1/2"	"	0.145	3.32	9.42	12.74
3/4"	"	0.145	5.21	9.42	14.63
1"	"	0.170	9.04	11.00	20.04
1-1/4"	"	0.182	18.25	11.75	30.00
1-1/2"	"	0.200	29.75	13.00	42.75
2"	"	0.211	37.00	13.75	50.75
2-1/2"	"	0.229	120	14.75	135
3"	"	0.267	170	17.25	187
90 deg insulated throat connectors					
3/8"	EA.	0.145	2.44	9.42	11.86
1/2"	"	0.145	3.68	9.42	13.10
3/4"	"	0.145	6.14	9.42	15.56
1"	"	0.170	10.00	11.00	21.00
1-1/4"	"	0.182	19.50	11.75	31.25
1-1/2"	"	0.200	34.75	13.00	47.75
2"	"	0.211	44.25	13.75	58.00
2-1/2"	"	0.229	120	14.75	135
3"	"	0.267	170	17.25	187
3-1/2"	"	0.333	480	21.50	502
4"	"	0.421	730	27.25	757
16110.24 GALVANIZED CONDUIT					
Galvanized rigid steel conduit					
1/2"	L.F.	0.040	2.25	2.59	4.84
3/4"	"	0.050	2.49	3.24	5.73
1"	"	0.059	3.60	3.84	7.44
1-1/4"	"	0.080	4.98	5.18	10.16
1-1/2"	"	0.089	5.86	5.76	11.62
2"	"	0.100	7.45	6.48	13.93
2-1/2"	"	0.145	13.75	9.42	23.17
3"	"	0.182	14.25	11.75	26.00
3-1/2"	"	0.190	20.50	12.25	32.75
4"	"	0.211	23.50	13.75	37.25
5"	"	0.286	43.50	18.50	62.00
6"	"	0.381	63.00	24.75	87.75
90 degree ell					
1/2"	EA.	0.250	12.50	16.25	28.75
3/4"	"	0.308	13.00	20.00	33.00
1"	"	0.381	20.00	24.75	44.75
1-1/4"	"	0.444	27.50	28.75	56.25
1-1/2"	"	0.500	33.75	32.50	66.25
2"	"	0.533	49.00	34.50	83.50

BASIC MATERIALS

16110.24 GALVANIZED CONDUIT, Cont'd...	UNIT	HOURS	MAT.	INST.	TOTAL
2-1/2"	EA.	0.667	91.00	43.25	134
3"	"	0.889	130	58.00	188
3-1/2"	"	1.000	200	65.00	265
4"	"	1.333	230	86.00	316
5"	"	2.222	630	140	770
6"	"	3.333	950	220	1,170
Couplings, with set screws					
1/2"	EA.	0.050	5.17	3.24	8.41
3/4"	"	0.059	6.82	3.84	10.66
1"	"	0.080	11.00	5.18	16.18
1-1/4"	"	0.100	18.50	6.48	24.98
1-1/2"	"	0.123	24.00	7.97	31.97
2"	"	0.145	54.00	9.42	63.42
2-1/2"	"	0.190	130	12.25	142
3"	"	0.250	160	16.25	176
3-1/2"	"	0.286	220	18.50	239
4"	"	0.308	290	20.00	310
5"	"	0.444	420	28.75	449
6"	"	0.500	550	32.50	583
Split couplings					
1/2"	EA.	0.190	4.40	12.25	16.65
3/4"	"	0.250	5.72	16.25	21.97
1"	"	0.276	8.03	17.75	25.78
1-1/4"	"	0.308	15.75	20.00	35.75
1-1/2"	"	0.381	20.50	24.75	45.25
2"	"	0.571	47.25	37.00	84.25
2-1/2"	"	0.571	96.00	37.00	133
3"	"	0.727	140	47.00	187
3-1/2"	"	1.000	220	65.00	285
4"	"	1.333	260	86.00	346
5"	"	1.633	460	110	570
6"	"	2.051	620	130	750
Erickson couplings					
1/2"	EA.	0.444	5.22	28.75	33.97
3/4"	"	0.500	6.38	32.50	38.88
1"	"	0.615	12.75	39.75	52.50
1-1/4"	"	0.889	23.25	58.00	81.25
1-1/2"	"	1.000	30.00	65.00	95.00
2"	"	1.333	58.00	86.00	144
2-1/2"	"	1.860	120	120	240
3"	"	2.105	170	140	310
3-1/2"	"	2.500	310	160	470
4"	"	2.667	370	170	540
5"	"	2.963	740	190	930
6"	"	3.200	1,080	210	1,290
Seal fittings					
1/2"	EA.	0.667	16.50	43.25	59.75
3/4"	"	0.800	18.25	52.00	70.25
1"	"	1.000	23.00	65.00	88.00
1-1/4"	"	1.143	27.50	74.00	102
1-1/2"	"	1.333	41.75	86.00	128
2"	"	1.600	53.00	100	153
2-1/2"	"	1.905	83.00	120	203

BASIC MATERIALS

16110.24 GALVANIZED CONDUIT, Cont'd...	UNIT	HOURS	MAT.	INST.	TOTAL
3"	EA.	2.105	99.00	140	239
3-1/2"	"	2.500	260	160	420
4"	"	2.963	400	190	590
5"	"	4.444	620	290	910
6"	"	5.000	680	320	1,000
Entrance fitting, (weather head), threaded					
1/2"	EA.	0.444	8.80	28.75	37.55
3/4"	"	0.500	10.75	32.50	43.25
1"	"	0.571	13.75	37.00	50.75
1-1/4"	"	0.727	18.00	47.00	65.00
1-1/2"	"	0.800	31.75	52.00	83.75
2"	"	0.889	48.50	58.00	107
2-1/2"	"	1.000	170	65.00	235
3"	"	1.333	240	86.00	326
3-1/2"	"	1.739	310	110	420
4"	"	2.500	400	160	560
5"	"	3.478	420	230	650
6"	"	4.444	520	290	810
Locknuts					
1/2"	EA.	0.050	0.19	3.24	3.43
3/4"	"	0.050	0.24	3.24	3.48
1"	"	0.050	0.38	3.24	3.62
1-1/4"	"	0.050	0.52	3.24	3.76
1-1/2"	"	0.059	0.86	3.84	4.70
2"	"	0.059	1.26	3.84	5.10
2-1/2"	"	0.080	3.52	5.18	8.70
3"	"	0.080	4.51	5.18	9.69
3-1/2"	"	0.080	7.62	5.18	12.80
4"	"	0.089	9.49	5.76	15.25
5"	"	0.089	20.25	5.76	26.01
6"	"	0.089	34.75	5.76	40.51
Plastic conduit bushings					
1/2"	EA.	0.123	0.33	7.97	8.30
3/4"	"	0.145	0.50	9.42	9.92
1"	"	0.190	0.71	12.25	12.96
1-1/4"	"	0.222	0.93	14.50	15.43
1-1/2"	"	0.250	1.26	16.25	17.51
2"	"	0.308	2.20	20.00	22.20
2-1/2"	"	0.500	5.50	32.50	38.00
3"	"	0.667	6.38	43.25	49.63
3-1/2"	"	0.800	7.15	52.00	59.15
4"	"	0.889	9.79	58.00	67.79
5"	"	1.143	18.75	74.00	92.75
6"	"	1.600	36.00	100	136
Conduit bushings, steel					
1/2"	EA.	0.123	0.50	7.97	8.47
3/4"	"	0.145	0.63	9.42	10.05
1"	"	0.190	0.96	12.25	13.21
1-1/4"	"	0.222	1.38	14.50	15.88
1-1/2"	"	0.250	1.98	16.25	18.23
2"	"	0.308	3.08	20.00	23.08
2-1/2"	"	0.500	7.04	32.50	39.54
3"	"	0.667	8.69	43.25	51.94

BASIC MATERIALS

16110.24 GALVANIZED CONDUIT, Cont'd...	UNIT	HOURS	MAT.	INST.	TOTAL
3-1/2"	EA.	0.800	18.00	52.00	70.00
4"	"	0.889	22.00	58.00	80.00
5"	"	1.143	45.00	74.00	119
6"	"	1.600	83.00	100	183
Pipe cap					
1/2"	EA.	0.050	0.57	3.24	3.81
3/4"	"	0.050	0.61	3.24	3.85
1"	"	0.050	0.99	3.24	4.23
1-1/4"	"	0.080	1.69	5.18	6.87
1-1/2"	"	0.080	2.64	5.18	7.82
2"	"	0.080	2.97	5.18	8.15
2-1/2"	"	0.089	5.06	5.76	10.82
3"	"	0.089	6.27	5.76	12.03
3-1/2"	"	0.089	8.58	5.76	14.34
4"	"	0.107	11.00	6.91	17.91
5"	"	0.145	14.75	9.42	24.17
6"	"	0.200	18.25	13.00	31.25
GRS elbows, 36" radius					
2"	EA.	0.667	150	43.25	193
2-1/2"	"	0.808	200	52.00	252
3"	"	1.053	260	68.00	328
3-1/2"	"	1.250	360	81.00	441
4"	"	1.509	400	98.00	498
5"	"	2.500	650	160	810
6"	"	3.810	690	250	940
42" radius					
2"	EA.	0.808	160	52.00	212
2-1/2"	"	1.000	220	65.00	285
3"	"	1.250	290	81.00	371
3-1/2"	"	1.509	410	98.00	508
4"	"	1.739	490	110	600
5"	"	2.857	730	190	920
6"	"	4.000	770	260	1,030
48" radius					
2"	EA.	0.930	180	60.00	240
2-1/2"	"	1.127	250	73.00	323
3"	"	1.429	330	93.00	423
3-1/2"	"	1.739	460	110	570
4"	"	2.162	550	140	690
5"	"	3.077	820	200	1,020
6"	"	4.444	860	290	1,150
Threaded couplings					
1/2"	EA.	0.050	1.91	3.24	5.15
3/4"	"	0.059	2.34	3.84	6.18
1"	"	0.080	3.47	5.18	8.65
1-1/4"	"	0.089	4.34	5.76	10.10
1-1/2"	"	0.100	5.32	6.48	11.80
2"	"	0.107	7.24	6.91	14.15
2-1/2"	"	0.123	18.00	7.97	25.97
3"	"	0.145	23.25	9.42	32.67
3-1/2"	"	0.145	31.25	9.42	40.67
4"	"	0.160	31.25	10.25	41.50
5"	"	0.182	72.00	11.75	83.75

BASIC MATERIALS

16110.24 GALVANIZED CONDUIT, Cont'd...	UNIT	HOURS	MAT.	INST.	TOTAL
6"	EA.	0.190	100	12.25	112
Threadless couplings					
1/2"	EA.	0.100	2.91	6.48	9.39
3/4"	"	0.123	3.03	7.97	11.00
1"	"	0.145	3.93	9.42	13.35
1-1/4"	"	0.190	4.58	12.25	16.83
1-1/2"	"	0.250	5.45	16.25	21.70
2"	"	0.308	7.97	20.00	27.97
2-1/2"	"	0.500	19.75	32.50	52.25
3"	"	0.615	24.00	39.75	63.75
3-1/2"	"	0.808	30.75	52.00	82.75
4"	"	1.000	36.00	65.00	101
5"	"	1.250	120	81.00	201
6"	"	5.333	130	350	480
Threadless connectors					
1/2"	EA.	0.100	2.13	6.48	8.61
3/4"	"	0.123	3.41	7.97	11.38
1"	"	0.145	5.39	9.42	14.81
1-1/4"	"	0.190	9.18	12.25	21.43
1-1/2"	"	0.250	14.00	16.25	30.25
2"	"	0.308	26.75	20.00	46.75
2-1/2"	"	0.500	62.00	32.50	94.50
3"	"	0.615	82.00	39.75	122
3-1/2"	"	0.808	110	52.00	162
4"	"	1.000	130	65.00	195
5"	"	1.250	350	81.00	431
6"	"	1.509	460	98.00	558
Setscrew connectors					
1/2"	EA.	0.080	2.56	5.18	7.74
3/4"	"	0.089	3.55	5.76	9.31
1"	"	0.100	5.53	6.48	12.01
1-1/4"	"	0.123	9.82	7.97	17.79
1-1/2"	"	0.145	14.25	9.42	23.67
2"	"	0.190	28.25	12.25	40.50
2-1/2"	"	0.250	84.00	16.25	100
3"	"	0.308	120	20.00	140
3-1/2"	"	0.381	160	24.75	185
4"	"	0.500	200	32.50	233
5"	"	0.615	330	39.75	370
6"	"	0.808	430	52.00	482
Clamp type entrance caps					
1/2"	EA.	0.308	8.58	20.00	28.58
3/4"	"	0.381	10.00	24.75	34.75
1"	"	0.444	14.00	28.75	42.75
1-1/4"	"	0.500	16.50	32.50	49.00
1-1/2"	"	0.615	29.75	39.75	69.50
2"	"	0.727	35.75	47.00	82.75
3-1/2"	"	0.941	140	61.00	201
3"	"	1.127	210	73.00	283
3-1/2"	"	1.379	260	89.00	349
4"	"	2.424	390	160	550
"LB" condulets					
1/2"	EA.	0.308	8.41	20.00	28.41

BASIC MATERIALS

16110.24 GALVANIZED CONDUIT, Cont'd...	UNIT	HOURS	MAT.	INST.	TOTAL
3/4"	EA.	0.381	10.25	24.75	35.00
1"	"	0.444	15.25	28.75	44.00
1-1/4"	"	0.500	26.50	32.50	59.00
1-1/2"	"	0.615	34.25	39.75	74.00
2"	"	0.727	57.00	47.00	104
2-1/2"	"	1.000	120	65.00	185
3"	"	1.379	160	89.00	249
3-1/2"	"	1.739	280	110	390
4"	"	2.105	310	140	450
"T" condulets					
1/2"	EA.	0.381	10.50	24.75	35.25
3/4"	"	0.444	12.75	28.75	41.50
1"	"	0.500	19.00	32.50	51.50
1-1/4"	"	0.571	28.00	37.00	65.00
1-1/2"	"	0.615	37.25	39.75	77.00
2"	"	0.727	58.00	47.00	105
2-1/2"	"	1.127	120	73.00	193
3"	"	1.509	160	98.00	258
3-1/2"	"	1.860	300	120	420
4"	"	2.222	330	140	470
"X" condulets					
1/2"	EA.	0.444	15.50	28.75	44.25
3/4"	"	0.500	16.75	32.50	49.25
1"	"	0.571	27.75	37.00	64.75
1-1/4"	"	0.615	36.25	39.75	76.00
1-1/2"	"	0.667	46.75	43.25	90.00
2"	"	0.879	96.00	57.00	153
Blank steel condulet covers					
1/2"	EA.	0.100	2.39	6.48	8.87
3/4"	"	0.100	2.97	6.48	9.45
1"	"	0.100	4.04	6.48	10.52
1-1/4"	"	0.123	4.95	7.97	12.92
1-1/2"	"	0.123	5.20	7.97	13.17
2"	"	0.123	8.74	7.97	16.71
2-1/2"	"	0.145	13.75	9.42	23.17
3"	"	0.145	14.75	9.42	24.17
3-1/2"	"	0.145	16.25	9.42	25.67
4"	"	0.200	17.75	13.00	30.75
Solid condulet gaskets					
1/2"	EA.	0.050	1.98	3.24	5.22
3/4"	"	0.050	2.14	3.24	5.38
1"	"	0.050	2.47	3.24	5.71
1-1/4"	"	0.080	3.08	5.18	8.26
1-1/2"	"	0.080	3.24	5.18	8.42
2"	"	0.080	3.63	5.18	8.81
2-1/2"	"	0.100	5.99	6.48	12.47
3"	"	0.100	6.16	6.48	12.64
3-1/2"	"	0.100	7.59	6.48	14.07
4"	"	0.145	8.19	9.42	17.61
One-hole malleable straps					
1/2"	EA.	0.040	0.33	2.59	2.92
3/4"	"	0.040	0.46	2.59	3.05
1"	"	0.040	0.66	2.59	3.25

BASIC MATERIALS

16110.24 GALVANIZED CONDUIT, Cont'd...	UNIT	HOURS	MAT.	INST.	TOTAL
1-1/4"	EA.	0.050	1.32	3.24	4.56
1-1/2"	"	0.050	1.51	3.24	4.75
2"	"	0.050	2.97	3.24	6.21
2-1/2"	"	0.059	6.14	3.84	9.98
3"	"	0.059	8.80	3.84	12.64
3-1/2"	"	0.059	12.75	3.84	16.59
4"	"	0.080	28.00	5.18	33.18
5"	"	0.080	99.00	5.18	104
6"	"	0.080	110	5.18	115
One-hole steel straps					
1/2"	EA.	0.040	0.07	2.59	2.66
3/4"	"	0.040	0.11	2.59	2.70
1"	"	0.040	0.18	2.59	2.77
1-1/4"	"	0.050	0.26	3.24	3.50
1-1/2"	"	0.050	0.35	3.24	3.59
2"	"	0.050	0.46	3.24	3.70
2-1/2"	"	0.059	1.60	3.84	5.44
3"	"	0.059	2.16	3.84	6.00
3-1/2"	"	0.059	3.21	3.84	7.05
4"	"	0.080	3.32	5.18	8.50
Bushed chase nipples					
1/2"	EA.	0.059	0.68	3.84	4.52
3/4"	"	0.070	0.94	4.50	5.44
1"	"	0.089	1.91	5.76	7.67
1-1/4"	"	0.100	2.87	6.48	9.35
1-1/2"	"	0.123	3.66	7.97	11.63
2"	"	0.145	4.91	9.42	14.33
2-1/2"	"	0.145	12.50	9.42	21.92
3"	"	0.182	16.25	11.75	28.00
3-1/2"	"	0.250	38.25	16.25	54.50
4"	"	0.296	54.00	19.25	73.25
Offset nipples					
1/2"	EA.	0.059	4.18	3.84	8.02
3/4"	"	0.070	4.34	4.50	8.84
1"	"	0.089	5.30	5.76	11.06
1-1/4"	"	0.107	12.75	6.91	19.66
1-1/2"	"	0.123	16.00	7.97	23.97
2"	"	0.145	25.00	9.42	34.42
3"	"	0.182	78.00	11.75	89.75
Short elbows					
1/2"	EA.	0.145	3.04	9.42	12.46
3/4"	"	0.200	4.16	13.00	17.16
1"	"	0.250	6.80	16.25	23.05
1-1/4"	"	0.296	20.50	19.25	39.75
1-1/2"	"	0.348	28.00	22.50	50.50
2"	"	0.400	50.00	26.00	76.00
Pulling elbows, female to female					
1/2"	EA.	0.250	7.34	16.25	23.59
3/4"	"	0.296	8.66	19.25	27.91
1"	"	0.400	14.25	26.00	40.25
1-1/4"	"	0.533	21.00	34.50	55.50
1-1/2"	"	0.727	39.50	47.00	86.50
2"	"	0.851	32.50	55.00	87.50

BASIC MATERIALS

16110.24 GALVANIZED CONDUIT, Cont'd...	UNIT	HOURS	MAT.	INST.	TOTAL
Grounding locknuts					
1/2"	EA.	0.080	1.90	5.18	7.08
3/4"	"	0.080	2.39	5.18	7.57
1"	"	0.080	3.46	5.18	8.64
1-1/4"	"	0.089	3.71	5.76	9.47
1-1/2"	"	0.089	3.88	5.76	9.64
2"	"	0.089	5.28	5.76	11.04
2-1/2"	"	0.100	9.73	6.48	16.21
3"	"	0.100	12.25	6.48	18.73
3-1/2"	"	0.100	20.00	6.48	26.48
4"	"	0.145	26.75	9.42	36.17
Insulated grounding metal bushings					
1/2"	EA.	0.190	1.35	12.25	13.60
3/4"	"	0.222	1.99	14.50	16.49
1"	"	0.250	2.83	16.25	19.08
1-1/4"	"	0.308	4.53	20.00	24.53
1-1/2"	"	0.381	5.65	24.75	30.40
2"	"	0.444	8.18	28.75	36.93
2-1/2"	"	0.667	21.25	43.25	64.50
3"	"	0.808	24.75	52.00	76.75
3-1/2"	"	0.941	35.75	61.00	96.75
4"	"	1.053	44.50	68.00	113
5"	"	1.569	89.00	100	189
6"	"	1.739	130	110	240
Nipples					
1/2" x					
4"	EA.	0.145	2.54	9.42	11.96
6"	"	0.145	3.39	9.42	12.81
8"	"	0.145	5.90	9.42	15.32
10"	"	0.145	6.76	9.42	16.18
12"	"	0.145	7.79	9.42	17.21
3/4" x					
4"	EA.	0.145	2.95	9.42	12.37
6"	"	0.145	3.97	9.42	13.39
8"	"	0.145	6.54	9.42	15.96
10"	"	0.145	7.85	9.42	17.27
12"	"	0.145	8.83	9.42	18.25
1" x					
4"	EA.	0.145	4.23	9.42	13.65
6"	"	0.145	5.25	9.42	14.67
8"	"	0.145	8.28	9.42	17.70
10"	"	0.145	10.75	9.42	20.17
12"	"	0.145	12.25	9.42	21.67
1-1/4" x					
4"	EA.	0.250	5.20	16.25	21.45
6"	"	0.250	6.77	16.25	23.02
8"	"	0.250	11.00	16.25	27.25
10"	"	0.250	14.00	16.25	30.25
12"	"	0.250	16.25	16.25	32.50
1-1/2" x					
4"	EA.	0.250	6.58	16.25	22.83
6"	"	0.250	9.08	16.25	25.33
8"	"	0.250	14.00	16.25	30.25

BASIC MATERIALS

16110.24 GALVANIZED CONDUIT, Cont'd...	UNIT	HOURS	MAT.	INST.	TOTAL
10"	EA.	0.250	16.75	16.25	33.00
12"	"	0.250	18.00	16.25	34.25
2" x					
4"	EA.	0.250	8.59	16.25	24.84
6"	"	0.250	11.50	16.25	27.75
8"	"	0.250	16.50	16.25	32.75
10"	"	0.250	19.75	16.25	36.00
12"	"	0.250	22.50	16.25	38.75
2-1/2" x					
6"	EA.	0.300	23.50	19.50	43.00
8"	"	0.300	30.75	19.50	50.25
10"	"	0.300	35.75	19.50	55.25
12"	"	0.300	41.50	19.50	61.00
3" x					
6"	EA.	0.300	28.25	19.50	47.75
8"	"	0.300	36.75	19.50	56.25
10"	"	0.300	43.25	19.50	62.75
12"	"	0.300	53.00	19.50	72.50
3-1/2" x					
6"	EA.	0.300	33.50	19.50	53.00
8"	"	0.300	42.00	19.50	61.50
10"	"	0.300	51.00	19.50	70.50
12"	"	0.300	59.00	19.50	78.50
4" x					
8"	EA.	0.400	47.25	26.00	73.25
10"	"	0.400	58.00	26.00	84.00
12"	"	0.400	70.00	26.00	96.00
5" x					
8"	EA.	0.400	85.00	26.00	111
10"	"	0.400	100	26.00	126
12"	"	0.400	120	26.00	146
6" x					
8"	EA.	0.400	110	26.00	136
10"	"	0.400	130	26.00	156
12"	"	0.400	150	26.00	176

16110.25 PLASTIC CONDUIT	UNIT	HOURS	MAT.	INST.	TOTAL
PVC conduit, schedule 40					
1/2"	L.F.	0.030	0.97	1.95	2.92
3/4"	"	0.030	1.25	1.95	3.20
1"	"	0.040	1.79	2.59	4.38
1-1/4"	"	0.040	2.47	2.59	5.06
1-1/2"	"	0.050	2.95	3.24	6.19
2"	"	0.050	3.85	3.24	7.09
2-1/2"	"	0.059	6.30	3.84	10.14
3"	"	0.059	7.64	3.84	11.48
3-1/2"	"	0.080	9.88	5.18	15.06
4"	"	0.080	10.75	5.18	15.93
5"	"	0.089	16.00	5.76	21.76
6"	"	0.100	21.50	6.48	27.98
Couplings					
1/2"	EA.	0.050	0.42	3.24	3.66
3/4"	"	0.050	0.51	3.24	3.75
1"	"	0.050	0.80	3.24	4.04

BASIC MATERIALS

16110.25 PLASTIC CONDUIT, Cont'd...	UNIT	HOURS	MAT.	INST.	TOTAL
1-1/4"	EA.	0.059	1.05	3.84	4.89
1-1/2"	"	0.059	1.46	3.84	5.30
2"	"	0.059	1.92	3.84	5.76
2-1/2"	"	0.059	3.35	3.84	7.19
3"	"	0.080	5.55	5.18	10.73
3-1/2"	"	0.080	6.20	5.18	11.38
4"	"	0.100	9.13	6.48	15.61
5"	"	0.100	21.75	6.48	28.23
6"	"	0.100	28.00	6.48	34.48
90 degree elbows					
1/2"	EA.	0.100	1.66	6.48	8.14
3/4"	"	0.123	1.81	7.97	9.78
1"	"	0.123	2.87	7.97	10.84
1-1/4"	"	0.145	4.00	9.42	13.42
1-1/2"	"	0.190	5.42	12.25	17.67
2"	"	0.222	7.56	14.50	22.06
2-1/2"	"	0.250	13.25	16.25	29.50
3"	"	0.308	24.25	20.00	44.25
3-1/2"	"	0.381	31.50	24.75	56.25
4"	"	0.500	39.75	32.50	72.25
5"	"	0.615	72.00	39.75	112
6"	"	0.727	120	47.00	167
Terminal adapters					
1/2"	EA.	0.100	0.62	6.48	7.10
3/4"	"	0.100	1.01	6.48	7.49
1"	"	0.100	1.26	6.48	7.74
1-1/4"	"	0.160	1.59	10.25	11.84
1-1/2"	"	0.160	2.03	10.25	12.28
2"	"	0.160	2.80	10.25	13.05
2-1/2"	"	0.222	4.78	14.50	19.28
3"	"	0.222	6.76	14.50	21.26
3-1/2"	"	0.222	8.69	14.50	23.19
4"	"	0.381	11.25	24.75	36.00
5"	"	0.381	22.50	24.75	47.25
6"	"	0.381	27.00	24.75	51.75
End bells					
1"	EA.	0.100	3.66	6.48	10.14
1-1/4"	"	0.160	4.33	10.25	14.58
1-1/2"	"	0.160	4.51	10.25	14.76
2"	"	0.160	6.71	10.25	16.96
2-1/2"	"	0.222	7.42	14.50	21.92
3"	"	0.222	7.84	14.50	22.34
3-1/2"	"	0.222	8.61	14.50	23.11
4"	"	0.381	9.38	24.75	34.13
5"	"	0.381	14.75	24.75	39.50
6"	"	0.381	16.25	24.75	41.00
LB conduit body					
1/2"	EA.	0.190	4.73	12.25	16.98
3/4"	"	0.190	6.09	12.25	18.34
1	"	0.190	6.71	12.25	18.96
1-1/4"	"	0.308	10.25	20.00	30.25
1-1/2"	"	0.308	12.25	20.00	32.25
2"	"	0.308	21.75	20.00	41.75

BASIC MATERIALS

16110.25 PLASTIC CONDUIT, Cont'd...	UNIT	HOURS	MAT.	INST.	TOTAL
2-1/2"	EA.	0.444	79.00	28.75	108
3"	"	0.533	81.00	34.50	116
3-1/2"	"	0.615	87.00	39.75	127
4"	"	0.727	89.00	47.00	136
Direct burial, conduit					
2"	L.F.	0.050	1.01	3.24	4.25
3"	"	0.059	1.87	3.84	5.71
4"	"	0.080	3.74	5.18	8.92
5"	"	0.089	5.33	5.76	11.09
6"	"	0.100	7.59	6.48	14.07
Encased burial conduit					
2"	L.F.	0.050	1.05	3.24	4.29
3"	"	0.059	1.76	3.84	5.60
4"	"	0.080	2.69	5.18	7.87
5"	"	0.089	3.85	5.76	9.61
6"	"	0.100	5.00	6.48	11.48
"EB" and "DB" duct, 90 degree elbows					
1-1/2"	EA.	0.145	10.75	9.42	20.17
2"	"	0.229	11.75	14.75	26.50
3"	"	0.381	16.75	24.75	41.50
3-1/2"	"	0.444	22.00	28.75	50.75
4"	"	0.533	23.75	34.50	58.25
5"	"	0.667	60.00	43.25	103
6"	"	0.899	110	58.00	168
45 degree elbows					
1-1/2"	EA.	0.229	11.50	14.75	26.25
2"	"	0.229	11.75	14.75	26.50
3"	"	0.381	17.00	24.75	41.75
3-1/2"	"	0.444	21.00	28.75	49.75
4"	"	0.533	22.25	34.50	56.75
5"	"	0.667	42.50	43.25	85.75
6"	"	0.899	98.00	58.00	156
Couplings					
1-1/2"	EA.	0.059	1.04	3.84	4.88
2"	"	0.059	1.17	3.84	5.01
3"	"	0.080	4.25	5.18	9.43
3-1/2"	"	0.080	5.06	5.18	10.24
4"	"	0.100	6.66	6.48	13.14
5"	"	0.100	12.00	6.48	18.48
6"	"	0.160	37.25	10.25	47.50
Bell ends					
1-1/2"	EA.	0.160	6.49	10.25	16.74
2"	"	0.160	8.25	10.25	18.50
3"	"	0.222	10.50	14.50	25.00
3-1/2"	"	0.222	10.50	14.50	25.00
4"	"	0.381	12.25	24.75	37.00
5"	"	0.381	18.50	24.75	43.25
6"	"	0.381	36.00	24.75	60.75
Female adapters, 1-1/2"	"	0.200	1.98	13.00	14.98
5 degree couplings					
1-1/2"	EA.	0.070	7.56	4.50	12.06
2"	"	0.070	8.53	4.50	13.03
3"	"	0.100	11.00	6.48	17.48

ELECTRICAL

BASIC MATERIALS

16110.25 PLASTIC CONDUIT, Cont'd...	UNIT	HOURS	MAT.	INST.	TOTAL
4"	EA.	0.145	11.50	9.42	20.92
5"	"	0.145	14.25	9.42	23.67
6"	"	0.145	15.00	9.42	24.42
45 degree elbows					
1/2"	EA.	0.123	1.26	7.97	9.23
3/4"	"	0.145	1.59	9.42	11.01
1"	"	0.145	2.25	9.42	11.67
1-1/4"	"	0.182	3.24	11.75	14.99
1-1/2"	"	0.229	4.45	14.75	19.20
2"	"	0.267	6.60	17.25	23.85
2-1/2"	"	0.296	12.25	19.25	31.50
3"	"	0.381	21.25	24.75	46.00
3-1/2"	"	0.444	23.75	28.75	52.50
4"	"	0.615	33.50	39.75	73.25
5"	"	0.727	54.00	47.00	101
6"	"	0.899	78.00	58.00	136
Female adapters					
1/2"	EA.	0.123	0.66	7.97	8.63
3/4"	"	0.123	1.05	7.97	9.02
1"	"	0.123	1.32	7.97	9.29
1-1/4"	"	0.200	1.70	13.00	14.70
1-1/2"	"	0.200	1.87	13.00	14.87
2"	"	0.200	2.69	13.00	15.69
2-1/2"	"	0.267	4.62	17.25	21.87
3"	"	0.267	7.70	17.25	24.95
3-1/2"	"	0.267	9.57	17.25	26.82
4"	"	0.444	12.25	28.75	41.00
5"	"	0.444	27.25	28.75	56.00
6"	"	0.444	31.00	28.75	59.75
Expansion couplings					
1/2"	EA.	0.123	28.50	7.97	36.47
3/4"	"	0.123	28.00	7.97	35.97
1"	"	0.145	29.25	9.42	38.67
1-1/4"	"	0.200	29.50	13.00	42.50
1-1/2"	"	0.200	29.50	13.00	42.50
2"	"	0.200	32.50	13.00	45.50
2-1/2"	"	0.296	44.75	19.25	64.00
3"	"	0.296	57.00	19.25	76.25
3-1/2"	"	0.296	71.00	19.25	90.25
4"	"	0.444	83.00	28.75	112
5"	"	0.444	130	28.75	159
6"	"	0.444	170	28.75	199
Plugs					
2"	EA.	0.200	2.11	13.00	15.11
3"	"	0.296	3.11	19.25	22.36
3-1/2"	"	0.296	3.35	19.25	22.60
4"	"	0.444	3.50	28.75	32.25
5"	"	0.444	4.75	28.75	33.50
6"	"	0.500	5.92	32.50	38.42
PVC cement					
1 pint	EA.				15.00
1 quart	"				22.00
1 gallon	"				72.00

BASIC MATERIALS

16110.25 PLASTIC CONDUIT, Cont'd...	UNIT	HOURS	MAT.	INST.	TOTAL
Type "T" condulets					
1/2"	EA.	0.296	7.42	19.25	26.67
3/4"	"	0.296	8.41	19.25	27.66
1"	"	0.296	9.57	19.25	28.82
1-1/4"	"	0.500	14.25	32.50	46.75
1-1/2"	"	0.500	18.75	32.50	51.25
2"	"	0.500	26.50	32.50	59.00
EB & DB female adapters					
2"	EA.	0.250	1.15	16.25	17.40
3"	"	0.381	3.19	24.75	27.94
3-1/2"	"	0.615	4.18	39.75	43.93
4"	"	0.727	4.29	47.00	51.29
5"	"	1.000	10.50	65.00	75.50
6"	"	1.600	14.00	100	114

16110.27 PLASTIC COATED CONDUIT					
Rigid steel conduit, plastic coated					
1/2"	L.F.	0.050	4.37	3.24	7.61
3/4"	"	0.059	5.08	3.84	8.92
1"	"	0.080	6.57	5.18	11.75
1-1/4"	"	0.100	8.32	6.48	14.80
1-1/2"	"	0.123	10.00	7.97	17.97
2"	"	0.145	13.25	9.42	22.67
2-1/2"	"	0.190	20.00	12.25	32.25
3"	"	0.222	25.25	14.50	39.75
3-1/2"	"	0.250	30.75	16.25	47.00
4"	"	0.308	37.50	20.00	57.50
5"	"	0.381	64.00	24.75	88.75
90 degree elbows					
1/2"	EA.	0.308	17.25	20.00	37.25
3/4"	"	0.381	17.75	24.75	42.50
1"	"	0.444	20.50	28.75	49.25
1-1/4"	"	0.500	25.25	32.50	57.75
1-1/2"	"	0.615	31.00	39.75	70.75
2"	"	0.800	43.25	52.00	95.25
2-1/2"	"	1.143	81.00	74.00	155
3"	"	1.333	130	86.00	216
3-1/2"	"	1.633	170	110	280
4"	"	2.000	190	130	320
5"	"	2.500	450	160	610
Couplings					
1/2"	EA.	0.059	4.91	3.84	8.75
3/4"	"	0.080	5.14	5.18	10.32
1"	"	0.089	6.82	5.76	12.58
1-1/4"	"	0.107	7.97	6.91	14.88
1-1/2"	"	0.123	11.00	7.97	18.97
2"	"	0.145	14.00	9.42	23.42
2-1/2"	"	0.182	34.75	11.75	46.50
3"	"	0.190	40.50	12.25	52.75
3-1/2"	"	0.200	56.00	13.00	69.00
4"	"	0.222	69.00	14.50	83.50
5"	"	0.250	200	16.25	216
1 hole conduit straps					
3/4"	EA.	0.050	8.37	3.24	11.61

BASIC MATERIALS

16110.27 PLASTIC COATED CONDUIT, Cont'd...	UNIT	HOURS	MAT.	INST.	TOTAL
1"	EA.	0.050	8.63	3.24	11.87
1-1/4"	"	0.059	12.50	3.84	16.34
1-1/2"	"	0.059	13.25	3.84	17.09
2"	"	0.059	19.50	3.84	23.34
3"	"	0.080	35.25	5.18	40.43
3-1/2"	"	0.080	63.00	5.18	68.18
4"	"	0.100	67.00	6.48	73.48
"L.B." condulets with covers					
1/2"	EA.	0.500	45.00	32.50	77.50
3/4"	"	0.500	50.00	32.50	82.50
1"	"	0.615	67.00	39.75	107
1-1/4"	"	0.727	97.00	47.00	144
1-1/2"	"	0.879	120	57.00	177
2"	"	1.000	170	65.00	235
2-1/2"	"	1.379	320	89.00	409
3"	"	1.739	400	110	510
3-1/2"	"	2.162	590	140	730
4"	"	2.500	670	160	830
"T" condulets with covers					
1/2"	EA.	0.571	52.00	37.00	89.00
3/4"	"	0.615	65.00	39.75	105
1"	"	0.667	78.00	43.25	121
1-1/4"	"	0.808	110	52.00	162
1-1/2"	"	0.941	140	61.00	201
2"	"	1.053	200	68.00	268
2-1/2"	"	1.509	340	98.00	438
3-1/2"	"	2.222	620	140	760
4"	"	2.667	680	170	850
5"	"	3.333	730	220	950
16110.28 STEEL CONDUIT					
Intermediate metal conduit (IMC)					
1/2"	L.F.	0.030	1.54	1.95	3.49
3/4"	"	0.040	1.89	2.59	4.48
1"	"	0.050	2.86	3.24	6.10
1-1/4"	"	0.059	3.66	3.84	7.50
1-1/2"	"	0.080	4.57	5.18	9.75
2"	"	0.089	5.97	5.76	11.73
2-1/2"	"	0.119	11.75	7.73	19.48
3"	"	0.145	15.25	9.42	24.67
3-1/2"	"	0.182	18.00	11.75	29.75
4"	"	0.190	19.75	12.25	32.00
90 degree ell					
1/2"	EA.	0.250	12.75	16.25	29.00
3/4"	"	0.308	13.50	20.00	33.50
1"	"	0.381	20.50	24.75	45.25
1-1/4"	"	0.444	28.50	28.75	57.25
1-1/2"	"	0.500	35.25	32.50	67.75
2"	"	0.571	51.00	37.00	88.00
2-1/2"	"	0.667	94.00	43.25	137
3"	"	0.889	130	58.00	188
3-1/2"	"	1.143	210	74.00	284
4"	"	1.333	230	86.00	316
Couplings					

BASIC MATERIALS

16110.28 STEEL CONDUIT, Cont'd...	UNIT	HOURS	MAT.	INST.	TOTAL
1/2"	EA.	0.050	3.14	3.24	6.38
3/4"	"	0.059	3.86	3.84	7.70
1"	"	0.080	5.72	5.18	10.90
1-1/4"	"	0.089	7.16	5.76	12.92
1-1/2"	"	0.100	9.05	6.48	15.53
2"	"	0.107	12.00	6.91	18.91
2-1/2"	"	0.123	29.50	7.97	37.47
3"	"	0.145	38.00	9.42	47.42
3-1/2"	"	0.145	51.00	9.42	60.42
4"	"	0.160	51.00	10.25	61.25

16110.32 FLEXIBLE WIRING SYSTEMS	UNIT	HOURS	MAT.	INST.	TOTAL
Single circuit cables					
5'	EA.	0.059	23.00	3.84	26.84
10'	"	0.100	32.75	6.48	39.23
15'	"	0.145	40.75	9.42	50.17
20'	"	0.200	57.00	13.00	70.00
25'	"	0.267	73.00	17.25	90.25
30'	"	0.296	90.00	19.25	109
40'	"	0.400	120	26.00	146
Two circuit cables					
5'	EA.	0.059	31.25	3.84	35.09
10'	"	0.100	36.75	6.48	43.23
15'	"	0.145	46.00	9.42	55.42
20'	"	0.200	65.00	13.00	78.00
25'	"	0.267	84.00	17.25	101
30'	"	0.296	100	19.25	119
40'	"	0.400	150	26.00	176
Two wire switch and receptacle cables					
5'	EA.	0.059	13.00	3.84	16.84
10'	"	0.100	26.25	6.48	32.73
15'	"	0.145	33.50	9.42	42.92
20'	"	0.200	58.00	13.00	71.00
25'	"	0.267	77.00	17.25	94.25
30'	"	0.296	100	19.25	119
40'	"	0.348	130	22.50	153
Three wire switch					
5'	EA.	0.059	15.00	3.84	18.84
10'	"	0.100	30.00	6.48	36.48
15'	"	0.145	39.25	9.42	48.67
20'	"	0.200	58.00	13.00	71.00
25'	"	0.267	77.00	17.25	94.25
30'	"	0.296	100	19.25	119
40'	"	0.348	130	22.50	153
Distribution boxes					
2 circuit	EA.	0.533	22.25	34.50	56.75
3 circuit	"	0.667	25.50	43.25	68.75
4 circuit	"	0.800	38.50	52.00	90.50
6 circuit	"	1.096	51.00	71.00	122
12 circuit	"	2.222	79.00	140	219
18 circuit	"	2.963	120	190	310
Tap boxes					
1 single pole switch	EA.	0.400	44.75	26.00	70.75
2 single pole switches	"	0.533	49.25	34.50	83.75

BASIC MATERIALS

16110.32 FLEXIBLE WIRING SYSTEMS, Cont'd...	UNIT	HOURS	MAT.	INST.	TOTAL
1 3 way switch	EA.	0.444	52.00	28.75	80.75
1 4 way switch	"	0.533	65.00	34.50	99.50
1 receptacle	"	0.400	40.25	26.00	66.25
2 receptacles	"	0.533	50.00	34.50	84.50
4 receptacles	"	0.800	63.00	52.00	115
1 clock	"	0.400	50.00	26.00	76.00
2 clocks	"	0.533	58.00	34.50	92.50
4 clocks	"	0.800	65.00	52.00	117
Dust cap	"	0.100	6.61	6.48	13.09
Cable coupler	"	0.200	15.50	13.00	28.50
Reversing connector	"	0.296	22.25	19.25	41.50
16110.35 SURFACE MOUNTED RACEWAY					
Single Raceway					
3/4" x 17/32" Conduit	L.F.	0.040	1.67	2.59	4.26
Mounting Strap	EA.	0.053	0.45	3.45	3.90
Connector	"	0.053	0.60	3.45	4.05
Elbow					
45 degree	EA.	0.050	7.62	3.24	10.86
90 degree	"	0.050	2.43	3.24	5.67
internal	"	0.050	3.05	3.24	6.29
external	"	0.050	2.82	3.24	6.06
Switch	"	0.400	19.75	26.00	45.75
Utility Box	"	0.400	13.25	26.00	39.25
Receptacle	"	0.400	23.50	26.00	49.50
3/4" x 21/32" Conduit	L.F.	0.040	1.90	2.59	4.49
Mounting Strap	EA.	0.053	0.70	3.45	4.15
Connector	"	0.053	0.72	3.45	4.17
Elbow					
45 degree	EA.	0.050	9.41	3.24	12.65
90 degree	"	0.050	2.59	3.24	5.83
internal	"	0.050	3.52	3.24	6.76
external	"	0.050	3.52	3.24	6.76
Switch	"	0.400	19.75	26.00	45.75
Utility Box	"	0.400	13.25	26.00	39.25
Receptacle	"	0.400	23.50	26.00	49.50
1-1/4" x 7/8" Conduit	L.F.	0.040	4.51	2.59	7.10
Mounting Strap	EA.	0.053	0.75	3.45	4.20
Connector	"	0.053	1.21	3.45	4.66
Elbow					
90 degree	EA.	0.050	9.87	3.24	13.11
internal	"	0.050	7.85	3.24	11.09
external	"	0.050	15.50	3.24	18.74
Switch Box	"	0.400	15.75	26.00	41.75
Receptacle Box	"	0.400	15.75	26.00	41.75
1-29/32" x 7/8" Conduit	L.F.	0.040	3.52	2.59	6.11
Mounting Strap	EA.	0.053	0.70	3.45	4.15
Connector	"	0.053	2.48	3.45	5.93
Elbow					
90 degree	EA.	0.050	9.18	3.24	12.42
internal	"	0.050	22.25	3.24	25.49
external	"	0.050	13.50	3.24	16.74
Switch Box	"	0.400	13.75	26.00	39.75
Receptacle Box	"	0.400	13.75	26.00	39.75

BASIC MATERIALS

16110.35 SURFACE MOUNTED RACEWAY, Cont'd...	UNIT	HOURS	MAT.	INST.	TOTAL
2-3/4" x 1-15/32" Conduit	L.F.	0.040	6.75	2.59	9.34
Mounting Strap	EA.	0.053	2.13	3.45	5.58
Connector	"	0.053	4.21	3.45	7.66
Elbow					
90 degree	EA.	0.050	30.75	3.24	33.99
internal	"	0.050	17.25	3.24	20.49
external	"	0.050	26.25	3.24	29.49
Switch Cover	"	0.400	13.00	26.00	39.00
Receptacle Cover	"	0.400	12.25	26.00	38.25
Double Raceway					
5-1/2" x 2" Conduit	L.F.	0.044	12.50	2.88	15.38
Mounting Strap	EA.	0.067	2.43	4.32	6.75
Connector	"	0.067	5.20	4.32	9.52
Elbow					
90 degree	EA.	0.057	51.00	3.70	54.70
internal	"	0.057	69.00	3.70	72.70
external	"	0.057	74.00	3.70	77.70
Receptacle Cover	"	0.400	12.25	26.00	38.25
16110.40 UNDERFLOOR DUCT					
Underfloor blank duct, insert duct					
7/8"	L.F.	0.050	13.50	3.24	16.74
1-3/8"	"	0.050	14.75	3.24	17.99
1-7/8"	"	0.050	15.00	3.24	18.24
Box opening plugs	EA.	0.145	5.22	9.42	14.64
Duct end plugs	"	0.145	6.08	9.42	15.50
Sleeve couplings	"	0.348	14.00	22.50	36.50
Expansion couplings	"	0.348	79.00	22.50	102
Vertical elbow	"	0.348	67.00	22.50	89.50
Offset elbow	"	0.348	53.00	22.50	75.50
Horizontal elbow	"	0.348	130	22.50	153
Adjustable elbow	"	0.348	23.75	22.50	46.25
Cabinet connector	"	1.194	19.25	77.00	96.25
Y-take off	"	0.615	60.00	39.75	99.75
Underfloor duct leveling legs	"	0.145	6.00	9.42	15.42
Conduit adapters					
1/2"	EA.	0.250	23.75	16.25	40.00
3/4"	"	0.250	24.00	16.25	40.25
1"	"	0.250	20.75	16.25	37.00
1-1/4"	"	0.296	27.00	19.25	46.25
2"	"	0.348	37.50	22.50	60.00
Reducer bushings					
1-1/4" x 3/4"	EA.	0.200	12.00	13.00	25.00
1-1/4" x 1"	"	0.200	14.00	13.00	27.00
2" x 1-1/2"	"	0.250	16.25	16.25	32.50
Support couplers					
1 standard	EA.	0.250	33.50	16.25	49.75
2 standard	"	0.296	33.50	19.25	52.75
3 standard	"	0.348	33.50	22.50	56.00
Supports					
1 duct	EA.	0.145	33.50	9.42	42.92
2 duct	"	0.170	33.50	11.00	44.50
3 duct	"	0.190	33.50	12.25	45.75
4 duct	"	0.250	45.75	16.25	62.00

BASIC MATERIALS

16110.40 UNDERFLOOR DUCT, Cont'd...	UNIT	HOURS	MAT.	INST.	TOTAL
5 duct	EA.	0.296	49.75	19.25	69.00
Single level junction box					
1 standard	EA.	0.800	330	52.00	382
2 standard	"	1.509	490	98.00	588
3 standard	"	2.963	940	190	1,130
4 standard	"	4.000	1,210	260	1,470
Two level junction boxes					
1 standard	EA.	1.000	360	65.00	425
2 standard	"	2.000	560	130	690
Sealing compound	"				7.37
Insert adapters	"	0.145	17.75	9.42	27.17
Ellipsoids	"	0.348	19.75	22.50	42.25
Insert closing cap	"	0.145	2.09	9.42	11.51
Marker Screws	"	0.145	5.50	9.42	14.92
Access boxes	"	1.000	390	65.00	455
Closing caps	"	0.145	2.09	9.42	11.51
Afterset markers	"	0.145	5.44	9.42	14.86
Cell markers	"	0.145	12.00	9.42	21.42
Tie down straps	"	0.145	11.00	9.42	20.42
Plastic grommets	"	0.400	5.50	26.00	31.50
Metal grommets	"	0.400	38.25	26.00	64.25
Receptacle					
Duplex, 20a	EA.	0.500	67.00	32.50	99.50
Single					
30a	EA.	0.500	88.00	32.50	121
50a	"	0.615	98.00	39.75	138
Double duplex	"	0.615	70.00	39.75	110
Single, 20a	"	0.444	62.00	28.75	90.75
Double single	"	0.500	73.00	32.50	106
Twist lock	"	0.444	67.00	28.75	95.75
1 conduit opening	"	0.444	65.00	28.75	93.75
2 conduit openings	"	0.500	73.00	32.50	106
1 bushed opening	"	0.444	65.00	28.75	93.75
2 bushed openings	"	0.500	73.00	32.50	106
Amphenol connector					
1"	EA.	0.500	110	32.50	143
2"	"	0.533	120	34.50	155
5"	"	0.615	140	39.75	180
Standpipes					
Aluminum	EA.	0.250	81.00	16.25	97.25
Brass	"	0.250	85.00	16.25	101
Abandonment plates					
Aluminum	EA.	0.250	22.75	16.25	39.00
Brass	"	0.250	37.75	16.25	54.00
Split bell caps					
Aluminum	EA.	0.250	130	16.25	146
Brass	"	0.250	170	16.25	186
Flush floor receptacles					
Aluminum	EA.	0.727	110	47.00	157
Brass	"	0.727	120	47.00	167
Flush floor telephone					
Aluminum	EA.	0.500	78.00	32.50	111
Brass	"	0.500	97.00	32.50	130

BASIC MATERIALS

16110.40 UNDERFLOOR DUCT, Cont'd...	UNIT	HOURS	MAT.	INST.	TOTAL
Super underfloor duct blank duct					
1/2"	L.F.	0.059	19.00	3.84	22.84
7/8"	"	0.059	19.75	3.84	23.59
1-3/8"	"	0.059	20.00	3.84	23.84
1-7/8"	"	0.059	22.50	3.84	26.34
Box opening plugs	EA.	0.145	4.34	9.42	13.76
End plugs	"	0.145	4.62	9.42	14.04
Conduit adapters	"	0.727	18.25	47.00	65.25
Sleeve coupling	"	0.444	14.75	28.75	43.50
Expansion coupling	"	0.444	48.75	28.75	77.50
Reducing coupling	"	0.444	63.00	28.75	91.75
Vertical elbow	"	0.444	38.75	28.75	67.50
Offset elbow	"	0.444	38.75	28.75	67.50
Horizontal elbow	"	0.444	98.00	28.75	127
Adjustable elbow	"	0.444	38.75	28.75	67.50
Cabinet connector	"	1.509	29.50	98.00	128
Super underfloor duct Y-take off	"	0.727	59.00	47.00	106
Leveling legs	"	0.145	5.33	9.42	14.75
Support couplers					
1 super	EA.	0.250	26.00	16.25	42.25
2 super	"	0.296	35.00	19.25	54.25
1 super, 1 standard	"	0.296	32.00	19.25	51.25
2 super, 2 standard	"	0.348	38.00	22.50	60.50
Single level junction boxes					
1 super	EA.	1.509	340	98.00	438
2 super	"	2.000	740	130	870
4 super	"	3.478	940	230	1,170
Double level junction boxes					
1 super	EA.	1.194	420	77.00	497
2 super	"	1.509	560	98.00	658
16110.50 WALL DUCT					
Lay-in wall duct, 10"	L.F.	0.059	55.00	3.84	58.84
Horizontal elbow	EA.	0.727	270	47.00	317
Edgewise elbow	"	0.727	61.00	47.00	108
Tee	"	0.899	210	58.00	268
Cross	"	1.096	130	71.00	201
Cabinet connector	"	1.600	130	100	230
Reverse elbow	"	0.533	110	34.50	145
Sweep elbow	"	0.727	190	47.00	237
Partition	"	0.059	40.00	3.84	43.84
Straight tunnel	"	0.276	55.00	17.75	72.75
Elbow tunnel	"	0.348	83.00	22.50	106
Tee kit	"	0.400	83.00	26.00	109
Ceiling dropout	"	1.000	320	65.00	385
Coupling device	"	0.145	34.25	9.42	43.67
End cap	"	0.276	46.25	17.75	64.00
Lay-in wall duct, 18"	L.F.	0.080	68.00	5.18	73.18
Horizontal elbow	EA.	0.800	98.00	52.00	150
Edgeware elbow	"	1.000	210	65.00	275
Tee	"	1.096	220	71.00	291
Cross	"	1.250	270	81.00	351
Reverse elbow	"	0.727	130	47.00	177
Sweep elbow	"	0.800	290	52.00	342

BASIC MATERIALS

16110.50 WALL DUCT, Cont'd...	UNIT	HOURS	MAT.	INST.	TOTAL
Partition	EA.	0.100	55.00	6.48	61.48
Straight tunnel	"	0.400	68.00	26.00	94.00
Elbow tunnel	"	0.500	120	32.50	153
Tee kit	"	0.533	120	34.50	155
Ceiling dropout	"	1.096	320	71.00	391
Coupling device	"	0.200	35.25	13.00	48.25
Reducer coupling	"	0.400	83.00	26.00	109
Cabinet connector	"	2.000	89.00	130	219
End cap	"	0.400	57.00	26.00	83.00

16110.60 TRENCH DUCT	UNIT	HOURS	MAT.	INST.	TOTAL
Trench duct, with cover					
9"	L.F.	0.170	91.00	11.00	102
12"	"	0.200	100	13.00	113
18"	"	0.267	140	17.25	157
24"	"	0.348	180	22.50	203
30"	"	0.400	200	26.00	226
36"	"	0.571	230	37.00	267
Tees					
9"	EA.	1.739	330	110	440
12"	"	2.000	390	130	520
18"	"	2.222	500	140	640
24"	"	2.500	720	160	880
30"	"	2.963	930	190	1,120
36"	"	3.376	1,220	220	1,440
Vertical elbows					
9"	EA.	0.800	120	52.00	172
12"	"	1.096	130	71.00	201
18"	"	1.356	150	88.00	238
24"	"	1.667	180	110	290
30"	"	2.000	200	130	330
36"	"	2.500	220	160	380
Cabinet connectors					
9"	EA.	2.000	190	130	320
12"	"	2.105	210	140	350
18"	"	2.424	240	160	400
24"	"	2.500	300	160	460
30"	"	2.759	350	180	530
36"	"	2.963	390	190	580
End closers					
9"	EA.	0.615	34.50	39.75	74.25
12"	"	0.667	39.25	43.25	82.50
18"	"	0.800	60.00	52.00	112
24"	"	1.096	80.00	71.00	151
30"	"	1.290	100	84.00	184
36"	"	1.455	120	94.00	214
Horizontal elbows					
9"	EA.	1.509	310	98.00	408
12"	"	1.739	360	110	470
18"	"	2.105	440	140	580
24"	"	2.500	700	160	860
30"	"	2.857	930	190	1,120
36"	"	3.200	1,220	210	1,430
Crosses					

BASIC MATERIALS

16110.60 TRENCH DUCT, Cont'd...	UNIT	HOURS	MAT.	INST.	TOTAL
9"	EA.	2.000	550	130	680
12"	"	2.222	580	140	720
18"	"	2.500	700	160	860
24"	"	2.759	890	180	1,070
30"	"	3.200	1,150	210	1,360
36"	"	3.478	1,440	230	1,670

16110.80 WIREWAYS	UNIT	HOURS	MAT.	INST.	TOTAL
Wireway, hinge cover type					
2-1/2" x 2-1/2"					
1' section	EA.	0.154	18.50	9.96	28.46
2'	"	0.190	26.50	12.25	38.75
3'	"	0.250	35.75	16.25	52.00
5'	"	0.381	61.00	24.75	85.75
10'	"	0.667	120	43.25	163
4" x 4"					
1'	EA.	0.250	20.25	16.25	36.50
2'	"	0.250	29.75	16.25	46.00
3'	"	0.308	44.00	20.00	64.00
4'	"	0.308	61.00	20.00	81.00
10'	"	0.800	180	52.00	232
6" x 6"					
1'	EA.	0.381	39.00	24.75	63.75
2'	"	0.381	47.50	24.75	72.25
3'	"	0.444	68.00	28.75	96.75
4'	"	0.444	90.00	28.75	119
5'	"	0.571	97.00	37.00	134
10'	"	0.889	190	58.00	248
8" x 8"					
1'	EA.	0.444	63.00	28.75	91.75
2'	"	0.444	96.00	28.75	125
3'	"	0.500	130	32.50	163
4'	"	0.500	160	32.50	193
5'	"	0.615	200	39.75	240
12" x 12"					
1'	EA.	0.615	87.00	39.75	127
2'	"	0.615	130	39.75	170
3'	"	0.727	190	47.00	237
4'	"	0.727	220	47.00	267
5'	"	0.889	260	58.00	318
Fittings					
2-1/2" x 2-1/2"					
Drop hanger	EA.	0.123	18.50	7.97	26.47
Bracket hanger	"	0.123	13.75	7.97	21.72
Panel adapter	"	0.500	16.25	32.50	48.75
End plate	"	0.123	14.00	7.97	21.97
U-connector	"	0.123	11.50	7.97	19.47
Tee	"	0.200	76.00	13.00	89.00
Cross	"	0.250	48.50	16.25	64.75
90 degree elbow	"	0.200	39.00	13.00	52.00
Sweep elbow	"	0.200	66.00	13.00	79.00
45 degree elbow	"	0.200	38.00	13.00	51.00
Lay-in adapter	"	0.145	17.25	9.42	26.67
4" x 4"					

ELECTRICAL

BASIC MATERIALS

16110.80 WIREWAYS, Cont'd...	UNIT	HOURS	MAT.	INST.	TOTAL
Drop hanger	EA.	0.145	12.25	9.42	21.67
Bracket hanger	"	0.145	16.25	9.42	25.67
Panel adapter	"	0.615	19.25	39.75	59.00
End plate	"	0.145	13.50	9.42	22.92
U-connector	"	0.145	11.00	9.42	20.42
Tee	"	0.250	86.00	16.25	102
Cross	"	0.348	59.00	22.50	81.50
90 degree elbow	"	0.250	46.75	16.25	63.00
Sweep elbow	"	0.250	75.00	16.25	91.25
45 degree elbow	"	0.250	46.50	16.25	62.75
Lay-in adapter	"	0.200	32.50	13.00	45.50
6" x 6"					
Drop hanger	EA.	0.145	27.00	9.42	36.42
Bracket hanger	"	0.145	23.25	9.42	32.67
Reducing bushing	"	0.145	49.25	9.42	58.67
Panel adapter	"	0.727	25.50	47.00	72.50
End plate	"	0.145	16.50	9.42	25.92
U-connector	"	0.145	15.50	9.42	24.92
Tee	"	0.250	100	16.25	116
Cross	"	0.348	73.00	22.50	95.50
90 degree elbow	"	0.250	54.00	16.25	70.25
Sweep elbow	"	0.250	110	16.25	126
45 degree elbow	"	0.250	52.00	16.25	68.25
Lay-in adapter	"	0.250	43.00	16.25	59.25
8" x 8"					
Drop hanger	EA.	0.145	28.75	9.42	38.17
Bracket hanger	"	0.145	24.75	9.42	34.17
Reducing bushing	"	0.145	56.00	9.42	65.42
Panel adapter	"	0.899	34.00	58.00	92.00
End plate	"	0.145	11.00	9.42	20.42
U-connector	"	0.145	13.75	9.42	23.17
Tee	"	0.400	110	26.00	136
Cross	"	0.444	120	28.75	149
90 degree elbow	"	0.400	85.00	26.00	111
Sweep elbow	"	0.400	70.00	26.00	96.00
45 degree elbow	"	0.400	79.00	26.00	105
Lay-in adapter	"	0.250	42.50	16.25	58.75
10" x 10"					
Drop hanger	EA.	0.145	29.00	9.42	38.42
Bracket hanger	"	0.145	29.50	9.42	38.92
Reducing bushing	"	0.145	85.00	9.42	94.42
Panel adapter	"	1.000	54.00	65.00	119
End plate	"	0.145	17.75	9.42	27.17
U-connector	"	0.145	34.50	9.42	43.92
Tee	"	0.444	110	28.75	139
Cross	"	0.500	150	32.50	183
90 degree elbow	"	0.444	91.00	28.75	120
Sweep elbow	"	0.444	87.00	28.75	116
45 degree elbow	"	0.444	110	28.75	139
Lay-in adapter	"	0.296	48.50	19.25	67.75
12" x 12"					
Drop hanger	EA.	0.145	81.00	9.42	90.42
Bracket hanger	"	0.145	55.00	9.42	64.42

BASIC MATERIALS

16110.80 WIREWAYS, Cont'd...	UNIT	HOURS	MAT.	INST.	TOTAL
Reducing bushing	EA.	0.145	83.00	9.42	92.42
Panel adapter	"	1.250	57.00	81.00	138
End plate	"	0.145	24.50	9.42	33.92
U-connector	"	0.615	52.00	39.75	91.75
Tee	"	0.533	220	34.50	255
Cross	"	0.615	220	39.75	260
90 degree elbow	"	0.615	140	39.75	180
Sweep elbow	"	0.615	200	39.75	240
45 degree elbow	"	0.615	220	39.75	260
Lay-in adapter	"	0.533	53.00	34.50	87.50
Raintight wireway, 4" x 4"					
1' section	EA.	0.400	63.00	26.00	89.00
5'	"	0.400	100	26.00	126
10'	"	1.000	150	65.00	215
Fittings					
90 degree elbow	EA.	0.400	61.00	26.00	87.00
Tee	"	0.444	110	28.75	139
Cross	"	0.500	110	32.50	143
Panel adapter	"	0.727	28.25	47.00	75.25
End plate	"	0.145	14.75	9.42	24.17
Gusset bracket	"	0.145	10.75	9.42	20.17
6" x 6"					
1' section	EA.	0.500	51.00	32.50	83.50
5'	"	0.727	120	47.00	167
10'	"	1.509	210	98.00	308
Fittings					
90 degree elbow	EA.	0.500	76.00	32.50	109
Tee	"	0.500	130	32.50	163
Cross	"	0.727	130	47.00	177
Panel adapter	"	1.000	37.50	65.00	103
End plate	"	0.145	16.50	9.42	25.92
Gusset bracket	"	0.145	13.75	9.42	23.17
16120.41 ALUMINUM CONDUCTORS					
Type XHHW, stranded aluminum, 600v					
#8	L.F.	0.005	0.28	0.32	0.60
#6	"	0.006	0.30	0.39	0.69
#4	"	0.008	0.37	0.51	0.88
#2	"	0.009	0.51	0.58	1.09
1/0	"	0.011	0.82	0.71	1.53
2/0	"	0.012	1.06	0.77	1.83
3/0	"	0.014	1.32	0.90	2.22
4/0	"	0.015	1.47	0.96	2.43
300 MCM	"	0.020	2.47	1.29	3.76
350 MCM	"	0.023	2.51	1.48	3.99
400 MCM	"	0.028	2.94	1.81	4.75
500 MCM	"	0.033	3.24	2.16	5.40
600 MCM	"	0.040	4.10	2.59	6.69
700 MCM	"	0.047	4.76	3.04	7.80
750 MCM	"	0.052	4.80	3.34	8.14
THW, stranded					
#8	L.F.	0.005	0.28	0.32	0.60
#6	"	0.006	0.30	0.39	0.69
#4	"	0.008	0.37	0.51	0.88

BASIC MATERIALS

16120.41 ALUMINUM CONDUCTORS, Cont'd...	UNIT	HOURS	MAT.	INST.	TOTAL
#3	L.F.	0.009	0.48	0.57	1.05
#1	"	0.010	0.82	0.64	1.46
1/0	"	0.011	0.90	0.71	1.61
2/0	"	0.012	1.06	0.76	1.82
3/0	"	0.012	1.32	0.76	2.08
4/0	"	0.015	1.47	0.96	2.43
250 MCM	"	0.018	1.79	1.16	2.95
300 MCM	"	0.020	2.47	1.29	3.76
350 MCM	"	0.023	2.51	1.48	3.99
400 MCM	"	0.028	2.94	1.81	4.75
500 MCM	"	0.033	3.24	2.16	5.40
600 MCM	"	0.040	4.10	2.59	6.69
700 MCM	"	0.047	4.76	3.04	7.80
750 MCM	"	0.052	4.80	3.34	8.14
XLP, stranded					
#6	L.F.	0.005	0.36	0.32	0.68
#4	"	0.008	0.41	0.51	0.92
#2	"	0.009	0.57	0.58	1.15
#1	"	0.010	0.79	0.64	1.43
1/0	"	0.011	0.96	0.71	1.67
2/0	"	0.012	1.14	0.77	1.91
3/0	"	0.014	1.36	0.90	2.26
4/0	"	0.015	1.50	0.96	2.46
250 MCM	"	0.016	2.02	1.04	3.06
300 MCM	"	0.020	2.62	1.29	3.91
350 MCM	"	0.023	2.68	1.48	4.16
400 MCM	"	0.028	3.28	1.81	5.09
500 MCM	"	0.033	3.60	2.16	5.76
600 MCM	"	0.040	4.64	2.59	7.23
700 MCM	"	0.047	5.32	3.04	8.36
750 MCM	"	0.052	5.40	3.34	8.74
1000 MCM	"	0.057	7.17	3.70	10.87
Bare stranded aluminum wire					
#4	L.F.	0.008	0.26	0.51	0.77
#2	"	0.009	0.37	0.58	0.95
1/0	"	0.011	0.50	0.71	1.21
2/0	"	0.012	0.62	0.77	1.39
3/0	"	0.014	0.78	0.90	1.68
4/0	"	0.015	0.97	0.96	1.93
Triplex XLP cable					
#4	L.F.	0.015	0.85	0.96	1.81
#2	"	0.020	1.05	1.29	2.34
1/0	"	0.030	1.68	1.95	3.63
4/0	"	0.048	3.09	3.14	6.23
Aluminum quadruplex XLP cable					
#4	L.F.	0.018	1.14	1.16	2.30
#2	"	0.023	1.47	1.48	2.95
1/0	"	0.032	2.33	2.07	4.40
2/0	"	0.042	2.79	2.72	5.51
4/0	"	0.064	4.02	4.14	8.16
Triplexed URD-XLP cable					
#6	L.F.	0.011	0.69	0.71	1.40
#4	"	0.014	0.99	0.90	1.89

BASIC MATERIALS

16120.41	ALUMINUM CONDUCTORS, Cont'd...	UNIT	HOURS	MAT.	INST.	TOTAL
#2		L.F.	0.018	1.27	1.16	2.43
1/0		"	0.028	2.03	1.81	3.84
2/0		"	0.033	2.33	2.16	4.49
3/0		"	0.040	2.79	2.59	5.38
4/0		"	0.047	3.26	3.04	6.30
250 MCM		"	0.055	3.74	3.57	7.31
350 MCM		"	0.057	4.84	3.70	8.54
Type S.E.U. cable						
#8/3		L.F.	0.025	1.34	1.62	2.96
#6/3		"	0.028	1.34	1.81	3.15
#4/3		"	0.035	1.72	2.25	3.97
#2/3		"	0.038	2.29	2.46	4.75
#1/3		"	0.040	3.12	2.59	5.71
1/0-3		"	0.042	3.50	2.72	6.22
2/0-3		"	0.044	4.02	2.88	6.90
3/0-3		"	0.052	5.61	3.34	8.95
4/0-3		"	0.057	5.64	3.70	9.34
Type S.E.R. cable with ground						
#8/3		L.F.	0.028	1.62	1.81	3.43
#6/3		"	0.035	1.83	2.25	4.08
#4/3		"	0.038	2.05	2.46	4.51
#2/3		"	0.040	3.02	2.59	5.61
#1/3		"	0.044	3.93	2.88	6.81
1/0-3		"	0.050	4.58	3.24	7.82
2/0-3		"	0.055	5.40	3.57	8.97
3/0-3		"	0.059	6.65	3.84	10.49
4/0-3		"	0.067	7.70	4.32	12.02
#6/4		"	0.038	3.12	2.46	5.58
#4/4		"	0.044	3.52	2.88	6.40
#2/4		"	0.044	5.13	2.88	8.01
#1/4		"	0.050	6.65	3.24	9.89
1/0-4		"	0.052	7.76	3.34	11.10
2/0-4		"	0.057	9.13	3.70	12.83
3/0-4		"	0.064	11.25	4.14	15.39
4/0-4		"	0.076	13.25	4.93	18.18
16120.43	COPPER CONDUCTORS					
Copper conductors, type THW, solid						
#14		L.F.	0.004	0.12	0.25	0.37
#12		"	0.005	0.18	0.32	0.50
#10		"	0.006	0.28	0.39	0.67
Stranded						
#14		L.F.	0.004	0.13	0.25	0.38
#12		"	0.005	0.16	0.32	0.48
#10		"	0.006	0.25	0.39	0.64
#8		"	0.008	0.41	0.51	0.92
#6		"	0.009	0.67	0.58	1.25
#4		"	0.010	1.05	0.64	1.69
#3		"	0.010	1.33	0.64	1.97
#2		"	0.012	1.67	0.77	2.44
#1		"	0.014	2.11	0.90	3.01
1/0		"	0.016	2.53	1.03	3.56
2/0		"	0.020	3.16	1.29	4.45
3/0		"	0.025	3.99	1.62	5.61

BASIC MATERIALS

16120.43 COPPER CONDUCTORS, Cont'd...	UNIT	HOURS	MAT.	INST.	TOTAL
4/0	L.F.	0.028	4.98	1.81	6.79
250 MCM	"	0.030	6.14	1.95	8.09
300 MCM	"	0.033	7.23	2.16	9.39
350 MCM	"	0.040	8.47	2.59	11.06
400 MCM	"	0.044	9.63	2.88	12.51
500 MCM	"	0.052	12.00	3.34	15.34
600 MCM	"	0.059	15.75	3.84	19.59
750 MCM	"	0.067	20.00	4.32	24.32
1000 MCM	"	0.076	25.00	4.93	29.93
THHN-THWN, solid					
#14	L.F.	0.004	0.12	0.25	0.37
#12	"	0.005	0.18	0.32	0.50
#10	"	0.006	0.28	0.39	0.67
Stranded					
#14	L.F.	0.004	0.12	0.25	0.37
#12	"	0.005	0.18	0.32	0.50
#10	"	0.006	0.28	0.39	0.67
#8	"	0.008	0.49	0.51	1.00
#6	"	0.009	0.78	0.58	1.36
#4	"	0.010	1.23	0.64	1.87
#2	"	0.012	1.71	0.77	2.48
#1	"	0.014	2.16	0.90	3.06
1/0	"	0.016	2.67	1.03	3.70
2/0	"	0.020	3.30	1.29	4.59
3/0	"	0.025	4.14	1.62	5.76
4/0	"	0.028	5.18	1.81	6.99
250 MCM	"	0.030	6.33	1.95	8.28
350 MCM	"	0.040	7.55	2.59	10.14
XHHW					
#14	L.F.	0.004	0.20	0.25	0.45
#10	"	0.006	0.46	0.39	0.85
#8	"	0.008	0.67	0.51	1.18
#6	"	0.009	1.05	0.58	1.63
#4	"	0.009	1.63	0.58	2.21
#2	"	0.011	2.55	0.71	3.26
#1	"	0.014	3.25	0.90	4.15
1/0	"	0.016	3.83	1.03	4.86
2/0	"	0.019	4.80	1.23	6.03
3/0	"	0.025	5.99	1.62	7.61
XLP, 600v					
#12	L.F.	0.005	0.31	0.32	0.63
#10	"	0.006	0.46	0.39	0.85
#8	"	0.008	0.60	0.51	1.11
#6	"	0.009	0.93	0.58	1.51
#4	"	0.010	1.44	0.64	2.08
#3	"	0.011	1.79	0.71	2.50
#2	"	0.012	2.22	0.77	2.99
#1	"	0.014	2.86	0.90	3.76
1/0	"	0.016	3.22	1.03	4.25
2/0	"	0.020	4.02	1.29	5.31
3/0	"	0.026	5.04	1.67	6.71
4/0	"	0.028	6.31	1.81	8.12
250 MCM	"	0.030	7.37	1.95	9.32

BASIC MATERIALS

16120.43 COPPER CONDUCTORS, Cont'd...	UNIT	HOURS	MAT.	INST.	TOTAL
300 MCM	L.F.	0.033	8.78	2.16	10.94
350 MCM	"	0.039	10.25	2.52	12.77
400 MCM	"	0.044	11.75	2.88	14.63
500 MCM	"	0.052	14.50	3.34	17.84
600 MCM	"	0.059	17.50	3.84	21.34
750 MCM	"	0.067	27.00	4.32	31.32
1000 MCM	"	0.076	35.75	4.93	40.68
Bare solid wire					
#14	L.F.	0.004	0.12	0.25	0.37
#12	"	0.005	0.20	0.32	0.52
#10	"	0.006	0.30	0.38	0.68
#8	"	0.008	0.41	0.51	0.92
#6	"	0.009	0.74	0.58	1.32
#4	"	0.010	1.23	0.64	1.87
#2	"	0.012	1.95	0.77	2.72
Bare stranded wire					
#8	L.F.	0.008	0.42	0.51	0.93
#6	"	0.010	0.71	0.64	1.35
#4	"	0.010	1.12	0.64	1.76
#2	"	0.011	1.78	0.71	2.49
#1	"	0.014	2.23	0.90	3.13
1/0	"	0.018	2.64	1.16	3.80
2/0	"	0.020	3.32	1.29	4.61
3/0	"	0.025	4.19	1.62	5.81
4/0	"	0.028	5.28	1.81	7.09
250 MCM	"	0.030	6.34	1.95	8.29
300 MCM	"	0.033	7.90	2.16	10.06
350 MCM	"	0.040	8.74	2.59	11.33
400 MCM	"	0.044	10.25	2.88	13.13
500 MCM	"	0.052	12.50	3.34	15.84
Type "BX" solid armored cable					
#14/2	L.F.	0.025	0.82	1.62	2.44
#14/3	"	0.028	1.29	1.81	3.10
#14/4	"	0.031	1.81	1.99	3.80
#12/2	"	0.028	0.84	1.81	2.65
#12/3	"	0.031	1.35	1.99	3.34
#12/4	"	0.035	1.87	2.25	4.12
#10/2	"	0.031	1.56	1.99	3.55
#10/3	"	0.035	2.23	2.25	4.48
#10/4	"	0.040	3.47	2.59	6.06
#8/2	"	0.035	3.11	2.25	5.36
#8/3	"	0.040	4.37	2.59	6.96
Steel type, metal clad cable, solid, with					
#14/2	L.F.	0.018	0.74	1.16	1.90
#14/3	"	0.020	1.14	1.29	2.43
#14/4	"	0.023	1.54	1.48	3.02
#12/2	"	0.020	0.77	1.29	2.06
#12/3	"	0.025	1.26	1.62	2.88
#12/4	"	0.030	1.70	1.95	3.65
#10/2	"	0.023	1.58	1.48	3.06
#10/3	"	0.028	2.20	1.81	4.01
#10/4	"	0.033	3.42	2.16	5.58
Metal clad cable, stranded, with ground					

BASIC MATERIALS

16120.43 COPPER CONDUCTORS, Cont'd...	UNIT	HOURS	MAT.	INST.	TOTAL
#8/2	L.F.	0.028	2.78	1.81	4.59
#8/3	"	0.035	3.98	2.25	6.23
#8/4	"	0.042	5.20	2.72	7.92
#6/2	"	0.030	3.79	1.95	5.74
#6/3	"	0.038	4.56	2.46	7.02
#6/4	"	0.044	5.44	2.88	8.32
#4/2	"	0.040	4.95	2.59	7.54
#4/3	"	0.044	5.61	2.88	8.49
#4/4	"	0.055	6.35	3.57	9.92
#3/3	"	0.050	6.50	3.24	9.74
#3/4	"	0.059	7.21	3.84	11.05
#2/3	"	0.057	5.22	3.70	8.92
#2/4	"	0.067	8.83	4.32	13.15
#1/3	"	0.076	9.18	4.93	14.11
#1/4	"	0.084	10.75	5.45	16.20
16120.45 FLAT CONDUCTOR CABLE					
Flat conductor cable, with shield, 3 conductor					
#12 awg	L.F.	0.059	8.03	3.84	11.87
#10 awg	"	0.059	9.40	3.84	13.24
4 conductor					
#12 awg	L.F.	0.080	11.00	5.18	16.18
#10 awg	"	0.080	12.25	5.18	17.43
Transition boxes					
#12 awg	L.F.	0.089	13.50	5.76	19.26
#10 awg	"	0.089	15.25	5.76	21.01
Flat conductor cable communication, with					
10 conductor	L.F.	0.059	5.28	3.84	9.12
16 conductor	"	0.070	6.10	4.50	10.60
24 conductor	"	0.100	6.82	6.48	13.30
Power and communication heads, duplex	EA.	0.800	72.00	52.00	124
Double duplex receptacle	"	0.952	80.00	62.00	142
Telephone	"	0.800	45.75	52.00	97.75
Receptacle and telephone	"	0.952	110	62.00	172
Blank cover	"	0.145	11.50	9.42	20.92
Transition boxes					
Surface	EA.	0.727	210	47.00	257
Flush	"	1.000	120	65.00	185
Flat conductor cable fittings					
End caps	EA.	0.145	2.20	9.42	11.62
Insulators	"	0.296	24.00	19.25	43.25
Splice connectors	"	0.444	1.65	28.75	30.40
Tap connectors	"	0.444	1.81	28.75	30.56
Cable connectors	"	0.444	2.03	28.75	30.78
Terminal blocks	"	0.615	14.00	39.75	53.75
Tape	"				21.50
16120.47 SHEATHED CABLE					
Non-metallic sheathed cable					
Type NM cable with ground					
#14/2	L.F.	0.015	0.35	0.96	1.31
#12/2	"	0.016	0.53	1.03	1.56
#10/2	"	0.018	0.85	1.15	2.00
#8/2	"	0.020	1.39	1.29	2.68
#6/2	"	0.025	2.20	1.62	3.82

BASIC MATERIALS

16120.47 SHEATHED CABLE, Cont'd...	UNIT	HOURS	MAT.	INST.	TOTAL
#14/3	L.F.	0.026	0.49	1.67	2.16
#12/3	"	0.027	0.77	1.72	2.49
#10/3	"	0.027	1.22	1.75	2.97
#8/3	"	0.028	2.05	1.78	3.83
#6/3	"	0.028	3.32	1.81	5.13
#4/3	"	0.032	6.87	2.07	8.94
#2/3	"	0.035	10.25	2.25	12.50
Type U.F. cable with ground					
#14/2	L.F.	0.016	0.40	1.03	1.43
#12/2	"	0.019	0.61	1.23	1.84
#10/2	"	0.020	0.97	1.29	2.26
#8/2	"	0.023	1.68	1.48	3.16
#6/2	"	0.027	2.62	1.75	4.37
#14/3	"	0.020	0.57	1.29	1.86
#12/3	"	0.022	0.86	1.42	2.28
#10/3	"	0.025	1.35	1.62	2.97
#8/3	"	0.028	2.55	1.81	4.36
#6/3	"	0.032	4.12	2.07	6.19
Type S.F.U. cable, 3 conductor					
#8	L.F.	0.028	1.76	1.81	3.57
#6	"	0.031	3.06	1.99	5.05
#3	"	0.040	5.97	2.59	8.56
#2	"	0.044	7.41	2.88	10.29
#1	"	0.050	9.58	3.24	12.82
#1/0	"	0.055	11.75	3.57	15.32
#2/0	"	0.064	14.75	4.14	18.89
#3/0	"	0.070	18.50	4.50	23.00
#4/0	"	0.076	20.50	4.93	25.43
Type SER cable, 4 conductor					
#6	L.F.	0.036	4.38	2.35	6.73
#4	"	0.039	6.14	2.52	8.66
#3	"	0.044	8.29	2.88	11.17
#2	"	0.048	9.61	3.14	12.75
#1	"	0.055	12.00	3.57	15.57
#1/0	"	0.064	15.25	4.14	19.39
#2/0	"	0.067	19.00	4.32	23.32
#3/0	"	0.076	23.75	4.93	28.68
#4/0	"	0.084	29.75	5.45	35.20
Flexible cord, type STO cord					
#18/2	L.F.	0.004	0.74	0.25	0.99
#18/3	"	0.005	0.86	0.32	1.18
#18/4	"	0.006	1.21	0.38	1.59
#16/2	"	0.004	0.85	0.25	1.10
#16/3	"	0.004	0.72	0.28	1.00
#16/4	"	0.005	1.01	0.32	1.33
#14/2	"	0.005	1.34	0.32	1.66
#14/3	"	0.006	1.22	0.39	1.61
#14/4	"	0.007	1.51	0.45	1.96
#12/2	"	0.006	1.70	0.38	2.08
#12/3	"	0.007	1.28	0.43	1.71
#12/4	"	0.008	1.85	0.51	2.36
#10/2	"	0.007	2.11	0.45	2.56
#10/3	"	0.008	2.02	0.51	2.53

ELECTRICAL

BASIC MATERIALS

16120.47 SHEATHED CABLE, Cont'd...	UNIT	HOURS	MAT.	INST.	TOTAL
#10/4	L.F.	0.009	3.13	0.58	3.71
#8/2	"	0.008	3.52	0.51	4.03
#8/3	"	0.009	3.90	0.57	4.47
#8/4	"	0.010	5.47	0.64	6.11
16130.10 FLOOR BOXES					
Adjustable floor boxes, steel	EA.	0.533	24.00	34.50	58.50
Cast bronze round	"	0.727	30.75	47.00	77.75
1 gang	"	0.800	35.75	52.00	87.75
2 gang	"	0.952	66.00	62.00	128
3 gang	"	1.000	94.00	65.00	159
Aluminum round	"	0.727	53.00	47.00	100
1 gang	"	0.800	40.75	52.00	92.75
2 gang	"	0.952	49.50	62.00	112
3 gang	"	1.000	59.00	65.00	124
Steel plate single recept	"	0.145	13.50	9.42	22.92
Duplex receptacle	"	0.182	13.00	11.75	24.75
Twist lock receptacle	"	0.182	13.75	11.75	25.50
Plug, 3/4"	"	0.145	17.25	9.42	26.67
1" plug	"	0.145	16.00	9.42	25.42
Carpet flange	"	0.145	21.00	9.42	30.42
Adjustable bronze plates for round cast boxes					
1/2" plug	EA.	0.145	7.04	9.42	16.46
3/4" plug	"	0.145	7.04	9.42	16.46
1" plug	"	0.145	8.85	9.42	18.27
1-1/4" plug	"	0.182	9.96	11.75	21.71
2" plug	"	0.200	13.25	13.00	26.25
Combination plug	"	0.200	15.50	13.00	28.50
Duplex receptacle plug	"	0.200	26.25	13.00	39.25
Adjustable aluminum plates for round cast					
1/2" plug	EA.	0.145	21.00	9.42	30.42
3/4" plug	"	0.145	21.25	9.42	30.67
1" plug	"	0.145	21.75	9.42	31.17
1-1/4" plug	"	0.182	23.25	11.75	35.00
2" plug	"	0.200	23.50	13.00	36.50
Combination plug	"	0.200	21.00	13.00	34.00
Duplex receptacle plug	"	0.200	35.75	13.00	48.75
Adjustable bronze plates for gang type boxes					
1/2" plug	EA.	0.145	22.00	9.42	31.42
3/4" plug	"	0.145	22.25	9.42	31.67
1" plug	"	0.145	22.50	9.42	31.92
1-1/4" plug	"	0.182	23.50	11.75	35.25
2" plug	"	0.200	24.50	13.00	37.50
Carpet plate					
1 gang	EA.	0.145	19.50	9.42	28.92
2 gang	"	0.145	29.25	9.42	38.67
3 gang	"	0.200	39.25	13.00	52.25
Adjustable aluminum plates for gang type					
1/2" plug	EA.	0.145	19.75	9.42	29.17
3/4" plug	"	0.145	20.25	9.42	29.67
1" plug	"	0.145	20.50	9.42	29.92
1-1/4" plug	"	0.182	23.25	11.75	35.00
2" plug	"	0.200	23.25	13.00	36.25
Duplex recept	"	0.200	19.75	13.00	32.75

BASIC MATERIALS

16130.10 FLOOR BOXES, Cont'd...	UNIT	HOURS	MAT.	INST.	TOTAL
Carpet plate					
1 gang	EA.	0.145	43.25	9.42	52.67
2 gang	"	0.145	60.00	9.42	69.42
3 gang	"	0.200	95.00	13.00	108
4 gang carpet plate	"	0.571	32.00	37.00	69.00
Telephone	"	0.500	29.25	32.50	61.75
Floor box nozzles, horizontal					
Duplex recept	EA.	0.533	49.50	34.50	84.00
Single recept	"	0.533	66.00	34.50	101
Double duplex recept	"	0.727	54.00	47.00	101
Vertical with duplex recept	"	0.615	44.00	39.75	83.75
Double duplex recept	"	0.727	46.75	47.00	93.75
Floor box bell nozzles split bell	"	0.250	16.00	16.25	32.25
One piece bell	"	0.250	50.00	16.25	66.25
Floor box standpipe					
1/2" x 3"	EA.	0.145	13.75	9.42	23.17
1/2" x 1"	"	0.145	13.75	9.42	23.17
Poke thru floor outlets					
2" floor	EA.	1.000	43.00	65.00	108
3" floor	"	1.194	46.75	77.00	124
4" floor	"	1.290	47.50	84.00	132
7" floor	"	1.509	50.00	98.00	148
9" floor	"	1.600	72.00	100	172
11" floor	"	1.818	72.00	120	192
13" floor	"	2.000	77.00	130	207
16130.40 BOXES					
Round cast box, type SEH					
1/2"	EA.	0.348	20.00	22.50	42.50
3/4"	"	0.421	20.00	27.25	47.25
SEHC					
1/2"	EA.	0.348	24.00	22.50	46.50
3/4"	"	0.421	24.00	27.25	51.25
SEHL					
1/2"	EA.	0.348	24.50	22.50	47.00
3/4"	"	0.444	24.00	28.75	52.75
SEHT					
1/2"	EA.	0.421	26.25	27.25	53.50
3/4"	"	0.500	26.25	32.50	58.75
SEHX					
1/2"	EA.	0.500	28.50	32.50	61.00
3/4"	"	0.615	28.50	39.75	68.25
Blank cover	"	0.145	4.84	9.42	14.26
1/2", hub cover	"	0.145	4.62	9.42	14.04
Cover with gasket	"	0.178	5.06	11.50	16.56
Rectangle, type FS boxes					
1/2"	EA.	0.348	10.25	22.50	32.75
3/4"	"	0.400	11.00	26.00	37.00
1"	"	0.500	11.75	32.50	44.25
FSA					
1/2"	EA.	0.348	18.50	22.50	41.00
3/4"	"	0.400	17.25	26.00	43.25
FSC					
1/2"	EA.	0.348	11.50	22.50	34.00

BASIC MATERIALS

16130.40 BOXES, Cont'd...	UNIT	HOURS	MAT.	INST.	TOTAL
3/4"	EA.	0.421	12.50	27.25	39.75
1"	"	0.500	15.75	32.50	48.25
FSL					
1/2"	EA.	0.348	18.25	22.50	40.75
3/4"	"	0.400	18.25	26.00	44.25
FSR					
1/2"	EA.	0.348	19.00	22.50	41.50
3/4"	"	0.400	19.50	26.00	45.50
FSS					
1/2"	EA.	0.348	11.50	22.50	34.00
3/4"	"	0.400	12.50	26.00	38.50
FSLA					
1/2"	EA.	0.348	7.83	22.50	30.33
3/4"	"	0.400	8.86	26.00	34.86
FSCA					
1/2"	EA.	0.348	23.00	22.50	45.50
3/4"	"	0.400	22.25	26.00	48.25
FSCC					
1/2"	EA.	0.400	14.00	26.00	40.00
3/4"	"	0.500	21.00	32.50	53.50
FSCT					
1/2"	EA.	0.400	14.00	26.00	40.00
3/4"	"	0.500	17.50	32.50	50.00
1"	"	0.571	14.25	37.00	51.25
FST					
1/2"	EA.	0.500	20.50	32.50	53.00
3/4"	"	0.571	20.50	37.00	57.50
FSX					
1/2"	EA.	0.615	23.50	39.75	63.25
3/4"	"	0.727	21.75	47.00	68.75
FSCD boxes					
1/2"	EA.	0.615	19.50	39.75	59.25
3/4"	"	0.727	20.50	47.00	67.50
Rectangle, type FS, 2 gang boxes					
1/2"	EA.	0.348	22.00	22.50	44.50
3/4"	"	0.400	22.50	26.00	48.50
1"	"	0.500	23.75	32.50	56.25
FSC, 2 gang boxes					
1/2"	EA.	0.348	23.25	22.50	45.75
3/4"	"	0.400	25.75	26.00	51.75
1"	"	0.500	31.25	32.50	63.75
FSS, 2 gang boxes					
3/4"	EA.	0.400	24.25	26.00	50.25
FS, tandem boxes					
1/2"	EA.	0.400	24.25	26.00	50.25
3/4"	"	0.444	25.00	28.75	53.75
FSC, tandem boxes					
1/2"	EA.	0.400	32.75	26.00	58.75
3/4"	"	0.444	35.00	28.75	63.75
FS, three gang boxes					
3/4"	EA.	0.444	35.75	28.75	64.50
1"	"	0.500	39.25	32.50	71.75
FSS, three gang boxes, 3/4"	"	0.500	46.00	32.50	78.50

BASIC MATERIALS

16130.40 BOXES, Cont'd...	UNIT	HOURS	MAT.	INST.	TOTAL
Weatherproof cast aluminum boxes, 1 gang,					
1/2"	EA.	0.400	6.54	26.00	32.54
3/4"	"	0.500	7.09	32.50	39.59
2 gang, 3 outlets					
1/2"	EA.	0.500	12.50	32.50	45.00
3/4"	"	0.533	13.25	34.50	47.75
1 gang, 4 outlets					
1/2"	EA.	0.615	11.50	39.75	51.25
3/4"	"	0.727	12.50	47.00	59.50
2 gang, 4 outlets					
1/2"	EA.	0.615	12.00	39.75	51.75
3/4"	"	0.727	13.25	47.00	60.25
1 gang, 5 outlets					
1/2"	EA.	0.727	9.44	47.00	56.44
3/4"	"	0.800	11.25	52.00	63.25
2 gang, 5 outlets					
1/2"	EA.	0.727	17.00	47.00	64.00
3/4"	"	0.800	20.75	52.00	72.75
2 gang, 6 outlets					
1/2"	EA.	0.851	19.25	55.00	74.25
3/4"	"	0.899	20.75	58.00	78.75
2 gang, 7 outlets					
1/2"	EA.	1.000	20.50	65.00	85.50
3/4"	"	1.096	25.50	71.00	96.50
Weatherproof and type FS box covers, blank,	"	0.145	2.98	9.42	12.40
Tumbler switch, 1 gang	"	0.145	6.11	9.42	15.53
1 gang, single recept	"	0.145	3.85	9.42	13.27
Duplex recept	"	0.145	4.91	9.42	14.33
Despard	"	0.145	4.93	9.42	14.35
Red pilot light	"	0.145	23.25	9.42	32.67
SW and					
Single recept	EA.	0.200	10.25	13.00	23.25
Duplex recept	"	0.200	8.47	13.00	21.47
2 gang					
Blank	EA.	0.182	3.10	11.75	14.85
Tumbler switch	"	0.182	4.07	11.75	15.82
Single recept	"	0.182	4.07	11.75	15.82
Duplex recept	"	0.182	4.07	11.75	15.82
3 gang					
Blank	EA.	0.200	7.09	13.00	20.09
Tumbler switch	"	0.200	8.80	13.00	21.80
4 gang					
Tumbler switch	EA.	0.250	11.25	16.25	27.50
Explosion proof boxes type E					
1/2"	EA.	0.348	40.00	22.50	62.50
3/4"	"	0.400	38.75	26.00	64.75
1"	"	0.500	40.00	32.50	72.50
1-1/4"	"	0.571	69.00	37.00	106
1-1/2"	"	0.615	160	39.75	200
Type L.B.					
1/2"	EA.	0.400	38.25	26.00	64.25
3/4"	"	0.500	40.75	32.50	73.25
1"	"	0.571	42.25	37.00	79.25

BASIC MATERIALS

16130.40 BOXES, Cont'd...	UNIT	HOURS	MAT.	INST.	TOTAL
1-1/4"	EA.	0.667	75.00	43.25	118
1-1/2"	"	0.727	150	47.00	197
2"	"	0.800	170	52.00	222
Type C					
1/2"	EA.	0.400	34.25	26.00	60.25
3/4"	"	0.500	35.75	32.50	68.25
1"	"	0.571	37.00	37.00	74.00
1-1/4"	"	0.667	62.00	43.25	105
1-1/2"	"	0.727	130	47.00	177
2"	"	0.800	140	52.00	192
Type CA					
1/2"	EA.	0.571	33.50	37.00	70.50
3/4"	"	0.727	38.00	47.00	85.00
Type L					
1/2"	EA.	0.400	34.75	26.00	60.75
3/4"	"	0.500	37.00	32.50	69.50
1"	"	0.571	38.50	37.00	75.50
1-1/4"	"	0.667	65.00	43.25	108
1-1/2"	"	0.727	130	47.00	177
2"	"	0.800	130	52.00	182
Type N					
1/2"	EA.	0.400	35.25	26.00	61.25
3/4"	"	0.500	36.75	32.50	69.25
1"	"	0.615	38.00	39.75	77.75
1-1/4"	"	0.667	66.00	43.25	109
Type T					
1/2"	EA.	0.533	34.00	34.50	68.50
3/4"	"	0.727	36.00	47.00	83.00
1"	"	0.851	37.25	55.00	92.25
1-1/4"	"	1.000	64.00	65.00	129
1-1/2"	"	1.159	130	75.00	205
2"	"	1.290	130	84.00	214
Type TA					
1/2"	EA.	0.727	39.00	47.00	86.00
3/4"	"	0.800	41.25	52.00	93.25
Type X					
1/2"	EA.	0.727	35.25	47.00	82.25
3/4"	"	0.851	37.75	55.00	92.75
1"	"	1.000	41.50	65.00	107
1-1/4"	"	1.159	75.00	75.00	150
1-1/2"	"	1.290	140	84.00	224
2"	"	1.455	150	94.00	244
With union hubs					
1/2"	EA.	0.727	73.00	47.00	120
3/4"	"	0.800	76.00	52.00	128
Box covers					
Surface	EA.	0.200	15.50	13.00	28.50
Sealing	"	0.200	17.00	13.00	30.00
Dome	"	0.200	23.50	13.00	36.50
1/2" nipple	"	0.200	30.00	13.00	43.00
3/4" nipple	"	0.200	31.00	13.00	44.00

BASIC MATERIALS

16130.45 EXPLOSION PROOF FITTINGS	UNIT	HOURS	MAT.	INST.	TOTAL
Flexible couplings with female unions					
1/2" x 18"	EA.	0.200	220	13.00	233
3/4" x 18"	"	0.276	270	17.75	288
1" x 18"	"	0.348	490	22.50	513
1-1/4" x 18"	"	0.421	820	27.25	847
1-1/2" x 18"	"	0.500	1,000	32.50	1,033
2" x 18"	"	0.571	1,390	37.00	1,427
1/2" x 24"	"	0.250	290	16.25	306
3/4" x 24"	"	0.296	360	19.25	379
1" x 24"	"	0.400	660	26.00	686
1-1/4" x 24"	"	0.444	1,050	28.75	1,079
1-1/2" x 24"	"	0.571	1,330	37.00	1,367
2" x 24"	"	0.615	1,850	39.75	1,890
Female seal-offs					
1/2"	EA.	0.571	15.00	37.00	52.00
3/4"	"	0.667	17.50	43.25	60.75
1"	"	0.727	22.75	47.00	69.75
1-1/4"	"	0.851	27.50	55.00	82.50
1-1/2"	"	1.000	41.75	65.00	107
2"	"	1.159	54.00	75.00	129
2-1/2"	"	1.739	83.00	110	193
3"	"	2.162	110	140	250
4"	"	2.667	410	170	580
Conduit plugs					
1/2"	EA.	0.145	2.54	9.42	11.96
3/4"	"	0.145	2.89	9.42	12.31
1"	"	0.145	3.47	9.42	12.89
1-1/4"	"	0.250	3.79	16.25	20.04
1-1/2"	"	0.250	5.39	16.25	21.64
2"	"	0.296	9.16	19.25	28.41
2-1/2"	"	0.296	14.75	19.25	34.00
3"	"	0.348	20.75	22.50	43.25
4"	"	0.348	34.75	22.50	57.25
Sealing cement					
1 pound	EA.				14.75
5 pound	"				41.00
Fibre					
1 ounce	EA.				6.87
8 ounce	"				49.00
Male unions					
1/2"	EA.	0.200	11.50	13.00	24.50
3/4"	"	0.242	16.25	15.75	32.00
1"	"	0.276	28.50	17.75	46.25
1-1/4"	"	0.296	43.50	19.25	62.75
1-1/2"	"	0.348	56.00	22.50	78.50
2"	"	0.421	72.00	27.25	99.25
2-1/2"	"	0.500	110	32.50	143
3"	"	0.727	150	47.00	197
4"	"	0.899	180	58.00	238
Female unions					
1/2"	EA.	0.200	7.97	13.00	20.97
3/4"	"	0.242	11.00	15.75	26.75
1"	"	0.276	19.75	17.75	37.50

BASIC MATERIALS

16130.45 EXPLOSION PROOF FITTINGS	UNIT	HOURS	MAT.	INST.	TOTAL
1-1/4"	EA.	0.296	29.75	19.25	49.00
1-1/2"	"	0.348	38.25	22.50	60.75
2"	"	0.421	49.25	27.25	76.50
2-1/2"	"	0.500	71.00	32.50	104
3"	"	0.727	100	47.00	147
4"	"	0.899	150	58.00	208
Male elbows					
1/2"	EA.	0.250	15.00	16.25	31.25
3/4"	"	0.296	16.75	19.25	36.00
1"	"	0.348	25.00	22.50	47.50
1-1/4"	"	0.444	28.50	28.75	57.25
Female elbows					
1/2"	EA.	0.250	12.50	16.25	28.75
3/4"	"	0.296	14.00	19.25	33.25
1"	"	0.348	19.25	22.50	41.75
1-1/4"	"	0.444	26.75	28.75	55.50
Pulling elbows					
1/2"	EA.	0.348	56.00	22.50	78.50
3/4"	"	0.444	60.00	28.75	88.75
1"	"	0.500	150	32.50	183
1-1/4"	"	0.615	170	39.75	210
1-1/2"	"	0.727	220	47.00	267
2"	"	1.905	240	120	360
2-1/2"	"	2.500	530	160	690
3"	"	2.963	500	190	690
3-1/2"	"	3.478	950	230	1,180
4"	"	4.211	960	270	1,230
Male expansion couplings					
1/2"	EA.	0.250	18.75	16.25	35.00
3/4"	"	0.296	24.50	19.25	43.75
1"	"	0.444	45.50	28.75	74.25
Female expansion couplings					
1/2"	EA.	0.250	16.75	16.25	33.00
3/4"	"	0.296	26.25	19.25	45.50
1"	"	0.444	45.50	28.75	74.25
16130.60 PULL AND JUNCTION BOXES					
4"					
Octagon box	EA.	0.114	3.33	7.40	10.73
Box extension	"	0.059	5.61	3.84	9.45
Plaster ring	"	0.059	3.08	3.84	6.92
Cover blank	"	0.059	1.36	3.84	5.20
Square box	"	0.114	4.79	7.40	12.19
Box extension	"	0.059	4.69	3.84	8.53
Plaster ring	"	0.059	2.57	3.84	6.41
Cover blank	"	0.059	1.32	3.84	5.16
4-11/16"					
Square box	EA.	0.114	9.70	7.40	17.10
Box extension	"	0.059	10.50	3.84	14.34
Plaster ring	"	0.059	6.40	3.84	10.24
Cover blank	"	0.059	2.37	3.84	6.21
Switch and device boxes					
2 gang	EA.	0.114	14.50	7.40	21.90
3 gang	"	0.114	25.50	7.40	32.90

BASIC MATERIALS

16130.60 PULL AND JUNCTION BOXES, Cont'd...	UNIT	HOURS	MAT.	INST.	TOTAL
4 gang	EA.	0.160	34.25	10.25	44.50
Device covers					
2 gang	EA.	0.059	11.50	3.84	15.34
3 gang	"	0.059	12.00	3.84	15.84
4 gang	"	0.059	16.25	3.84	20.09
Handy box	"	0.114	3.57	7.40	10.97
Extension	"	0.059	3.36	3.84	7.20
Switch cover	"	0.059	1.78	3.84	5.62
Switch box with knockout	"	0.145	5.36	9.42	14.78
Weatherproof cover, spring type	"	0.080	9.94	5.18	15.12
Cover plate, dryer receptacle 1 gang plastic	"	0.100	1.52	6.48	8.00
For 4" receptacle, 2 gang	"	0.100	2.71	6.48	9.19
Duplex receptacle cover plate, plastic	"	0.059	0.67	3.84	4.51
4", vertical bracket box, 1-1/2" with					
RMX clamps	EA.	0.145	6.90	9.42	16.32
BX clamps	"	0.145	7.41	9.42	16.83
4", octagon device cover					
1 switch	EA.	0.059	4.05	3.84	7.89
1 duplex recept	"	0.059	4.05	3.84	7.89
4", octagon swivel hanger box, 1/2" hub	"	0.059	10.75	3.84	14.59
3/4" hub	"	0.059	12.25	3.84	16.09
4" octagon adjustable bar hangers					
18-1/2"	EA.	0.050	5.03	3.24	8.27
26-1/2"	"	0.050	5.50	3.24	8.74
With clip					
18-1/2"	EA.	0.050	3.72	3.24	6.96
26-1/2"	"	0.050	4.18	3.24	7.42
4", square face bracket boxes, 1-1/2"					
RMX	EA.	0.145	8.25	9.42	17.67
BX	"	0.145	8.96	9.42	18.38
4" square to round plaster rings	"	0.059	2.75	3.84	6.59
2 gang device plaster rings	"	0.059	2.83	3.84	6.67
Surface covers					
1 gang switch	EA.	0.059	2.47	3.84	6.31
2 gang switch	"	0.059	2.53	3.84	6.37
1 single recept	"	0.059	3.72	3.84	7.56
1 20a twist lock recept	"	0.059	4.66	3.84	8.50
1 30a twist lock recept	"	0.059	5.97	3.84	9.81
1 duplex recept	"	0.059	2.31	3.84	6.15
2 duplex recept	"	0.059	2.31	3.84	6.15
Switch and duplex recept	"	0.059	3.85	3.84	7.69
4-11/16" square to round plaster rings	"	0.059	6.40	3.84	10.24
2 gang device plaster rings	"	0.059	5.28	3.84	9.12
Surface covers					
1 gang switch	EA.	0.059	7.10	3.84	10.94
2 gang switch	"	0.059	11.00	3.84	14.84
1 single recept	"	0.059	9.86	3.84	13.70
1 20a twist lock recept	"	0.059	9.69	3.84	13.53
1 30a twist lock recept	"	0.059	12.25	3.84	16.09
1 duplex recept	"	0.059	10.50	3.84	14.34
2 duplex recept	"	0.059	9.25	3.84	13.09
Switch and duplex recept	"	0.059	16.00	3.84	19.84
4" plastic round boxes, ground straps					

BASIC MATERIALS

16130.60 PULL AND JUNCTION BOXES, Cont'd...	UNIT	HOURS	MAT.	INST.	TOTAL
Box only	EA.	0.145	1.59	9.42	11.01
Box w/clamps	"	0.200	1.85	13.00	14.85
Box w/16" bar	"	0.229	3.94	14.75	18.69
Box w/24" bar	"	0.250	3.93	16.25	20.18
4" plastic round box covers					
Blank cover	EA.	0.059	1.04	3.84	4.88
Plaster ring	"	0.059	1.70	3.84	5.54
4" plastic square boxes					
Box only	EA.	0.145	1.23	9.42	10.65
Box w/clamps	"	0.200	1.52	13.00	14.52
Box w/hanger	"	0.250	1.88	16.25	18.13
Box w/nails and clamp	"	0.250	2.69	16.25	18.94
4" plastic square box covers					
Blank cover	EA.	0.059	1.01	3.84	4.85
1 gang ring	"	0.059	1.23	3.84	5.07
2 gang ring	"	0.059	1.72	3.84	5.56
Round ring	"	0.059	1.37	3.84	5.21
16130.65 PULL BOXES AND CABINETS					
Galvanized pull boxes, screw cover					
4x4x4	EA.	0.190	8.36	12.25	20.61
4x6x4	"	0.190	9.95	12.25	22.20
6x6x4	"	0.190	12.75	12.25	25.00
6x8x4	"	0.190	15.00	12.25	27.25
8x8x4	"	0.250	18.75	16.25	35.00
8x10x4	"	0.242	21.50	15.75	37.25
8x12x4	"	0.250	23.75	16.25	40.00
Screw cover					
10x10x4	EA.	0.308	23.75	20.00	43.75
12x12x6	"	0.444	35.00	28.75	63.75
12x15x6	"	0.444	41.50	28.75	70.25
12x18x6	"	0.500	46.25	32.50	78.75
15x18x6	"	0.571	51.00	37.00	88.00
18x24x6	"	0.615	96.00	39.75	136
18x30x6	"	0.727	110	47.00	157
24x36x6	"	0.727	160	47.00	207
Cast iron junction box, unflanged					
6x6x4					
3/4" tap	EA.	0.500	79.00	32.50	112
1" tap	"	0.500	86.00	32.50	119
Two 1/2" taps	"	0.500	86.00	32.50	119
3/4" taps	"	0.500	86.00	32.50	119
6" adapter plate	"	0.348	34.50	22.50	57.00
6" exterior collar	"	0.348	56.00	22.50	78.50
Screw cover cabinet					
12x12x4	EA.	0.615	66.00	39.75	106
12x16x4	"	0.615	86.00	39.75	126
12x16x6	"	0.615	100	39.75	140
12x18x4	"	0.667	93.00	43.25	136
12x18x6	"	0.667	110	43.25	153
18x18x4	"	1.000	110	65.00	175
18x18x6	"	1.000	130	65.00	195
18x24x6	"	1.143	180	74.00	254
24x24x6	"	1.333	210	86.00	296

BASIC MATERIALS

16130.65 PULL BOXES AND CABINETS, Cont'd...	UNIT	HOURS	MAT.	INST.	TOTAL
24x36x6	EA.	1.667	300	110	410
36x48x6	"	2.500	610	160	770
NEMA 3R, rain tight screw cover enclosures					
6x6x4	EA.	0.211	18.00	13.75	31.75
8x6x4	"	0.296	20.75	19.25	40.00
8x8x4	"	0.296	23.75	19.25	43.00
10x8x4	"	0.400	27.00	26.00	53.00
10x10x4	"	0.400	30.50	26.00	56.50
12x8x4	"	0.444	34.75	28.75	63.50
12x12x4	"	0.444	38.50	28.75	67.25
15x12x4	"	0.533	45.00	34.50	79.50
8x8x6	"	0.400	28.00	26.00	54.00
10x8x6	"	0.444	31.75	28.75	60.50
10x10x6	"	0.444	35.75	28.75	64.50
12x8x6	"	0.533	35.50	34.50	70.00
12x10x6	"	0.548	40.00	35.50	75.50
12x12x6	"	0.548	44.75	35.50	80.25
18x12x6	"	0.702	64.00	45.50	110
16130.80 RECEPTACLES					
Contractor grade duplex receptacles, 15a 120v					
Duplex	EA.	0.200	1.46	13.00	14.46
125 volt, 20a, duplex, grounding type,	"	0.200	10.75	13.00	23.75
Ground fault interrupter type	"	0.296	35.25	19.25	54.50
250 volt, 20a, 2 pole, single receptacle,	"	0.200	18.25	13.00	31.25
120/208v, 4 pole, single receptacle, twist lock					
20a	EA.	0.348	21.50	22.50	44.00
50a	"	0.348	41.00	22.50	63.50
125/250v, 3 pole, flush receptacle					
30a	EA.	0.296	21.75	19.25	41.00
50a	"	0.296	27.00	19.25	46.25
60a	"	0.348	70.00	22.50	92.50
277v, 20a, 2 pole, grounding type, twist lock	"	0.200	11.75	13.00	24.75
Dryer receptacle, 250v, 30a/50a, 3 wire	"	0.296	16.25	19.25	35.50
Clock receptacle, 2 pole, grounding type	"	0.200	10.75	13.00	23.75
125v, 20a single recept. grounding type					
Standard grade	EA.	0.200	11.75	13.00	24.75
Specification	"	0.200	14.25	13.00	27.25
Hospital	"	0.200	14.75	13.00	27.75
Isolated ground orange	"	0.250	49.50	16.25	65.75
Duplex					
Specification grade	EA.	0.200	11.75	13.00	24.75
Hospital	"	0.200	24.25	13.00	37.25
Isolated ground orange	"	0.250	49.50	16.25	65.75
250v, 20a, duplex, 2 pole, grounding, spec.	"	0.200	19.25	13.00	32.25
Combination recepts, 20a, 125v and 250v,	"	0.200	25.50	13.00	38.50
GFI hospital grade recepts, 20a, 125v, duplex	"	0.296	53.00	19.25	72.25
125/250v, 3 pole, 3 wire surface recepts					
30a	EA.	0.296	18.50	19.25	37.75
50a	"	0.296	20.50	19.25	39.75
60a	"	0.348	45.00	22.50	67.50
Cord set, 3 wire, 6' cord					
30a	EA.	0.296	16.50	19.25	35.75
50a	"	0.296	23.25	19.25	42.50

BASIC MATERIALS

16130.80 RECEPTACLES, Cont'd...	UNIT	HOURS	MAT.	INST.	TOTAL
125/250v, 3 pole, 3 wire cap					
30a	EA.	0.400	16.25	26.00	42.25
50a	"	0.400	29.75	26.00	55.75
60a	"	0.444	38.25	28.75	67.00
16198.10 ELECTRIC MANHOLES					
Precast, handhole, 4' deep					
2'x2'	EA.	3.478	350	230	580
3'x3'	"	5.556	460	360	820
4'x4'	"	10.256	1,000	660	1,660
Power manhole, complete, precast, 8' deep					
4'x4'	EA.	14.035	1,420	910	2,330
6'x6'	"	20.000	1,900	1,300	3,200
8'x8'	"	21.053	2,260	1,360	3,620
6' deep, 9' x 12'	"	25.000	2,490	1,620	4,110
Cast in place, power manhole, 8' deep					
4'x4'	EA.	14.035	1,690	910	2,600
6'x6'	"	20.000	2,180	1,300	3,480
8'x8'	"	21.053	2,420	1,360	3,780
16199.10 UTILITY POLES & FITTINGS					
Wood pole, creosoted					
25'	EA.	2.353	450	150	600
30'	"	2.963	540	190	730
35'	"	3.478	720	230	950
40'	"	3.791	860	250	1,110
45'	"	6.957	990	450	1,440
50'	"	7.207	1,170	470	1,640
55'	"	7.547	1,340	490	1,830
Treated, wood preservative, 6"x6"					
8'	EA.	0.500	95.00	32.50	128
10'	"	0.800	140	52.00	192
12'	"	0.889	150	58.00	208
14'	"	1.333	180	86.00	266
16'	"	1.600	220	100	320
18'	"	2.000	250	130	380
20'	"	2.000	320	130	450
Aluminum, brushed, no base					
8'	EA.	2.000	590	130	720
10'	"	2.667	680	170	850
15'	"	2.759	760	180	940
20'	"	3.200	920	210	1,130
25'	"	3.810	1,230	250	1,480
30'	"	4.396	1,850	280	2,130
35'	"	5.000	2,170	320	2,490
40'	"	6.250	2,780	400	3,180
Steel, no base					
10'	EA.	2.500	690	160	850
15'	"	2.963	760	190	950
20'	"	3.810	1,010	250	1,260
25'	"	4.520	1,140	290	1,430
30'	"	5.096	1,460	330	1,790
35'	"	6.250	1,710	400	2,110
Concrete, no base					
13'	EA.	5.517	890	360	1,250

BASIC MATERIALS

16199.10 UTILITY POLES & FITTINGS, Cont'd...	UNIT	HOURS	MAT.	INST.	TOTAL
16'	EA.	7.273	1,240	470	1,710
18'	"	8.791	1,490	570	2,060
25'	"	10.000	1,820	650	2,470
30'	"	12.121	2,430	790	3,220
35'	"	14.035	3,130	910	4,040
40'	"	16.000	3,650	1,040	4,690
45'	"	17.021	4,340	1,100	5,440
50'	"	18.182	5,380	1,180	6,560
55'	"	19.048	5,990	1,230	7,220
60'	"	20.000	6,860	1,300	8,160
Pole line hardware					
Wood crossarm					
4'	EA.	1.333	72.00	86.00	158
8'	"	1.667	140	110	250
10'	"	2.051	280	130	410
Angle steel brace					
1 piece	EA.	0.250	10.50	16.25	26.75
2 piece	"	0.348	22.25	22.50	44.75
Eye nut, 5/8"	"	0.050	2.57	3.24	5.81
Bolt (14-16"), 5/8"	"	0.200	19.25	13.00	32.25
Transformer, ground connection	"	0.250	6.10	16.25	22.35
Stirrup	"	0.308	13.50	20.00	33.50
Secondary lead support	"	0.400	20.75	26.00	46.75
Spool insulator	"	0.200	4.44	13.00	17.44
Guy grip, preformed					
7/16"	EA.	0.145	2.64	9.42	12.06
1/2"	"	0.145	4.56	9.42	13.98
Hook	"	0.250	3.30	16.25	19.55
Strain insulator	"	0.364	26.75	23.50	50.25
Wire					
5/16"	L.F.	0.005	1.47	0.32	1.79
7/16"	"	0.006	1.46	0.39	1.85
1/2"	"	0.008	3.52	0.51	4.03
Soft drawn ground, copper, #8	"	0.008	0.45	0.51	0.96
Ground clamp	EA.	0.308	3.67	20.00	23.67
Perforated strapping for conduit, 1-1/2"	L.F.	0.145	2.75	9.42	12.17
Hot line clamp	EA.	0.800	15.00	52.00	67.00
Lightning arrester					
3kv	EA.	1.000	480	65.00	545
10kv	"	1.600	750	100	850
30kv	"	2.000	1,360	130	1,490
36kv	"	2.500	2,770	160	2,930
Fittings					
Plastic molding	L.F.	0.145	3.23	9.42	12.65
Molding staples	EA.	0.050	0.77	3.24	4.01
Ground wires staples	"	0.030	0.33	1.95	2.28
Copper butt plate	"	0.296	0.92	19.25	20.17
Anchor bond clamp	"	0.145	4.04	9.42	13.46
Guy wire					
1/4"	L.F.	0.030	0.46	1.95	2.41
3/8"	"	0.050	0.71	3.24	3.95
Guy grip					
1/4"	EA.	0.050	7.86	3.24	11.10

BASIC MATERIALS

16199.10 UTILITY POLES & FITTINGS, Cont'd...	UNIT	HOURS	MAT.	INST.	TOTAL
3/8"	EA.	0.050	9.07	3.24	12.31

POWER GENERATION

16210.10 GENERATORS	UNIT	HOURS	MAT.	INST.	TOTAL
Diesel generator, with auto transfer switch					
30kw	EA.	30.769	27,180	1,990	29,170
50kw	"	30.769	34,420	1,990	36,410
75kw	"	42.105	43,700	2,730	46,430
100kw	"	47.059	48,500	3,050	51,550
125kw	"	50.000	51,830	3,240	55,070
150kw	"	57.143	59,750	3,700	63,450
175kw	"	66.667	62,270	4,320	66,590
200kw	"	80.000	64,590	5,180	69,770
250kw	"	88.889	70,590	5,760	76,350
300kw	"	100.000	84,900	6,480	91,380
350kw	"	114.286	90,890	7,410	98,300
400kw	"	133.333	111,580	8,640	120,220
450kw	"	145.455	119,520	9,430	128,950
500kw	"	160.000	129,470	10,370	139,840
600kw	"	200.000	177,330	12,960	190,290
750kw	"	200.000	247,530	12,960	260,490

16230.10 CAPACITORS	UNIT	HOURS	MAT.	INST.	TOTAL
Three phase capacitors					
240v					
1.5 kvar	EA.	2.500	520	160	680
2.5 kvar	"	3.200	570	210	780
3.0 kvar	"	4.000	640	260	900
4 kvar	"	5.000	690	320	1,010
5 kvar	"	5.333	740	350	1,090
6 kvar	"	5.714	830	370	1,200
7.5 kvar	"	6.154	910	400	1,310
10 kvar	"	8.000	1,010	520	1,530
15 kvar	"	9.501	1,380	620	2,000
20 kvar	"	11.994	1,670	780	2,450
25 kvar	"	13.008	1,960	840	2,800
40 kvar	"	18.018	3,490	1,170	4,660
50 kvar	"	20.997	4,220	1,360	5,580
60 kvar	"	21.505	5,320	1,390	6,710
75 kvar	"	25.000	6,060	1,620	7,680
100 kvar	"	29.963	7,170	1,940	9,110
480v					
1.5 kvar	EA.	2.500	440	160	600
2.5 kvar	"	3.200	460	210	670
3 kvar	"	4.000	500	260	760
4 kvar	"	5.000	540	320	860
5 kvar	"	5.333	580	350	930
6 kvar	"	5.714	620	370	990
7.5 kvar	"	6.154	630	400	1,030
10 kvar	"	8.000	720	520	1,240
12.5 kvar	"	9.501	800	620	1,420
15 kvar	"	11.994	880	780	1,660
18 kvar	"	12.500	910	810	1,720
20 kvar	"	13.008	960	840	1,800

POWER GENERATION

16230.10 CAPACITORS, Cont'd...	UNIT	HOURS	MAT.	INST.	TOTAL
22.5 kvar	EA.	13.491	990	870	1,860
25 kvar	"	14.842	1,070	960	2,030
30 kvar	"	14.842	1,250	960	2,210
35 kvar	"	16.000	1,410	1,040	2,450
40 kvar	"	18.018	1,580	1,170	2,750
45 kvar	"	20.000	1,650	1,300	2,950
50 kvar	"	20.997	2,110	1,360	3,470
60 kvar	"	21.978	2,480	1,420	3,900
70 kvar	"	24.024	2,390	1,560	3,950
75 kvar	"	25.000	2,570	1,620	4,190
80 kvar	"	27.027	2,940	1,750	4,690
90 kvar	"	28.986	3,120	1,880	5,000
100 kvar	"	29.963	3,310	1,940	5,250
125 kvar	"	33.058	4,220	2,140	6,360
150 kvar	"	37.037	4,960	2,400	7,360
16320.10 TRANSFORMERS					
Floor mounted, single phase, int. dry, 480v-					
3 kva	EA.	1.818	500	120	620
5 kva	"	3.077	660	200	860
7.5 kva	"	3.478	890	230	1,120
10 kva	"	3.810	1,110	250	1,360
15 kva	"	4.301	1,490	280	1,770
25 kva	"	7.547	2,730	490	3,220
37.5 kva	"	9.412	2,910	610	3,520
50 kva	"	10.256	3,460	660	4,120
75 kva	"	10.667	4,560	690	5,250
100 kva	"	11.594	6,000	750	6,750
Three phase, 480v-120/208v					
15 kva	EA.	6.015	1,630	390	2,020
30 kva	"	9.412	1,960	610	2,570
45 kva	"	10.811	2,600	700	3,300
75 kva	"	10.959	3,920	710	4,630
112.5 kva	"	12.698	5,130	820	5,950
150 kva	"	13.559	6,100	880	6,980
225 kva	"	15.385	9,350	1,000	10,350
Single phase, dry type, 2400v					
167 kva	EA.	22.472	16,660	1,460	18,120
250 kva	"	29.963	21,730	1,940	23,670
333 kva	"	37.559	26,690	2,430	29,120
5000v					
167 kva	EA.	22.472	18,130	1,460	19,590
250 kva	"	29.963	22,440	1,940	24,380
333 kva	"	37.559	28,060	2,430	30,490
8660v					
167 kva	EA.	27.491	18,760	1,780	20,540
250 kva	"	34.934	25,360	2,260	27,620
333 kva	"	67.797	30,110	4,390	34,500
1500v					
167 kva	EA.	27.491	21,150	1,780	22,930
250 kva	"	34.934	27,390	2,260	29,650
333 kva	"	42.553	32,710	2,760	35,470
Three phase, dry type transformer, 2400v					
225 kva	EA.	25.000	21,950	1,620	23,570

POWER GENERATION

16320.10 TRANSFORMERS, Cont'd...	UNIT	HOURS	MAT.	INST.	TOTAL
300 kva	EA.	27.491	26,480	1,780	28,260
500 kva	"	42.553	30,930	2,760	33,690
750 kva	"	52.632	38,730	3,410	42,140
5000v					
225.0 kva	EA.	25.000	23,750	1,620	25,370
300 kva	"	27.491	29,440	1,780	31,220
500 kva	"	42.553	36,070	2,760	38,830
750 kva	"	52.632	49,670	3,410	53,080
8660v					
225.0 kva	EA.	29.963	28,140	1,940	30,080
300 kva	"	32.520	33,960	2,110	36,070
500 kva	"	47.619	39,660	3,090	42,750
750 kva	"	57.554	49,660	3,730	53,390
1500v					
225 kva	EA.	29.963	31,600	1,940	33,540
300 kva	"	32.520	37,080	2,110	39,190
500 kva	"	47.619	46,090	3,090	49,180
750 kva	"	57.554	56,420	3,730	60,150
Buck boost transformers					
.25 kva	EA.	1.000	140	65.00	205
.50 kva	"	1.250	180	81.00	261
.75 kva	"	1.509	240	98.00	338
1.00 kva	"	1.739	290	110	400
1.50 kva	"	2.000	370	130	500
2.00 kva	"	2.500	460	160	620
3.00 kva	"	2.963	620	190	810
16350.10 CIRCUIT BREAKERS					
Molded case, 240v, 15-60a, bolt-on					
1 pole	EA.	0.250	16.50	16.25	32.75
2 pole	"	0.348	35.25	22.50	57.75
70-100a, 2 pole	"	0.533	100	34.50	135
15-60a, 3 pole	"	0.400	120	26.00	146
70-100a, 3 pole	"	0.615	200	39.75	240
480v, 2 pole					
15-60a	EA.	0.296	250	19.25	269
70-100a	"	0.400	330	26.00	356
3 pole					
15-60a	EA.	0.400	330	26.00	356
70-100a	"	0.444	390	28.75	419
70-225a	"	0.615	800	39.75	840
Draw out air circuit breakers					
600a	EA.	16.000	12,720	1,040	13,760
800a	"	18.182	16,430	1,180	17,610
1600a	"	24.242	26,390	1,570	27,960
2000a	"	27.586	35,360	1,790	37,150
3000a	"	32.000	61,370	2,070	63,440
4000a	"	38.095	94,260	2,470	96,730
Load center circuit breakers, 240v					
1 pole, 10-60a	EA.	0.250	16.50	16.25	32.75
2 pole					
10-60a	EA.	0.400	38.50	26.00	64.50
70-100a	"	0.667	120	43.25	163
110-150a	"	0.727	250	47.00	297

POWER GENERATION

16350.10 CIRCUIT BREAKERS, Cont'd...	UNIT	HOURS	MAT.	INST.	TOTAL
3 pole					
10-60a	EA.	0.500	110	32.50	143
70-100a	"	0.727	160	47.00	207
Load center, G.F.I. breakers, 240v					
1 pole, 15-30a	EA.	0.296	140	19.25	159
2 pole, 15-30a	"	0.400	250	26.00	276
Key operated breakers, 240v, 1 pole, 10-	"	0.296	90.00	19.25	109
Tandem breakers, 240v					
1 pole, 15-30a	EA.	0.400	31.25	26.00	57.25
2 pole, 15-30a	"	0.533	57.00	34.50	91.50
Bolt-on, G.F.I. breakers, 240v, 1 pole, 15-30a	"	0.348	130	22.50	153
Enclosed breaker, 120v, 1 pole, 15-50a,	"	0.800	150	52.00	202
240v, 2 pole					
15-60a, NEMA 1	EA.	1.250	220	81.00	301
70-100a, NEMA 1	"	1.739	280	110	390
3 pole					
15-60a, NEMA 1	EA.	1.509	280	98.00	378
70-100a, NEMA 1	"	2.222	360	140	500
Enclosed circuit breakers					
120v, 1 pole, NEMA 3R, 15-50a	EA.	0.899	300	58.00	358
240v, 2 pole, NEMA 3R					
15-60a	EA.	1.250	360	81.00	441
70-100a	"	1.739	420	110	530
3 pole, NEMA 3R					
15-60a	EA.	1.509	410	98.00	508
70-100a	"	2.222	500	140	640
480v, NEMA 1					
1 pole, 15-50a	EA.	0.800	190	52.00	242
2 pole, 15-60a	"	1.250	330	81.00	411
70-100a	"	1.509	410	98.00	508
3 pole, NEMA 1					
15-60a	EA.	1.509	400	98.00	498
70-100a	"	2.222	460	140	600
480v, 1 pole, 15-50a, NEMA 3R	"	1.000	310	65.00	375
2 pole					
2 pole, 15-60a, NEMA 3R	EA.	1.250	460	81.00	541
70-100a, NEMA 3R	"	1.739	530	110	640
3 pole					
15-60a, NEMA 3R	EA.	1.509	520	98.00	618
70-100a, NEMA 3R	"	2.222	580	140	720
70-100a, NEMA 1	"	1.739	440	110	550
3 pole					
15-60a, NEMA 1	EA.	1.739	440	110	550
70-100a, NEMA 1	"	2.222	530	140	670
Enclosed breakers, 600v, 2 phase, NEMA 3R					
15-60a	EA.	1.250	470	81.00	551
70-100a	"	1.739	580	110	690
3 phase, NEMA 3R					
15-60a	EA.	1.509	550	98.00	648
70-100a	"	2.222	630	140	770
600v, 3 phase, NEMA 1					
125a	EA.	2.222	770	140	910
150a	"	2.963	1,190	190	1,380

POWER GENERATION

16350.10 CIRCUIT BREAKERS, Cont'd...	UNIT	HOURS	MAT.	INST.	TOTAL
175a	EA.	2.963	1,190	190	1,380
200a	"	2.963	1,780	190	1,970
225a	"	2.963	1,780	190	1,970
250a	"	6.154	2,190	400	2,590
300a	"	6.154	2,190	400	2,590
350a	"	6.154	3,030	400	3,430
400a	"	6.154	3,030	400	3,430
500a	"	9.744	4,160	630	4,790
600a	"	9.744	4,160	630	4,790
700a	"	10.753	4,560	700	5,260
800a	"	10.753	5,750	700	6,450
900a	"	15.009	5,750	970	6,720
1000a	"	15.009	7,250	970	8,220
1200a	"	18.519	9,150	1,200	10,350
1400a	"	18.519	12,700	1,200	13,900
1600a	"	24.024	12,700	1,560	14,260
1800a	"	29.963	17,820	1,940	19,760
2000a	"	29.963	19,010	1,940	20,950
600v, 3 phase, NEMA 3R					
125-225a	EA.	2.222	1,480	140	1,620
250-400a	"	5.714	2,780	370	3,150
500-600a	"	9.744	4,170	630	4,800
700-800a	"	11.004	5,560	710	6,270
900-1000a	"	15.009	6,310	970	7,280
1000-1200a	"	19.002	14,900	1,230	16,130
1400-1600a	"	24.024	15,090	1,560	16,650
1800-2000a	"	29.963	15,280	1,940	17,220
16360.10 SAFETY SWITCHES					
Fused, 3 phase, 30 amp, 600v, heavy duty					
NEMA 1	EA.	1.143	200	74.00	274
NEMA 3r	"	1.143	460	74.00	534
NEMA 4	"	1.600	1,290	100	1,390
NEMA 12	"	1.739	410	110	520
60a					
NEMA 1	EA.	1.143	290	74.00	364
NEMA 3r	"	1.143	540	74.00	614
NEMA 4	"	1.600	1,420	100	1,520
NEMA 12	"	1.739	490	110	600
100a					
NEMA 1	EA.	1.739	480	110	590
NEMA 3r	"	1.739	850	110	960
NEMA 4	"	2.000	3,030	130	3,160
NEMA 12	"	2.500	740	160	900
200a					
NEMA 1	EA.	2.500	720	160	880
NEMA 3r	"	2.500	1,170	160	1,330
NEMA 4	"	2.759	3,980	180	4,160
NEMA 12	"	3.478	1,090	230	1,320
400a					
NEMA 1	EA.	5.517	1,740	360	2,100
NEMA 3r	"	5.517	3,360	360	3,720
NEMA 4	"	5.755	7,890	370	8,260
NEMA 12	"	7.018	2,570	450	3,020

POWER GENERATION

16360.10 SAFETY SWITCHES, Cont'd...	UNIT	HOURS	MAT.	INST.	TOTAL
600a					
NEMA 1	EA.	8.000	3,030	520	3,550
NEMA 3r	"	8.000	4,490	520	5,010
NEMA 4	"	8.989	7,280	580	7,860
NEMA 12	"	12.308	4,730	800	5,530
Non-fused, 240-600v, heavy duty, 3 phase, 30					
NEMA 1	EA.	1.143	140	74.00	214
NEMA 3r	"	1.143	230	74.00	304
NEMA 4	"	1.739	910	110	1,020
NEMA 12	"	1.739	280	110	390
60a					
NEMA1	EA.	1.143	190	74.00	264
NEMA 3r	"	1.143	350	74.00	424
NEMA 4	"	1.739	990	110	1,100
NEMA 12	"	1.739	330	110	440
100a					
NEMA 1	EA.	1.739	310	110	420
NEMA 3r	"	1.739	480	110	590
NEMA 4	"	2.500	2,000	160	2,160
NEMA 12	"	2.500	470	160	630
200a, NEMA 1	"	2.500	470	160	630
600a, NEMA 12	"	12.308	2,630	800	3,430
Bolt-on hubs					
3/4" - 1-1/2"	EA.	0.250	15.50	16.25	31.75
2"	"	0.296	28.00	19.25	47.25
2-1/2"	"	0.296	44.25	19.25	63.50
3"	"	0.348	82.00	22.50	105
3-1/2"	"	0.400	120	26.00	146
4"	"	0.400	150	26.00	176
Watertight hubs					
1/2"	EA.	0.250	12.50	16.25	28.75
3/4"	"	0.296	18.25	19.25	37.50
1"	"	0.400	19.00	26.00	45.00
1-1/4"	"	0.444	21.75	28.75	50.50
1-1/2"	"	0.471	32.00	30.50	62.50
2"	"	0.500	47.50	32.50	80.00
2-1/2"	"	0.533	58.00	34.50	92.50
3"	"	0.615	72.00	39.75	112
3-1/2"	"	0.800	110	52.00	162
4"	"	0.851	150	55.00	205
Non-fused, 600v, 3 pole, NEMA 7					
600a	EA.	2.222	1,380	140	1,520
100a	"	3.200	1,720	210	1,930
225a	"	4.000	3,740	260	4,000
NEMA 9					
60a	EA.	2.500	1,160	160	1,320
100a	"	3.333	1,450	220	1,670
225a	"	4.211	3,240	270	3,510
Fusible bolted pressure switches, 600v/3					
800a	EA.	16.000	5,590	1,040	6,630
1200a	"	21.978	6,770	1,420	8,190
1600a	"	25.000	7,300	1,620	8,920
2000a	"	29.963	7,510	1,940	9,450

POWER GENERATION

16360.10 SAFETY SWITCHES, Cont'd...	UNIT	HOURS	MAT.	INST.	TOTAL
2500a	EA.	34.934	8,590	2,260	10,850
3000a	"	44.944	11,600	2,910	14,510
4000a	"	51.948	15,480	3,370	18,850
Non-fusible					
800a	EA.	14.493	5,370	940	6,310
1200a	"	20.000	6,020	1,300	7,320
1600a	"	22.989	6,450	1,490	7,940
2000a	"	27.972	6,830	1,810	8,640
2500a	"	34.934	7,840	2,260	10,100
3000a	"	44.944	11,180	2,910	14,090
4000a	"	51.948	15,050	3,370	18,420
Fusible load interrupter switches, 4.16 kv,					
200a	EA.	29.963	6,140	1,940	8,080
600a	"	70.175	7,740	4,550	12,290
Fusible load interrupter switch, 13.8 kv					
NEMA 1, 600a	EA.	100.000	8,590	6,480	15,070
NEMA 3R, 600a	"	100.000	10,310	6,480	16,790
4.16 kv, NEMA 3R					
200a	EA.	29.963	5,370	1,940	7,310
600a	"	70.175	9,670	4,550	14,220
Non-fused load interrupter switch, 4.16 kv,					
200a	EA.	29.963	4,290	1,940	6,230
600a	"	70.175	7,400	4,550	11,950
13.8 kv, NEMA 1, 600a	"	100.000	7,940	6,480	14,420
4.16 kv, NEMA 3R					
200a	EA.	29.963	4,510	1,940	6,450
600a	"	70.175	9,030	4,550	13,580
13.8 kv, NEMA 3R, 600a	"	100.000	9,670	6,480	16,150
Interrupter switch accessories, strip heater	"				580
Cable lugs	"				110
Key interlock	"				750
Auxiliary switch	"				420
Lightning arrester					
5 kva	EA.				2,660
15 kv	"				2,900
16365.10 FUSES					
Fuse, one-time, 250v					
30a	EA.	0.050	2.17	3.24	5.41
60a	"	0.050	3.68	3.24	6.92
100a	"	0.050	15.50	3.24	18.74
200a	"	0.050	37.25	3.24	40.49
400a	"	0.050	84.00	3.24	87.24
600a	"	0.050	140	3.24	143
600v					
30a	EA.	0.050	11.00	3.24	14.24
60a	"	0.050	17.50	3.24	20.74
100a	"	0.050	33.00	3.24	36.24
200a	"	0.050	88.00	3.24	91.24
400a	"	0.050	180	3.24	183
Fusetron, 600v					
200a	EA.	0.050	76.00	3.24	79.24
400a	"	0.050	150	3.24	153
Fuse, amp-trap, K1, 250v					

POWER GENERATION

16365.10 FUSES, Cont'd...	UNIT	HOURS	MAT.	INST.	TOTAL
30a	EA.	0.050	7.09	3.24	10.33
60a	"	0.050	13.00	3.24	16.24
100a	"	0.050	29.25	3.24	32.49
200a	"	0.050	64.00	3.24	67.24
400a	"	0.050	140	3.24	143
600a	"	0.050	190	3.24	193
600v					
30a	EA.	0.050	21.25	3.24	24.49
60a	"	0.050	38.25	3.24	41.49
100a	"	0.050	77.00	3.24	80.24
200a	"	0.050	110	3.24	113
400a	"	0.050	240	3.24	243
K5, 250v					
30a	EA.	0.050	5.32	3.24	8.56
60a	"	0.050	9.72	3.24	12.96
100a	"	0.050	21.75	3.24	24.99
200a	"	0.050	48.00	3.24	51.24
400a	"	0.050	87.00	3.24	90.24
600a	"	0.050	140	3.24	143
600v					
30a	EA.	0.050	11.75	3.24	14.99
60a	"	0.050	20.25	3.24	23.49
100a	"	0.050	41.75	3.24	44.99
200a	"	0.050	84.00	3.24	87.24
400a	"	0.050	170	3.24	173
600a	"	0.050	240	3.24	243
J, 600v					
30a	EA.	0.050	19.25	3.24	22.49
60a	"	0.050	32.00	3.24	35.24
100a	"	0.050	57.00	3.24	60.24
200a	"	0.050	110	3.24	113
400a	"	0.050	230	3.24	233
L, 600v					
1200a	EA.	0.400	550	26.00	576
1600a	"	0.400	710	26.00	736
2000a	"	0.400	950	26.00	976
2500a	"	0.400	1,260	26.00	1,286
3000a	"	0.400	1,450	26.00	1,476
4000a	"	0.400	1,990	26.00	2,016
5000a	"	0.400	3,130	26.00	3,156
Fuse cl-ay 250v					
600a	EA.	0.296	460	19.25	479
1200a	"	0.296	460	19.25	479
1600a	"	0.296	570	19.25	589
2000a	"	0.296	740	19.25	759
600v					
1200a	EA.	0.296	550	19.25	569
1600a	"	0.296	640	19.25	659
2000a	"	0.296	770	19.25	789
Reducers, 600v					
60a-30a	EA.	0.145	11.75	9.42	21.17
100a-30a	"	0.145	41.00	9.42	50.42
100a-60a	"	0.145	26.50	9.42	35.92

ELECTRICAL

POWER GENERATION

16365.10 FUSES, Cont'd...	UNIT	HOURS	MAT.	INST.	TOTAL
200a-60a	EA.	0.250	100	16.25	116
200a-100a	"	0.250	38.75	16.25	55.00
400a-100a	"	0.348	190	22.50	213
400a-200a	"	0.348	160	22.50	183
600a-100a	"	0.400	250	26.00	276
600a-200a	"	0.400	280	26.00	306
600a-400a	"	0.400	250	26.00	276
16395.10 GROUNDING					
Ground rods, copper clad, 1/2" x					
6'	EA.	0.667	10.75	43.25	54.00
8'	"	0.727	14.75	47.00	61.75
10'	"	1.000	18.50	65.00	83.50
5/8" x					
5'	EA.	0.615	13.25	39.75	53.00
6'	"	0.727	14.25	47.00	61.25
8'	"	1.000	18.50	65.00	83.50
10'	"	1.250	22.75	81.00	104
3/4" x					
8'	EA.	0.727	32.75	47.00	79.75
10'	"	0.800	35.75	52.00	87.75
Ground rod clamp					
5/8"	EA.	0.123	5.46	7.97	13.43
3/4"	"	0.123	7.73	7.97	15.70
Coupling, on threaded rods, 3/4"	"	0.050	16.00	3.24	19.24
Ground receptacles	"	0.250	20.25	16.25	36.50
Bus bar, copper, 2" x 1/4"	L.F.	0.145	5.89	9.42	15.31
Copper braid, 1" x 1/8", for door ground	EA.	0.100	4.57	6.48	11.05
Brazed connection for					
#6 wire	EA.	0.500	19.00	32.50	51.50
#2 wire	"	0.800	24.00	52.00	76.00
#2/0 wire	"	1.000	32.00	65.00	97.00
#4/0 wire	"	1.143	44.00	74.00	118
Ground rod couplings					
1/2"	EA.	0.100	10.00	6.48	16.48
5/8"	"	0.100	14.00	6.48	20.48
Ground rod, driving stud					
1/2"	EA.	0.100	8.03	6.48	14.51
5/8"	"	0.100	9.50	6.48	15.98
3/4"	"	0.100	10.75	6.48	17.23
Ground rod clamps, #8-2 to					
1" pipe	EA.	0.200	8.69	13.00	21.69
2" pipe	"	0.250	11.00	16.25	27.25
3" pipe	"	0.296	43.50	19.25	62.75
5" pipe	"	0.348	70.00	22.50	92.50
6" pipe	"	0.444	96.00	28.75	125
#4-4/0 to					
1" pipe	EA.	0.200	20.75	13.00	33.75
2" pipe	"	0.250	32.75	16.25	49.00
3" pipe	"	0.296	50.00	19.25	69.25
3" pipe	"	0.348	74.00	22.50	96.50
8 pipe	"	0.444	110	28.75	139
8 pipe	"	0.667	120	43.25	163
10 pipe	"	0.952	140	62.00	202

POWER GENERATION

16395.10 GROUNDING, Cont'd...	UNIT	HOURS	MAT.	INST.	TOTAL
12 pipe	EA.	1.290	160	84.00	244

SERVICE AND DISTRIBUTION

16425.10 SWITCHBOARDS	UNIT	HOURS	MAT.	INST.	TOTAL
Switchboard, 90" high, no main disconnect,					
400a	EA.	7.921	2,630	510	3,140
600a	"	8.000	4,080	520	4,600
1000a	"	8.000	5,140	520	5,660
1200a	"	10.000	5,430	650	6,080
1600a	"	11.940	5,970	770	6,740
2000a	"	14.035	6,410	910	7,320
2500a	"	16.000	6,490	1,040	7,530
277/480v					
600a	EA.	8.163	4,690	530	5,220
800a	"	8.163	5,140	530	5,670
1600a	"	11.940	6,470	770	7,240
2000a	"	14.035	6,920	910	7,830
2500a	"	16.000	7,370	1,040	8,410
3000a	"	27.586	8,480	1,790	10,270
4000a	"	29.630	10,270	1,920	12,190
Main breaker sections, 600v					
1200a, GFI	EA.	16.985	19,460	1,100	20,560
1600a, GFI	"	19.512	22,980	1,260	24,240
2000a, GFI	"	20.000	24,390	1,300	25,690
2500a, GFI	"	25.000	26,970	1,620	28,590
3000a, GFI	"	29.963	35,640	1,940	37,580
4000a, GFI	"	34.934	32,410	2,260	34,670
Switchboard meter sections, 600v					
400a	EA.	8.000	3,510	520	4,030
600a	"	10.000	5,390	650	6,040
800a	"	11.004	6,560	710	7,270
1000a	"	13.491	7,970	870	8,840
2000a	"	16.000	9,850	1,040	10,890
2500a	"	20.000	11,020	1,300	12,320
3000a	"	25.000	11,490	1,620	13,110
4000a	"	29.963	12,900	1,940	14,840
Insulated case, draw out compartment,					
800a	EA.	2.500	2,230	160	2,390
1600a	"	2.963	2,670	190	2,860
2000a	"	3.478	3,340	230	3,570
2500a	"	3.478	4,010	230	4,240
3000a	"	4.000	6,700	260	6,960
4000a	"	4.790	9,380	310	9,690
Accessories for power trip breakers					
Shunt trip	EA.	0.500	1,070	32.50	1,103
Key interlock	"	2.222	520	140	660
Lifting and transport truck	"	4.494	3,340	290	3,630
Lifting device	"	1.333	340	86.00	426
Bus duct connection, 3 phase, 4 wire					
225a	EA.	2.963	490	190	680
400a	"	2.963	600	190	790
600a	"	3.333	790	220	1,010
800a	"	4.000	850	260	1,110

SERVICE AND DISTRIBUTION

16425.10 SWITCHBOARDS, Cont'd...	UNIT	HOURS	MAT.	INST.	TOTAL
2500a	EA.	6.015	1,590	390	1,980
3000a	"	7.477	2,400	480	2,880
4000a	"	8.791	4,310	570	4,880
Provision for mounting current transformers					
800a & below primary	EA.	2.963	1,800	190	1,990
1000 to 1500a primary	"	2.963	2,240	190	2,430
2000 to 6000a primary	"	2.963	2,700	190	2,890
Provision for mounting potential transformers					
2000a max	EA.	3.810	6,440	250	6,690
Switchboard instruments					
Voltmeter	EA.	1.000	2,200	65.00	2,265
Ammeter, incoming line	"	1.000	2,090	65.00	2,155
Wattmeter	"	1.000	3,500	65.00	3,565
Varmeter	"	1.000	3,620	65.00	3,685
Power factor meter	"	1.000	4,180	65.00	4,245
Frequency meter	"	1.000	4,690	65.00	4,755
Recording voltmeter	"	2.000	9,350	130	9,480
Wattmeter	"	2.000	9,950	130	10,080
Power factor meter	"	2.000	11,620	130	11,750
Frequency meter	"	2.000	11,620	130	11,750
Instrument phase select switch	"	0.500	440	32.50	473
Enclosure, 90" high, 3 phase, 4 wire					
1000a	EA.	6.838	3,800	440	4,240
1200a	"	7.018	4,010	450	4,460
1600a	"	8.602	4,470	560	5,030
2000a	"	13.333	4,690	860	5,550
5500a	"	15.686	5,810	1,020	6,830
3000a	"	18.182	6,470	1,180	7,650
4000a	"	23.529	8,480	1,520	10,000
Circuit breakers, 600v, 100a, frame					
15-30a, 1 pole	EA.	0.296	150	19.25	169
15-60a, 2 pole	"	0.348	380	22.50	403
70-100a, 2 pole	"	0.400	480	26.00	506
15-60a, 3 pole	"	0.444	490	28.75	519
70-100a, 3 pole	"	0.500	570	32.50	603
Bolt on breakers, 600v, 225a frame, 110-					
2 pole	EA.	0.615	1,110	39.75	1,150
3 pole	"	1.096	1,390	71.00	1,461
400a frame, 250-400a, 2 pole	"	1.250	2,030	81.00	2,111
800a frame					
450-600a, 2 pole	EA.	1.905	3,580	120	3,700
700-800a, 2 pole	"	2.500	4,170	160	4,330
450-600a, 3 pole	"	4.211	4,090	270	4,360
700-800a, 3 pole	"	4.444	5,290	290	5,580
Bolt on branch breakers, 600v					
1000-2000a, 2 pole	EA.	5.333	7,430	350	7,780
2500a, 2 pole	"	10.753	13,710	700	14,410
1000-2000a, 3 pole	"	8.000	9,470	520	9,990
2500a, 3 pole	"	11.004	16,720	710	17,430
3000a, 3 pole	"	20.000	31,820	1,300	33,120
Metal clad substation switch board, selector					
600a, 5kv	EA.	42.105	24,560	2,730	27,290
15kv	"	47.904	27,250	3,100	30,350

SERVICE AND DISTRIBUTION

16425.10 SWITCHBOARDS, Cont'd...	UNIT	HOURS	MAT.	INST.	TOTAL
Fused switch, 600a					
5kv	EA.	34.934	17,880	2,260	20,140
15kv	"	34.934	24,780	2,260	27,040
1200a					
5kv	EA.	40.000	19,880	2,590	22,470
15kv	"	40.000	26,630	2,590	29,220
Oil cutout switch					
5 kv	EA.	15.009	6,920	970	7,890
15 kv	"	18.018	9,600	1,170	10,770
Liquid air terminal section	"	8.000	890	520	1,410
Dry air terminal section	"	8.502	1,780	550	2,330
Auxiliary compartment	"	29.963	12,730	1,940	14,670
16430.20 METERING					
Outdoor wp meter sockets, 1 gang, 240v, 1					
Includes sealing ring, 100a	EA.	1.509	43.25	98.00	141
150a	"	1.778	57.00	120	177
200a	"	2.000	73.00	130	203
Die cast hubs, 1-1/4"	"	0.320	6.65	20.75	27.40
1-1/2"	"	0.320	7.64	20.75	28.39
2"	"	0.320	9.24	20.75	29.99
Indoor meter center, main switch single phase,					
400a	EA.	8.000	1,780	520	2,300
600a	"	11.004	3,120	710	3,830
800a	"	11.696	4,880	760	5,640
Main breaker					
400a	EA.	8.000	3,190	520	3,710
600a	"	11.004	4,300	710	5,010
800a	"	11.696	5,020	760	5,780
1000a	"	16.000	6,920	1,040	7,960
Terminal box	"	16.495	7,570	1,070	8,640
1600a	"	18.018	11,360	1,170	12,530
Terminal box					
800a	EA.	10.000	500	650	1,150
1600a	"	18.018	1,720	1,170	2,890
Main switch, three phase, 208v					
400a	EA.	8.502	1,820	550	2,370
600a	"	11.994	3,280	780	4,060
800a	"	13.491	6,580	870	7,450
Main breaker					
400a	EA.	8.502	3,180	550	3,730
600a	"	11.994	5,020	780	5,800
800a	"	13.491	6,670	870	7,540
1000a	"	16.985	8,540	1,100	9,640
1200a	"	18.018	11,900	1,170	13,070
1600a	"	20.997	17,520	1,360	18,880
Terminal box					
800a	EA.	13.008	570	840	1,410
1600a	"	20.997	1,810	1,360	3,170
Indoor meter center					
2 meters	EA.	5.000	520	320	840
3 meters	"	6.154	670	400	1,070
4 meters	"	7.273	860	470	1,330
5 meters	"	8.000	1,080	520	1,600

© 2009 BNI Publications Inc.

SERVICE AND DISTRIBUTION

16430.20 METERING, Cont'd...	UNIT	HOURS	MAT.	INST.	TOTAL
6 meters	EA.	8.999	1,380	580	1,960
Plug on breakers, single phase, 208v					
60a	EA.	0.250	29.25	16.25	45.50
70a	"	0.250	58.00	16.25	74.25
80a	"	0.250	80.00	16.25	96.25
90a	"	0.250	84.00	16.25	100
100a	"	0.348	89.00	22.50	112
Indoor meter center, single phase, 125a					
3 meters	EA.	6.154	690	400	1,090
4 meters	"	7.273	820	470	1,290
5 meters	"	8.000	1,030	520	1,550
6 meters	"	8.502	1,190	550	1,740
7 meters	"	10.000	1,510	650	2,160
8 meters	"	11.004	1,660	710	2,370
10 meters	"	11.994	2,060	780	2,840
150a breakers					
3 meters	EA.	6.154	2,340	400	2,740
4 meters	"	7.273	3,120	470	3,590
6 meters	"	8.000	4,690	520	5,210
7 meters	"	10.000	5,480	650	6,130
8 meters	"	11.004	6,260	710	6,970
200a breakers					
3 meters	EA.	6.154	1,930	400	2,330
4 meters	"	7.273	2,610	470	3,080
6 meters	"	8.000	3,870	520	4,390
7 meters	"	10.000	4,550	650	5,200
8 meters	"	11.004	5,230	710	5,940
Indoor meter center, three phase, 125a					
3 meters	EA.	6.154	680	400	1,080
4 meters	"	7.273	810	470	1,280
5 meters	"	8.000	1,010	520	1,530
6 meters	"	8.999	1,160	580	1,740
7 meters	"	10.000	1,480	650	2,130
8 meters	"	11.004	1,630	710	2,340
10 meters	"	11.994	2,030	780	2,810
150a breakers					
3 meters	EA.	6.154	2,860	400	3,260
4 meters	"	7.273	3,830	470	4,300
6 meters	"	8.502	5,810	550	6,360
7 meters	"	11.004	6,710	710	7,420
8 meters	"	11.994	7,660	780	8,440
200a breakers					
3 meters	EA.	6.667	3,410	430	3,840
4 meters	"	7.273	4,560	470	5,030
6 meters	"	8.999	6,010	580	6,590
7 meters	"	11.004	7,020	710	7,730
8 meters	"	11.994	8,010	780	8,790
NEMA 3R, meter center, main switch, 1					
400a	EA.	8.000	1,580	520	2,100
600a	"	10.000	3,080	650	3,730
800a	"	11.004	4,730	710	5,440
Main breaker					
400a	EA.	8.000	3,930	520	4,450

SERVICE AND DISTRIBUTION

16430.20 METERING, Cont'd...	UNIT	HOURS	MAT.	INST.	TOTAL
600a	EA.	10.000	5,030	650	5,680
800a	"	12.308	6,180	800	6,980
1000a	"	15.009	7,290	970	8,260
1200a	"	16.000	10,280	1,040	11,320
Terminal box					
225a	EA.	7.273	380	470	850
800a	"	11.494	570	740	1,310
1600a	"	18.018	1,870	1,170	3,040
NEMA 3R, three phase, 280v					
400a	EA.	8.502	1,830	550	2,380
600a	"	11.994	3,460	780	4,240
800a	"	13.008	5,280	840	6,120
Main breaker					
400a	EA.	8.502	4,550	550	5,100
600a	"	11.994	5,850	780	6,630
800a	"	13.008	7,410	840	8,250
1000a	"	16.985	8,320	1,100	9,420
1200a	"	18.018	11,390	1,170	12,560
Terminal box					
225a	EA.	8.000	440	520	960
800a	"	13.008	630	840	1,470
1600a	"	20.997	1,950	1,360	3,310
NEMA 3R meter center, single phase, 208v,					
2 meters	EA.	5.000	480	320	800
3 meters	"	6.154	570	400	970
4 meters	"	7.273	830	470	1,300
5 meters	"	8.000	1,000	520	1,520
6 meters	"	8.999	1,580	580	2,160
4 meters	"	7.273		470	470
6 meters	"	8.000		520	520
7 meters	"	10.000	1,690	650	2,340
8 meters	"	11.004	1,870	710	2,580
125a, 3 meters	"	6.154	1,260	400	1,660
4 meters	"	7.273	1,610	470	2,080
6 meters	"	8.239	2,000	530	2,530
7 meters	"	10.000	2,350	650	3,000
8 meters	"	11.004	2,870	710	3,580
150a, 3 meters	"	6.154	2,490	400	2,890
4 meters	"	7.273	3,320	470	3,790
6 meters	"	8.502	5,980	550	6,530
7 meters	"	10.000	6,980	650	7,630
8 meters	"	11.004	7,970	710	8,680
NEMA 3R center, 3 phase, 208v, 125a					
3 meters	EA.	6.154	660	400	1,060
4 meters	"	7.273	900	470	1,370
6 meters	"	8.502	1,350	550	1,900
7 meters	"	10.000	1,570	650	2,220
8 meters	"	11.004	1,800	710	2,510
150a					
3 meters	EA.	6.667	2,970	430	3,400
4 meters	"	7.273	3,890	470	4,360
6 meters	"	8.999	5,830	580	6,410
7 meters	"	10.499	6,810	680	7,490

SERVICE AND DISTRIBUTION

16430.20 METERING, Cont'd...	UNIT	HOURS	MAT.	INST.	TOTAL
8 meters	EA.	11.494	7,790	740	8,530
200a					
3 meters	EA.	6.667	2,300	430	2,730
4 meters	"	7.273	3,070	470	3,540
6 meters	"	8.999	4,600	580	5,180
7 meters	"	11.004	5,380	710	6,090
8 meters	"	11.494	6,150	740	6,890
NEMA 3R, center plug-on breakers, 208v, 1					
60a	EA.	0.250	35.00	16.25	51.25
70a	"	0.250	70.00	16.25	86.25
90a	"	0.250	100	16.25	116
100a	"	0.348	110	22.50	133
125a	"	0.400	210	26.00	236
16460.10 TRANSFORMERS					
Pad mounted, single phase, dry type, 480v-					
15 kva	EA.	8.000	1,730	520	2,250
25 kva	"	8.989	2,330	580	2,910
37.5 kva	"	10.000	3,400	650	4,050
50 kva	"	10.959	4,030	710	4,740
3 phase					
225 kva	EA.	25.000	10,080	1,620	11,700
300 kva	"	30.769	12,960	1,990	14,950
500 kva	"	38.095	20,400	2,470	22,870
750 kva	"	47.059	32,880	3,050	35,930
1000 kva	"	50.000	39,840	3,240	43,080
1500 kva	"	57.143	46,990	3,700	50,690
Substation transformers, outdoor, 5 kv - 208v					
112.5 kva	EA.	21.978	15,520	1,420	16,940
150 kva	"	24.024	16,870	1,560	18,430
225 kva	"	27.972	19,130	1,810	20,940
300 kva	"	29.963	22,050	1,940	23,990
500 kva	"	44.944	29,250	2,910	32,160
750 kva	"	55.172	40,510	3,580	44,090
1000 kva	"	65.041	49,960	4,210	54,170
15 kv, 208v					
112 kva	EA.	27.972	19,440	1,810	21,250
150 kva	"	29.963	19,880	1,940	21,820
225 kva	"	34.934	20,540	2,260	22,800
300 kva	"	40.000	23,160	2,590	25,750
500 kva	"	50.000	32,550	3,240	35,790
750 kva	"	60.150	32,550	3,900	36,450
1000 kva	"	70.175	48,930	4,550	53,480
5kv, 480v					
112kva	EA.	21.978	14,850	1,420	16,270
150 kva	"	24.024	15,730	1,560	17,290
225 kva	"	27.972	17,700	1,810	19,510
300 kva	"	29.963	19,880	1,940	21,820
500 kva	"	44.944	26,650	2,910	29,560
750 kva	"	55.172	36,270	3,580	39,850
1000 kva	"	65.041	42,600	4,210	46,810
1500 kva	"	74.766	55,700	4,840	60,540
2000 kva	"	89.888	68,600	5,820	74,420
2500 kva	"	109.589	81,480	7,100	88,580

SERVICE AND DISTRIBUTION

16460.10 TRANSFORMERS, Cont'd...	UNIT	HOURS	MAT.	INST.	TOTAL
15 kv, 480v					
112.5 kva	EA.	27.972	19,000	1,810	20,810
150 kva	"	29.963	19,440	1,940	21,380
225 kva	"	34.934	19,660	2,260	21,920
300 kva	"	40.000	21,410	2,590	24,000
500 kva	"	50.000	30,360	3,240	33,600
750 kva	"	60.150	36,920	3,900	40,820
1000 kva	"	70.175	42,600	4,550	47,150
1500 kva	"	80.000	55,920	5,180	61,100
2000 kva	"	89.888	68,820	5,820	74,640
2500 kva	"	119.403	81,710	7,740	89,450
Pad mounted 3 phase, 15 kv outdoor					
50 kva	EA.	10.256	4,810	660	5,470
75 kva	"	11.765	6,770	760	7,530
112 kva	"	12.903	8,720	840	9,560
150 kva	"	14.545	12,380	940	13,320
225 kva	"	15.385	14,910	1,000	15,910
300 kva	"	17.021	18,350	1,100	19,450
500 kva	"	27.586	22,480	1,790	24,270
750 kva	"	36.364	28,670	2,360	31,030
1000 kva	"	44.444	33,950	2,880	36,830
1500 kva	"	53.333	43,360	3,460	46,820
Dry type, for power gear, 5 kv indoor					
75 kva	EA.	16.000	13,300	1,040	14,340
112.5 kva	"	18.605	14,910	1,210	16,120
150 kva	"	21.053	17,200	1,360	18,560
225 kva	"	23.529	21,330	1,520	22,850
300 kva	"	25.000	25,220	1,620	26,840
500 kva	"	27.586	33,330	1,790	35,120
750 kva	"	36.364	43,800	2,360	46,160
16470.10 PANELBOARDS					
Indoor load center, 1 phase 240v main lug only					
30a - 2 spaces	EA.	2.000	20.25	130	150
100a - 8 spaces	"	2.424	64.00	160	224
150a - 16 spaces	"	2.963	170	190	360
200a - 24 spaces	"	3.478	350	230	580
200a - 42 spaces	"	4.000	360	260	620
Main circuit breaker					
100a - 8 spaces	EA.	2.424	200	160	360
100a - 16 spaces	"	2.759	220	180	400
150a - 16 spaces	"	2.963	360	190	550
150a - 24 spaces	"	3.200	430	210	640
200a - 24 spaces	"	3.478	400	230	630
200a - 42 spaces	"	3.636	570	240	810
3 phase, 480/277v, main lugs only, 120a, 30	"	3.478	1,040	230	1,270
277/480v, 4 wire, flush surface					
225a, 30 circuits	EA.	4.000	1,710	260	1,970
400a, 30 circuits	"	5.000	2,310	320	2,630
600a, 42 circuits	"	6.015	4,450	390	4,840
208/120v, main circuit breaker, 3 phase, 4					
100a					
12 circuits	EA.	5.096	900	330	1,230
20 circuits	"	6.299	1,120	410	1,530

SERVICE AND DISTRIBUTION

16470.10 PANELBOARDS, Cont'd...	UNIT	HOURS	MAT.	INST.	TOTAL
30 circuits	EA.	7.018	1,650	450	2,100
225a					
30 circuits	EA.	7.767	1,410	500	1,910
42 circuits	"	9.524	2,550	620	3,170
400a					
30 circuits	EA.	14.815	3,480	960	4,440
42 circuits	"	16.000	4,170	1,040	5,210
600a, 42 circuits	"	18.182	8,110	1,180	9,290
120/208v, flush, 3 ph., 4 wire, main only					
100a					
12 circuits	EA.	5.096	640	330	970
20 circuits	"	6.299	880	410	1,290
30 circuits	"	7.018	1,310	450	1,760
225a					
30 circuits	EA.	7.767	1,330	500	1,830
42 circuits	"	9.524	1,680	620	2,300
400a					
30 circuits	EA.	14.815	2,550	960	3,510
42 circuits	"	16.000	3,720	1,040	4,760
600a, 42 circuits	"	18.182	5,800	1,180	6,980
Panelboard accessories					
Grounding bus	EA.	0.348	29.75	22.50	52.25
Handle lock device	"	0.145	14.50	9.42	23.92
Factory assembled panel					
1 pole space	EA.	0.348	18.50	22.50	41.00
2 pole space	"	0.145	39.50	9.42	48.92
3 pole space	"	0.133	58.00	8.64	66.64
Panelboards 1 phase, 240/120v main circuit					
Single phase, 3 wire, 120/240v flush					
100a, 20 circuits	EA.	3.478	930	230	1,160
225a, 30 circuits	"	4.000	1,780	260	2,040
240/120v, main lugs only					
100a					
8 circuits	EA.	2.963	450	190	640
12 circuits	"	2.963	480	190	670
20 circuits	"	2.963	510	190	700
225a					
24 circuits	EA.	3.478	540	230	770
30 circuits	"	3.810	620	250	870
42 circuits	"	3.810	680	250	930
Distribution panelboards, 3 ph, main breaker					
225a	EA.	16.000	1,710	1,040	2,750
400a	"	18.018	3,120	1,170	4,290
600a	"	21.978	4,870	1,420	6,290
800a	"	24.024	6,260	1,560	7,820
1000a	"	27.972	8,120	1,810	9,930
1200a	"	29.963	9,980	1,940	11,920
Single phase					
225a	EA.	14.011	1,510	910	2,420
400a	"	16.000	2,780	1,040	3,820
600a	"	20.000	3,940	1,300	5,240
800a	"	24.024	5,340	1,560	6,900
1000a	"	27.972	6,950	1,810	8,760

SERVICE AND DISTRIBUTION

16470.10 PANELBOARDS, Cont'd...	UNIT	HOURS	MAT.	INST.	TOTAL
1200a	EA.	29.963	8,810	1,940	10,750
Fusible distribution panelboards, 3 phase,					
100a	EA.	14.011	1,620	910	2,530
200a	"	16.000	1,850	1,040	2,890
400a	"	20.000	3,250	1,300	4,550
600a	"	24.024	4,160	1,560	5,720
800a	"	27.972	6,260	1,810	8,070
Single phase					
100a	EA.	11.994	1,390	780	2,170
200a	"	14.011	1,620	910	2,530
400a	"	18.018	3,480	1,170	4,650
600a	"	21.978	3,710	1,420	5,130
800a	"	25.974	5,100	1,680	6,780
Hospital panels, operating room					
3kv - 208v	EA.	6.154	4,910	400	5,310
3kv - 277v	"	6.154	5,130	400	5,530
5kv - 208v	"	6.154	5,130	400	5,530
5kv - 277v	"	6.154	5,580	400	5,980
Coronary care					
3kv - 208v	EA.	7.273	5,800	470	6,270
3kv - 277v	"	7.273	6,250	470	6,720
5kv - 208v	"	7.273	6,250	470	6,720
5kv - 277v	"	7.273	6,690	470	7,160
Intensive care					
3kv - 208v	EA.	8.000	6,470	520	6,990
3kv - 277v	"	8.000	6,690	520	7,210
5kv - 208v	"	8.000	6,690	520	7,210
5kv - 277v	"	8.000	7,140	520	7,660
15kv - 208v	"	11.994	12,720	780	13,500
15kv - 277v	"	11.994	13,160	780	13,940
25kv - 208v	"	16.000	13,610	1,040	14,650
25kv - 277v	"	16.000	14,050	1,040	15,090
Explosion proof, 240v, m.l.b. 20a, single					
6 breakers	EA.	11.004	3,560	710	4,270
8 breakers	"	11.747	4,010	760	4,770
10 breakers	"	12.500	4,690	810	5,500
12 breakers	"	13.245	5,350	860	6,210
14 breakers	"	14.011	6,470	910	7,380
16 breakers	"	14.011	7,810	910	8,720
18 breakers	"	15.504	8,470	1,000	9,470
20 breakers	"	16.260	8,930	1,050	9,980
22 breakers	"	16.985	9,140	1,100	10,240
24 breakers	"	17.738	9,590	1,150	10,740
16480.10 MOTOR CONTROLS					
Motor generator set, 3 phase, 480/277v,					
10kw	EA.	27.586	11,680	1,790	13,470
15kw	"	30.769	15,230	1,990	17,220
20kw	"	32.000	16,910	2,070	18,980
25kw	"	34.783	19,500	2,250	21,750
30kw	"	36.364	21,820	2,360	24,180
40kw	"	38.095	23,800	2,470	26,270
50kw	"	40.000	26,560	2,590	29,150
60kw	"	44.444	30,100	2,880	32,980

SERVICE AND DISTRIBUTION

16480.10 MOTOR CONTROLS, Cont'd...	UNIT	HOURS	MAT.	INST.	TOTAL
75kw	EA.	50.000	33,800	3,240	37,040
100kw	"	61.538	39,010	3,990	43,000
125kw	"	66.667	70,590	4,320	74,910
150kw	"	66.667	78,020	4,320	82,340
200kw	"	72.727	89,170	4,710	93,880
250kw	"	72.727	96,590	4,710	101,300
300kw	"	80.000	111,450	5,180	116,630
2 pole, 230 volt starter, w/NEMA-1					
1 hp, 9a, size 00	EA.	1.000	140	65.00	205
2 hp, 18a, size 0	"	1.000	160	65.00	225
3 hp, 27a, size 1	"	1.000	230	65.00	295
5 hp, 45a, size 1p	"	1.000	230	65.00	295
7-1/2 hp, 45a, size 2	"	1.000	560	65.00	625
15 hp, 90a, size 3	"	1.000	840	65.00	905
2 pole, w/NEMA-4 enclosure					
2 hp, 18a, size 1	EA.	1.600	470	100	570
5 hp, 45a, size 1p	"	1.600	600	100	700
7-1/2 hp, 45a, size 2	"	1.600	950	100	1,050
3 pole, 2 hp, 9a, 200-575v starter					
W/NEMA-1, size 00	EA.	1.333	290	86.00	376
W/NEMA-4 enclosure, size 00	"	1.739	470	110	580
5hp, 18a					
W/NEMA-1 enclosure, size 0	EA.	1.333	360	86.00	446
W/NEMA-4 enclosure, size 0	"	1.739	720	110	830
7.5-10hp, 27a					
7.5-10hp 27a, w/NEMA-1 enclosure, size 1	EA.	1.333	420	86.00	506
W/NEMA-4 enclosure size 1	"	1.739	780	110	890
10-25hp, 45a					
W/NEMA-1 enclosure, size 2	EA.	1.333	820	86.00	906
W/NEMA-4 enclosure, size 2	"	1.739	1,540	110	1,650
25-50hp, 90a					
W/NEMA-1 enclosure, size 3	EA.	1.739	1,280	110	1,390
W/NEMA-4 enclosure, size 3	"	2.500	1,210	160	1,370
40-100hp, 135a					
W/NEMA-1 enclosure, size 4	EA.	2.500	2,070	160	2,230
W/NEMA-4 enclosure, size 4	"	3.478	3,190	230	3,420
75-200hp, 270a					
W/NEMA-1 enclosure, size 5	EA.	5.517	4,870	360	5,230
W/NEMA-4 enclosure, size 5	"	7.018	6,180	450	6,630
Magnetic starter accessories					
On-off-auto selector switch kit	EA.	0.320	33.50	20.75	54.25
With pilot light	"	0.348	63.00	22.50	85.50
Control center main lug only, 208v, 3 phase					
600a	EA.	11.994	1,950	780	2,730
1200a	"	16.000	4,180	1,040	5,220
Main circuit breakers, 208v, 3 phase					
400a	EA.	10.000	3,900	650	4,550
600a	"	14.011	4,350	910	5,260
800a	"	16.000	4,990	1,040	6,030
1000a	"	18.018	5,430	1,170	6,600
1200a	"	20.000	9,990	1,300	11,290
Non-reversing starters					
Size 1	EA.	0.727	420	47.00	467

ELECTRICAL

SERVICE AND DISTRIBUTION

16480.10 MOTOR CONTROLS, Cont'd...	UNIT	HOURS	MAT.	INST.	TOTAL
Size 2	EA.	1.250	820	81.00	901
Size 3	"	1.509	1,280	98.00	1,378
Size 4	"	1.739	2,640	110	2,750
Reversing starters					
Size 1	EA.	0.727	940	47.00	987
Size 2	"	1.096	2,180	71.00	2,251
Fusible switch, non-revolving starters					
Size 1	EA.	0.727	640	47.00	687
Size 2	"	1.250	800	81.00	881
Size 3	"	1.509	1,030	98.00	1,128
Size 4	"	1.739	1,650	110	1,760
Reversing starters					
Size 1	EA.	0.727	940	47.00	987
Size 2	"	1.096	990	71.00	1,061
Two speed, non-reversing starter					
Size 1	EA.	0.727	950	47.00	997
Size 2	"	1.096	1,390	71.00	1,461
Magnetic starter, 600v, 2 pole, NEMA 3R					
Size 0, 2 hp	EA.	1.000	240	65.00	305
Size 1, 5hp	"	1.096	320	71.00	391
NEMA 3R					
Size 2, 7.5 hp	EA.	1.143	660	74.00	734
Size 3, 15 hp	"	1.194	1,460	77.00	1,537
NEMA 7					
Size 0, 2 hp	EA.	1.739	1,210	110	1,320
Size 1, 5 hp	"	2.000	1,360	130	1,490
Size 2, 7.5 hp	"	2.222	2,360	140	2,500
NEMA 12					
Size 0, 2 hp	EA.	1.509	310	98.00	408
Size 1, 5 hp	"	1.739	410	110	520
Size 2, 7.5 hp	"	2.000	760	130	890
Size 3, 15 hp	"	2.222	1,210	140	1,350
3 pole, NEMA 1					
Size 6	EA.	10.000	13,200	650	13,850
Size 7	"	11.994	17,790	780	18,570
Size 8	"	16.000	24,680	1,040	25,720
NEMA 4					
Size 6	EA.	14.011	16,640	910	17,550
Size 7	"	16.000	21,230	1,040	22,270
Size 8	"	20.000	28,130	1,300	29,430
NEMA 3R					
Size 0	EA.	1.250	330	81.00	411
Size 1	"	1.356	370	88.00	458
Size 2	"	1.818	700	120	820
Size 3	"	1.905	1,100	120	1,220
Size 4	"	2.759	2,750	180	2,930
NEMA 7					
Size 0	EA.	2.000	1,350	130	1,480
Size 1	"	2.162	1,420	140	1,560
Size 2	"	2.222	2,280	140	2,420
Size 3	"	2.759	3,430	180	3,610
Size 4	"	4.444	5,720	290	6,010
Size 5	"	9.744	13,260	630	13,890

ELECTRICAL

SERVICE AND DISTRIBUTION

16480.10 MOTOR CONTROLS, Cont'd...	UNIT	HOURS	MAT.	INST.	TOTAL
Size 6	EA.	16.000	31,210	1,040	32,250
NEMA 12					
Size 00	EA.	1.739	230	110	340
Size 0	"	1.860	250	120	370
Size 1	"	1.905	350	120	470
Size 2	"	2.000	640	130	770
Size 3	"	2.500	1,030	160	1,190
Size 4	"	3.478	2,360	230	2,590
Size 5	"	7.273	5,720	470	6,190
Size 6	"	12.500	13,780	810	14,590
Size 7	"	14.011	19,760	910	20,670
Size 8	"	20.000	29,130	1,300	30,430
Reversing magnetic starters, 600v, 3 pole,					
Size 00	EA.	1.250	520	81.00	601
Size 0	"	1.290	600	84.00	684
Size 1	"	1.356	690	88.00	778
Size 2	"	1.509	1,370	98.00	1,468
Size 3	"	1.739	2,370	110	2,480
Size 4	"	2.000	5,420	130	5,550
Size 5	"	5.333	11,700	350	12,050
Size 6	"	9.501	26,220	620	26,840
Size 7	"	11.004	35,770	710	36,480
Size 8	"	18.018	50,940	1,170	52,110
NEMA 4					
Size 0	EA.	1.739	880	110	990
Size 4	"	1.818	1,080	120	1,200
Size 2	"	1.905	1,930	120	2,050
Size 3	"	2.000	2,950	130	3,080
Size 4	"	2.500	6,700	160	6,860
Size 5	"	7.273	12,210	470	12,680
Size 6	"	12.500	27,390	810	28,200
Size 7	"	15.009	35,860	970	36,830
Size 8	"	20.000	49,660	1,300	50,960
NEMA 7					
Size 0	EA.	2.000	1,810	130	1,940
Size 1	"	2.222	1,890	140	2,030
Size 2	"	2.500	3,260	160	3,420
Size 3	"	2.963	5,110	190	5,300
NEMA 12					
Size 0	EA.	1.739	790	110	900
Size 1	"	1.905	890	120	1,010
Size 2	"	2.000	1,640	130	1,770
Size 3	"	2.222	2,950	140	3,090
Size 4	"	2.500	6,360	160	6,520
Size 5	"	7.273	14,040	470	14,510
Size 6	"	14.011	29,690	910	30,600
Size 7	"	16.000	39,660	1,040	40,700
Size 8	"	20.000	55,520	1,300	56,820
Electrically held lighting contactors, NEMA 1,					
2 pole	EA.	1.000	310	65.00	375
3 pole	"	1.250	350	81.00	431
4 pole	"	1.509	430	98.00	528
6 pole	"	2.000	440	130	570

SERVICE AND DISTRIBUTION

16480.10 MOTOR CONTROLS, Cont'd...	UNIT	HOURS	MAT.	INST.	TOTAL
8 pole	EA.	2.500	570	160	730
10 pole	"	2.963	650	190	840
12 pole	"	3.478	760	230	990
30a					
2 pole	EA.	1.000	340	65.00	405
3 pole	"	1.250	360	81.00	441
4 pole	"	1.509	450	98.00	548
5 pole	"	1.739	560	110	670
60a					
2 pole	EA.	1.000	690	65.00	755
3 pole	"	1.250	730	81.00	811
4 pole	"	1.509	910	98.00	1,008
5 pole	"	1.739	1,320	110	1,430
100a					
2 pole	EA.	1.250	1,130	81.00	1,211
3 pole	"	1.739	1,210	110	1,320
4 pole	"	2.222	1,490	140	1,630
5 pole	"	2.759	2,040	180	2,220
200a					
2 pole	EA.	2.759	2,650	180	2,830
3 pole	"	2.963	2,840	190	3,030
4 pole	"	3.200	3,780	210	3,990
300a					
2 pole	EA.	4.211	5,000	270	5,270
3 pole	"	5.333	5,250	350	5,600
400a					
2 pole	EA.	4.211	10,210	270	10,480
3 pole	"	5.333	11,550	350	11,900
600a					
2 pole	EA.	6.667	12,570	430	13,000
3 pole	"	9.249	13,990	600	14,590
800a					
2 pole	EA.	8.000	15,000	520	15,520
3 pole	"	11.004	16,630	710	17,340
Mechanically held lighting contactors, NEMA 1,					
2 pole	EA.	1.000	340	65.00	405
3 pole	"	1.250	360	81.00	441
4 pole	"	1.509	390	98.00	488
6 pole	"	2.000	630	130	760
8 pole	"	2.500	690	160	850
10 pole	"	2.963	770	190	960
30a					
2 pole	EA.	1.000	360	65.00	425
3 pole	"	1.250	390	81.00	471
4 pole	"	1.509	400	98.00	498
5 pole	"	1.739	500	110	610
60a					
2 pole	EA.	1.000	730	65.00	795
3 pole	"	1.250	760	81.00	841
4 pole	"	1.509	910	98.00	1,008
5 pole	"	1.739	1,180	110	1,290
100a					
2 pole	EA.	1.250	1,010	81.00	1,091

SERVICE AND DISTRIBUTION

16480.10 MOTOR CONTROLS, Cont'd...	UNIT	HOURS	MAT.	INST.	TOTAL
3 pole	EA.	1.739	1,070	110	1,180
4 pole	"	2.000	1,290	130	1,420
5 pole	"	2.500	1,730	160	1,890
200a					
2 pole	EA.	1.739	2,610	110	2,720
3 pole	"	2.500	2,960	160	3,120
4 pole	"	3.200	3,600	210	3,810
300a					
2 pole	EA.	4.211	4,660	270	4,930
3 pole	"	5.333	5,070	350	5,420
400a					
2 pole	EA.	4.211	11,140	270	11,410
3 pole	"	5.333	12,570	350	12,920
600a					
2 pole	EA.	6.667	13,390	430	13,820
3 pole	"	8.889	15,000	580	15,580
800a					
2 pole	EA.	8.000	15,820	520	16,340
3 pole	"	11.429	17,640	740	18,380
AC relays, control type open, 15a, 600v					
2 pole	EA.	1.000	120	65.00	185
3 pole	"	1.250	130	81.00	211
4 pole	"	1.509	160	98.00	258
6 pole	"	2.000	200	130	330
8 pole	"	2.500	240	160	400
10 pole	"	2.963	390	190	580
12 pole	"	3.478	410	230	640
16490.10 SWITCHES					
Oil switches, medium voltage, bus components					
Switches, 277/120v, toggle device only	EA.	1.600	510	100	610
With oil 35kv, g&w gram 44, 4 way switch	"	8.000	16,740	520	17,260
Weatherproof enclosure					
3 way switch	EA.	10.000	20,680	650	21,330
4 way switch	"	10.959	19,690	710	20,400
Fused interrupter load, 35kv					21,660
20A					
1 pole	EA.	16.000	23,640	1,040	24,680
2 pole	"	17.021	25,610	1,100	26,710
3 way	"	17.021	27,580	1,100	28,680
4 way	"	18.182	29,550	1,180	30,730
30a, 1 pole	"	16.000	23,640	1,040	24,680
3 way	"	17.021	27,580	1,100	28,680
4 way	"	18.182	29,550	1,180	30,730
Weatherproof switch, including box & cover,					
1 pole	EA.	16.000	25,600	1,040	26,640
2 pole	"	17.021	27,580	1,100	28,680
3 way	"	18.182	29,550	1,180	30,730
4 way	"	18.182	31,530	1,180	32,710
3 way, oil switch, 15kv enclosure	"	11.940	21,660	770	22,430
Pedestal for 35kv double breaker switch	"	5.000	860	320	1,180
Bus terminal connector, 2	"	2.500	750	160	910
2 to 3	"	2.500	910	160	1,070
Support connector, 3	"	1.600	480	100	580

SERVICE AND DISTRIBUTION

16490.10 SWITCHES, Cont'd...	UNIT	HOURS	MAT.	INST.	TOTAL
Tee connector, 2 to 3	EA.	2.000	690	130	820
Flexible bus stud connector	"	1.739	590	110	700
End cap 3	"	1.333	640	86.00	726
Weldment connection, 3	"	1.000	260	65.00	325
Plate switch, 1 gang	"	0.050	0.64	3.24	3.88
Start stop stations, manual motor starters	"	0.727	64.00	47.00	111
Lockout switch	"	0.250	10.75	16.25	27.00
Forward-reverse switch	"	0.727	80.00	47.00	127
On-off switch	"	0.727	81.00	47.00	128
Open-close switch	"	0.727	80.00	47.00	127
Forward-reverse-stop switch	"	1.000	130	65.00	195
Standard 3 button switch any standard legend	"	1.000	86.00	65.00	151
Standard 3 button with lockout	"	1.000	86.00	65.00	151
Manual motor starters, tog, 115/230v					
Size 1 gp	EA.	1.000	140	65.00	205
Size 2	"	1.000	170	65.00	235
Button					
Size 0	EA.	1.000	100	65.00	165
Size 1	"	1.000	150	65.00	215
Size 2	"	1.000	180	65.00	245
3-phase					
Size 0	EA.	1.333	220	86.00	306
Size 1	"	1.333	270	86.00	356
Time & float switches	"	1.600	340	100	440
Astronomical time switch, 40a, 240v	"	1.000	530	65.00	595
Timer switch 0-5 minute, with box	"	0.500	25.75	32.50	58.25
Single pole/single throw time, 277v, NEMA-1	"	0.727	96.00	47.00	143
Single toggle switch, 20a, 120v, with pilot	"	0.250	23.00	16.25	39.25
3-way toggle	"	0.296	64.00	19.25	83.25
Photo electric switches					
1000 watt					
105-135v	EA.	0.727	33.50	47.00	80.50
208-277v	"	0.727	45.25	47.00	92.25
3000 watt, 105-130v					
Double throw	EA.	1.000	130	65.00	195
Single throw	"	1.000	120	65.00	185
Double pole/single throw, 210-250v	"	1.333	150	86.00	236
Dimmer switch and switch plate					
600w	EA.	0.308	30.75	20.00	50.75
1000w	"	0.348	51.00	22.50	73.50
Dimmer switch incandescent					
1500w	EA.	0.702	98.00	45.50	144
2000w	"	0.748	130	48.50	179
Fluorescent					
12 lamps	EA.	0.500	66.00	32.50	98.50
20 lamps	"	0.552	160	35.75	196
30 lamps	"	0.602	280	39.00	319
40 lamps	"	0.702	260	45.50	306
Time clocks with skip, 40a, 120v					
SPST	EA.	0.748	94.00	48.50	143
SPDT	"	0.748	200	48.50	249
DPST	"	0.748	130	48.50	179
DPDT	"	1.000	150	65.00	215

SERVICE AND DISTRIBUTION

16490.10 SWITCHES, Cont'd...	UNIT	HOURS	MAT.	INST.	TOTAL
SPST	EA.	1.000	160	65.00	225
Astronomic time clocks with skip, 40a, 120v					
DPST	EA.	0.748	130	48.50	179
SPST	"	1.000	190	65.00	255
SPDT	"	0.748	140	48.50	189
Raintight time clocks, 40a, 120v					
SPDT	EA.	1.000	140	65.00	205
DPST	"	1.000	130	65.00	195
Contractor grade wall switch 15a, 120v					
Single pole	EA.	0.160	1.62	10.25	11.87
Three way	"	0.200	2.97	13.00	15.97
Four way	"	0.267	10.00	17.25	27.25
Specification grade toggle switches, 20a, 120-					
Single pole	EA.	0.200	3.57	13.00	16.57
Double pole	"	0.296	8.58	19.25	27.83
3 way	"	0.250	9.29	16.25	25.54
4 way	"	0.296	28.25	19.25	47.50
30a, 120-277v					
Single pole	EA.	0.200	23.25	13.00	36.25
Double pole	"	0.296	32.25	19.25	51.50
3 way	"	0.250	32.25	16.25	48.50
Specification grade key switches, 20a, 120-					
Single pole	EA.	0.200	24.75	13.00	37.75
Double pole	"	0.296	31.25	19.25	50.50
3 way	"	0.250	26.75	16.25	43.00
4 way	"	0.296	52.00	19.25	71.25
Red pilot light handle switches, 20a, 120-277v					
Single pole	EA.	0.200	26.25	13.00	39.25
Double pole	"	0.296	30.50	19.25	49.75
3 way	"	0.250	46.25	16.25	62.50
30a, 120-277v					
Single pole	EA.	0.200	32.75	13.00	45.75
Double pole	"	0.296	40.00	19.25	59.25
3 way	"	0.250	61.00	16.25	77.25
Momentary contact switches, 20a					
SPDT, ivory	EA.	0.250	30.75	16.25	47.00
SPDT, locking	"	0.296	40.50	19.25	59.75
Maintained contact switches					
SPDT ivory	EA.	0.250	62.00	16.25	78.25
DPDT ivory	"	0.250	63.00	16.25	79.25
SPDT locking	"	0.296	73.00	19.25	92.25
DPDT locking	"	0.348	73.00	22.50	95.50
Mercury switch, 3 way	"	0.250	15.25	16.25	31.50
Door switches, open on or off	"	0.500	38.00	32.50	70.50
Combination switch and pilot light, single pole	"	0.296	12.25	19.25	31.50
3 way	"	0.348	15.25	22.50	37.75
Combination switch and receptacle, single pole	"	0.296	17.75	19.25	37.00
3 way	"	0.296	21.75	19.25	41.00
Combination two switches, single pole/single	"	0.250	14.75	16.25	31.00
3 way	"	0.400	18.00	26.00	44.00
Switch plates, plastic ivory					
1 gang	EA.	0.080	0.37	5.18	5.55
2 gang	"	0.100	0.88	6.48	7.36

SERVICE AND DISTRIBUTION

16490.10 SWITCHES, Cont'd...	UNIT	HOURS	MAT.	INST.	TOTAL
3 gang	EA.	0.119	1.37	7.73	9.10
4 gang	"	0.145	3.52	9.42	12.94
5 gang	"	0.160	3.68	10.25	13.93
6 gang	"	0.182	4.34	11.75	16.09
Stainless steel					
1 gang	EA.	0.080	3.16	5.18	8.34
2 gang	"	0.100	4.40	6.48	10.88
3 gang	"	0.123	6.75	7.97	14.72
4 gang	"	0.145	11.50	9.42	20.92
5 gang	"	0.160	13.50	10.25	23.75
6 gang	"	0.182	17.00	11.75	28.75
Brass					
1 gang	EA.	0.080	5.90	5.18	11.08
2 gang	"	0.100	12.75	6.48	19.23
3 gang	"	0.123	19.50	7.97	27.47
4 gang	"	0.145	22.50	9.42	31.92
5 gang	"	0.160	28.00	10.25	38.25
6 gang	"	0.182	33.75	11.75	45.50
16490.20 TRANSFER SWITCHES					
Automatic transfer switch 600v, 3 pole					
30a	EA.	3.478	2,960	230	3,190
60a	"	3.478	3,580	230	3,810
100a	"	4.762	3,920	310	4,230
150a	"	6.015	5,230	390	5,620
225a	"	8.000	6,530	520	7,050
260a	"	8.000	7,130	520	7,650
400a	"	10.000	8,840	650	9,490
600a	"	15.094	12,860	980	13,840
800a	"	18.182	16,280	1,180	17,460
1000a	"	21.053	23,210	1,360	24,570
1200a	"	22.857	26,830	1,480	28,310
1600a	"	25.000	33,860	1,620	35,480
2000a	"	29.630	34,250	1,920	36,170
2600a	"	42.105	70,300	2,730	73,030
3000a	"	50.000	110,470	3,240	113,710
16490.80 SAFETY SWITCHES					
Safety switch, 600v, 3 pole, heavy duty,					
30a	EA.	1.000	200	65.00	265
60a	"	1.143	260	74.00	334
100a	"	1.600	510	100	610
200a	"	2.500	790	160	950
400a	"	5.517	2,040	360	2,400
600a	"	8.000	3,620	520	4,140
800a	"	10.526	8,200	680	8,880
1200a	"	14.286	10,180	930	11,110

LIGHTING

16510.05 INTERIOR LIGHTING	UNIT	HOURS	MAT.	INST.	TOTAL
Recessed fluorescent fixtures, 2'x2'					
2 lamp	EA.	0.727	63.00	47.00	110
4 lamp	"	0.727	85.00	47.00	132
2 lamp w/flange	"	1.000	79.00	65.00	144

LIGHTING

16510.05 INTERIOR LIGHTING, Cont'd...	UNIT	HOURS	MAT.	INST.	TOTAL
4 lamp w/flange	EA.	1.000	97.00	65.00	162
1'x4'					
2 lamp	EA.	0.667	64.00	43.25	107
3 lamp	"	0.667	88.00	43.25	131
2 lamp w/flange	"	0.727	79.00	47.00	126
3 lamp w/flange	"	0.727	110	47.00	157
2'x4'					
2 lamp	EA.	0.727	79.00	47.00	126
3 lamp	"	0.727	97.00	47.00	144
4 lamp	"	0.727	88.00	47.00	135
2 lamp w/flange	"	1.000	97.00	65.00	162
3 lamp w/flange	"	1.000	110	65.00	175
4 lamp w/flange	"	1.000	110	65.00	175
4'x4'					
4 lamp	EA.	1.000	320	65.00	385
6 lamp	"	1.000	380	65.00	445
8 lamp	"	1.000	400	65.00	465
4 lamp w/flange	"	1.509	390	98.00	488
6 lamp w/flange	"	1.509	490	98.00	588
8 lamp, w/flange	"	1.509	540	98.00	638
Surface mounted incandescent fixtures					
40w	EA.	0.667	95.00	43.25	138
75w	"	0.667	98.00	43.25	141
100w	"	0.667	110	43.25	153
150w	"	0.667	140	43.25	183
Pendant					
40w	EA.	0.800	78.00	52.00	130
75w	"	0.800	86.00	52.00	138
100w	"	0.800	98.00	52.00	150
150w	"	0.800	110	52.00	162
Contractor grade recessed down lights					
100 watt housing only	EA.	1.000	64.00	65.00	129
150 watt housing only	"	1.000	93.00	65.00	158
100 watt trim	"	0.500	53.00	32.50	85.50
150 watt trim	"	0.500	82.00	32.50	115
Recessed incandescent fixtures					
40w	EA.	1.509	130	98.00	228
75w	"	1.509	140	98.00	238
100w	"	1.509	150	98.00	248
150w	"	1.509	160	98.00	258
Exit lights, 120v					
Recessed	EA.	1.250	44.00	81.00	125
Back mount	"	0.727	72.00	47.00	119
Universal mount	"	0.727	75.00	47.00	122
Emergency battery units, 6v-120v, 50 unit	"	1.509	150	98.00	248
With 1 head	"	1.509	180	98.00	278
With 2 heads	"	1.509	200	98.00	298
Mounting bucket	"	0.727	30.75	47.00	77.75
Light track single circuit					
2'	EA.	0.500	32.00	32.50	64.50
4'	"	0.500	38.00	32.50	70.50
8'	"	1.000	52.00	65.00	117
12'	"	1.509	73.00	98.00	171

LIGHTING

16510.05 INTERIOR LIGHTING, Cont'd...	UNIT	HOURS	MAT.	INST.	TOTAL
Fittings and accessories					
Dead end	EA.	0.145	15.25	9.42	24.67
Starter kit	"	0.250	20.50	16.25	36.75
Conduit feed	"	0.145	19.75	9.42	29.17
Straight connector	"	0.145	17.50	9.42	26.92
Center feed	"	0.145	28.00	9.42	37.42
L-connector	"	0.145	19.75	9.42	29.17
T-connector	"	0.145	26.50	9.42	35.92
X-connector	"	0.200	32.00	13.00	45.00
Cord and plug	"	0.100	32.00	6.48	38.48
Rigid corner	"	0.145	42.25	9.42	51.67
Flex connector	"	0.145	33.00	9.42	42.42
2 way connector	"	0.200	92.00	13.00	105
Spacer clip	"	0.050	1.43	3.24	4.67
Grid box	"	0.145	7.97	9.42	17.39
T-bar clip	"	0.050	2.13	3.24	5.37
Utility hook	"	0.145	6.18	9.42	15.60
Fixtures, square					
R-20	EA.	0.145	39.25	9.42	48.67
R-30	"	0.145	61.00	9.42	70.42
40w flood	"	0.145	99.00	9.42	108
40w spot	"	0.145	99.00	9.42	108
100w flood	"	0.145	110	9.42	119
100w spot	"	0.145	88.00	9.42	97.42
Mini spot	"	0.145	37.25	9.42	46.67
Mini flood	"	0.145	86.00	9.42	95.42
Quartz, 500w	"	0.145	220	9.42	229
R-20 sphere	"	0.145	66.00	9.42	75.42
R-30 sphere	"	0.145	34.50	9.42	43.92
R-20 cylinder	"	0.145	46.25	9.42	55.67
R-30 cylinder	"	0.145	54.00	9.42	63.42
R-40 cylinder	"	0.145	54.00	9.42	63.42
R-30 wall wash	"	0.145	86.00	9.42	95.42
R-40 wall wash	"	0.145	110	9.42	119
Explosion proof, incan., surface mounted					
100w - 200w	EA.	1.739	370	110	480
300w	"	1.739	520	110	630
500w	"	1.739	760	110	870
With guard					
100w-200w	EA.	2.222	350	140	490
300w	"	2.222	490	140	630
500w	"	2.222	720	140	860
Reflectors for incan. light fixtures, dome	"	0.250	64.00	16.25	80.25
Angle	"	0.250	72.00	16.25	88.25
Highbay	"	0.296	130	19.25	149
Explosion proof fluor. fixtures, 800 ms.					
1 lamp	EA.	2.222	1,430	140	1,570
2 lamp	"	2.667	1,770	170	1,940
3 lamp	"	2.963	2,650	190	2,840
4 lamp	"	3.200	3,430	210	3,640
Explosion proof hp sodium fixtures					
50w-70w	EA.	2.222	970	140	1,110
100w	"	2.222	990	140	1,130

LIGHTING

16510.05 INTERIOR LIGHTING, Cont'd...	UNIT	HOURS	MAT.	INST.	TOTAL
150w	EA.	2.500	1,030	160	1,190
200w	"	2.500	1,040	160	1,200
250w	"	2.500	1,100	160	1,260
310w	"	2.500	1,130	160	1,290
400w	"	2.500	1,710	160	1,870
With guard					
50w-70w	EA.	2.500	980	160	1,140
100w	"	2.500	1,000	160	1,160
150w	"	2.759	1,080	180	1,260
200w	"	2.759	1,100	180	1,280
250w	"	2.759	1,130	180	1,310
310w	"	2.759	1,180	180	1,360
400w	"	2.759	1,770	180	1,950
Explosion proof metal halide fixtures					
175w	EA.	2.500	840	160	1,000
250w	"	2.500	910	160	1,070
400w	"	2.500	1,350	160	1,510
With guard, 175w	"	2.759	860	180	1,040
250w	"	2.759	930	180	1,110
400w	"	2.759	1,410	180	1,590
Energy saving rapid start fluor. lamps					
F30 cw	EA.	0.100	8.14	6.48	14.62
F40 cw	"	0.100	8.14	6.48	14.62
F40 cwx	"	0.100	9.13	6.48	15.61
F30 ww	"	0.100	12.25	6.48	18.73
F40 ww	"	0.100	6.71	6.48	13.19
F40 wwx	"	0.100	9.13	6.48	15.61
Slimline					
F48 cw	EA.	0.145	13.75	9.42	23.17
F96 cwx	"	0.145	24.50	9.42	33.92
F48 ww	"	0.145	18.25	9.42	27.67
F96 ww	"	0.145	16.75	9.42	26.17
F96 wwx	"	0.145	15.50	9.42	24.92
High output	"	0.145	10.25	9.42	19.67
F96 cwx	"	0.145	15.25	9.42	24.67
F96 cw	"	0.145	11.50	9.42	20.92
Power groove, F48 cw	"	0.145	26.25	9.42	35.67
Circle					
Fc6 cw	EA.	0.100	11.25	6.48	17.73
Fc8 cw	"	0.100	9.46	6.48	15.94
Fc12 cw	"	0.100	10.00	6.48	16.48
Fc16 cw	"	0.100	14.75	6.48	21.23
Fc6 ww	"	0.100	12.00	6.48	18.48
Fc8 ww	"	0.100	10.25	6.48	16.73
Fc12 ww	"	0.100	12.25	6.48	18.73
Fc16 ww	"	0.100	18.00	6.48	24.48
Incandescent lamps					
200w	EA.	0.100	5.33	6.48	11.81
300w	"	0.100	5.83	6.48	12.31
500w	"	0.100	13.00	6.48	19.48
750w	"	0.145	31.75	9.42	41.17
1000w	"	0.200	34.75	13.00	47.75
1500w	"	0.200	51.00	13.00	64.00

LIGHTING

16510.05 INTERIOR LIGHTING, Cont'd...	UNIT	HOURS	MAT.	INST.	TOTAL
Energy saving reflector floodlight lamps					
25w	EA.	0.100	9.35	6.48	15.83
30w	"	0.100	10.00	6.48	16.48
50w	"	0.100	10.00	6.48	16.48
75w	"	0.100	11.50	6.48	17.98
120w	"	0.100	11.50	6.48	17.98
150w	"	0.100	16.00	6.48	22.48
200w	"	0.100	16.75	6.48	23.23
300w	"	0.100	22.50	6.48	28.98
500w	"	0.145	37.25	9.42	46.67
750w	"	0.145	48.50	9.42	57.92
Reflector spotlight					
75w	EA.	0.100	8.69	6.48	15.17
100w	"	0.100	10.50	6.48	16.98
125w	"	0.100	18.00	6.48	24.48
150w	"	0.100	19.00	6.48	25.48
250w	"	0.100	31.25	6.48	37.73
300w	"	0.100	49.75	6.48	56.23
400w	"	0.145	55.00	9.42	64.42
500w	"	0.145	69.00	9.42	78.42
1000w	"	0.200	150	13.00	163
Medium par flood lamps					
75w	EA.	0.100	8.58	6.48	15.06
100w	"	0.100	9.57	6.48	16.05
150w	"	0.100	10.25	6.48	16.73
200w	"	0.100	39.75	6.48	46.23
300w	"	0.100	44.00	6.48	50.48
500w	"	0.145	86.00	9.42	95.42
Medium par spot lamps					
75w	EA.	0.100	10.75	6.48	17.23
120w	"	0.100	11.00	6.48	17.48
150w	"	0.100	11.50	6.48	17.98
Tubular quartz lamps					
100w	EA.	0.145	71.00	9.42	80.42
150w	"	0.145	71.00	9.42	80.42
200w	"	0.145	83.00	9.42	92.42
400w	"	0.145	84.00	9.42	93.42
500w	"	0.200	86.00	13.00	99.00
750w	"	0.200	85.00	13.00	98.00
1000w	"	0.250	110	16.25	126
1250w	"	0.250	120	16.25	136
1500w	"	0.250	150	16.25	166
Ballast replacements rapid start fluor					
1f-40-120v	EA.	0.727	23.25	47.00	70.25
1f-40-277v	"	0.727	39.00	47.00	86.00
1f-96-120v	"	0.727	120	47.00	167
1f-96-277v	"	0.727	140	47.00	187
2f-40-120v	"	0.727	33.00	47.00	80.00
2f-40-277v	"	0.727	39.00	47.00	86.00
2f-96-120v	"	0.727	100	47.00	147
2f-96-277v	"	0.727	110	47.00	157
Circline, 1fc6-1fc16	"	0.727	30.50	47.00	77.50
Very high output, 1500ma					

LIGHTING

16510.05 INTERIOR LIGHTING, Cont'd...	UNIT	HOURS	MAT.	INST.	TOTAL
1f48-120v	EA.	0.727	180	47.00	227
1f48-277v	"	0.727	180	47.00	227
1f96-120v	"	0.727	150	47.00	197
1f96-277v	"	0.727	180	47.00	227
2f48-120v	"	0.727	150	47.00	197
2f48-277v	"	0.727	180	47.00	227
2f96-120v	"	0.727	180	47.00	227
2f96-277v	"	0.727	200	47.00	247
Mercury, multi tap					
475w	EA.	1.000	150	65.00	215
100w	"	1.000	150	65.00	215
175w	"	1.000	160	65.00	225
250w	"	1.000	200	65.00	265
400w	"	1.000	230	65.00	295
1000w	"	1.000	550	65.00	615
Metal halide, multi tap					
175w	EA.	1.000	130	65.00	195
250w	"	1.000	170	65.00	235
400w	"	1.000	210	65.00	275
1000w	"	1.000	370	65.00	435
1500w	"	1.000	480	65.00	545
High pressure sodium					
70w	EA.	1.000	220	65.00	285
100w	"	1.000	230	65.00	295
150w	"	1.000	250	65.00	315
250w	"	1.000	370	65.00	435
400w	"	1.000	420	65.00	485
1000w	"	1.000	570	65.00	635
16510.10 LIGHTING INDUSTRIAL					
Surface mounted fluorescent, wrap around					
1 lamp	EA.	0.800	86.00	52.00	138
2 lamps	"	0.889	140	58.00	198
4 lamps	"	1.000	130	65.00	195
Wall mounted fluorescent					
2-20w lamps	EA.	0.500	88.00	32.50	121
2-30w lamps	"	0.500	100	32.50	133
2-40w lamps	"	0.667	100	43.25	143
Indirect, with wood shielding, 2049w lamps					
4'	EA.	1.000	100	65.00	165
8'	"	1.600	130	100	230
Industrial fluorescent, 2 lamp					
4'	EA.	0.727	68.00	47.00	115
8'	"	1.333	110	86.00	196
Strip fluorescent					
4'					
1 lamp	EA.	0.667	43.25	43.25	86.50
2 lamps	"	0.667	53.00	43.25	96.25
8'					
1 lamp	EA.	0.727	63.00	47.00	110
2 lamps	"	0.889	95.00	58.00	153
Wire guard for strip fixture, 4' long	"	0.348	9.80	22.50	32.30
Strip fluorescent, 8' long, two 4' lamps	"	1.333	130	86.00	216
With four 4' lamps	"	1.600	160	100	260

LIGHTING

16510.10 LIGHTING INDUSTRIAL, Cont'd...	UNIT	HOURS	MAT.	INST.	TOTAL
Wet location fluorescent, plastic housing					
4' long					
1 lamp	EA.	1.000	140	65.00	205
2 lamps	"	1.333	150	86.00	236
8' long					
2 lamps	EA.	1.600	260	100	360
4 lamps	"	1.739	350	110	460
Parabolic troffer, 2'x2'					
With 2 "U" lamps	EA.	1.000	120	65.00	185
With 3 "U" lamps	"	1.143	140	74.00	214
2'x4'					
With 2 40w lamps	EA.	1.143	140	74.00	214
With 3 40w lamps	"	1.333	140	86.00	226
With 4 40w lamps	"	1.333	150	86.00	236
1'x4'					
With 1 T-12 lamp, 9 cell	EA.	0.727	110	47.00	157
With 2 T-12 lamps	"	0.889	130	58.00	188
With 1 T-12 lamp, 20 cell	"	0.727	130	47.00	177
With 2 T-12 lamps	"	0.889	140	58.00	198
Steel sided surface fluorescent, 2'x4'					
3 lamps	EA.	1.333	140	86.00	226
4 lamps	"	1.333	160	86.00	246
Outdoor sign fluor., 1 lamp, remote ballast					
4' long	EA.	6.015	3,010	390	3,400
6' long	"	8.000	3,620	520	4,140
Recess mounted, commercial, 2'x2', 13" high					
100w	EA.	4.000	1,000	260	1,260
250w	"	4.494	1,100	290	1,390
High pressure sodium, hi-bay open					
400w	EA.	1.739	430	110	540
1000w	"	2.424	750	160	910
Enclosed					
400w	EA.	2.424	700	160	860
1000w	"	2.963	980	190	1,170
Metal halide hi-bay, open					
400w	EA.	1.739	270	110	380
1000w	"	2.424	550	160	710
Enclosed					
400w	EA.	2.424	610	160	770
1000w	"	2.963	580	190	770
High pressure sodium, low bay, surface					
100w	EA.	1.000	220	65.00	285
150w	"	1.143	240	74.00	314
250w	"	1.333	270	86.00	356
400w	"	1.600	340	100	440
Metal halide, low bay, pendant mounted					
175w	EA.	1.333	350	86.00	436
250w	"	1.600	480	100	580
400w	"	2.222	520	140	660
Indirect luminare, square, metal halide,					
175w	EA.	1.000	440	65.00	505
250w	"	1.000	470	65.00	535
400w	"	1.000	490	65.00	555

ELECTRICAL

LIGHTING

16510.10 LIGHTING INDUSTRIAL, Cont'd...	UNIT	HOURS	MAT.	INST.	TOTAL
High pressure sodium					
150w	EA.	1.000	790	65.00	855
250w	"	1.000	850	65.00	915
400w	"	1.000	930	65.00	995
Round, metal halide					
175w	EA.	1.000	910	65.00	975
250w	"	1.000	950	65.00	1,015
400w	"	1.000	990	65.00	1,055
High pressure sodium					
150w	EA.	1.000	870	65.00	935
250w	"	1.000	1,010	65.00	1,075
400w	"	1.000	1,060	65.00	1,125
Wall mounted, metal halide					
175w	EA.	2.500	400	160	560
250w	"	2.500	390	160	550
400w	"	3.200	430	210	640
High pressure sodium					
150w	EA.	2.500	370	160	530
250w	"	2.500	390	160	550
400w	"	3.200	400	210	610
Wall pack lithonia, high pressure sodium					
35w	EA.	0.889	57.00	58.00	115
55w	"	1.000	72.00	65.00	137
150w	"	1.600	180	100	280
250w	"	1.739	190	110	300
Low pressure sodium					
35w	EA.	1.739	310	110	420
55w	"	2.000	420	130	550
Wall pack hubbell, high pressure sodium					
35w	EA.	0.889	250	58.00	308
150w	"	1.600	320	100	420
250w	"	1.739	410	110	520
Compact fluorescent					
2-7w	EA.	1.000	150	65.00	215
2-13w	"	1.333	180	86.00	266
1-18w	"	1.333	210	86.00	296
Handball & racquet ball court, 2'x2', metal					
250w	EA.	2.500	550	160	710
400w	"	2.759	660	180	840
High pressure sodium					
250w	EA.	2.500	600	160	760
400w	"	2.759	660	180	840
Bollard light, 42" w/found., high pressure					
70w	EA.	2.581	920	170	1,090
100w	"	2.581	950	170	1,120
150w	"	2.581	960	170	1,130
Light fixture lamps					
Lamp					
20w med. bipin base, cool white, 24"	EA.	0.145	7.41	9.42	16.83
30w cool white, rapid start, 36"	"	0.145	9.39	9.42	18.81
40w cool white "U", 3"	"	0.145	20.50	9.42	29.92
40w cool white, rapid start, 48"	"	0.145	8.74	9.42	18.16
70w high pressure sodium, mogul base	"	0.200	68.00	13.00	81.00

LIGHTING

16510.10 LIGHTING INDUSTRIAL, Cont'd...	UNIT	HOURS	MAT.	INST.	TOTAL
75w slimline, 96"	EA.	0.200	20.25	13.00	33.25
100w					
Incandescent, 100a, inside frost	EA.	0.100	3.52	6.48	10.00
Mercury vapor, clear, mogul base	"	0.200	61.00	13.00	74.00
High pressure sodium, mogul base	"	0.200	94.00	13.00	107
150w					
Par 38 flood or spot, incandescent	EA.	0.100	20.75	6.48	27.23
High pressure sodium, 1/2 mogul base	"	0.200	83.00	13.00	96.00
175w					
Mercury vapor, clear, mogul base	EA.	0.200	37.25	13.00	50.25
Metal halide, clear, mogul base	"	0.200	75.00	13.00	88.00
High pressure sodium, mogul base	"	0.200	83.00	13.00	96.00
250w					
Mercury vapor, clear, mogul base	EA.	0.200	52.00	13.00	65.00
Metal halide, clear, mogul base	"	0.200	75.00	13.00	88.00
High pressure sodium, mogul base	"	0.200	88.00	13.00	101
400w					
Mercury vapor, clear, mogul base	EA.	0.200	57.00	13.00	70.00
Metal halide, clear, mogul base	"	0.200	75.00	13.00	88.00
High pressure sodium, mogul base	"	0.200	90.00	13.00	103
1000w					
Mercury vapor, clear, mogul base	EA.	0.250	140	16.25	156
High pressure sodium, mogul base	"	0.250	240	16.25	256

16510.30 EXTERIOR LIGHTING	UNIT	HOURS	MAT.	INST.	TOTAL
Exterior light fixtures					
Rectangle, high pressure sodium					
70w	EA.	2.500	300	160	460
100w	"	2.581	310	170	480
150w	"	2.581	330	170	500
250w	"	2.759	450	180	630
400w	"	3.478	500	230	730
Flood, rectangular, high pressure sodium					
70w	EA.	2.500	180	160	340
100w	"	2.581	210	170	380
150w	"	2.581	200	170	370
400w	"	3.478	250	230	480
1000w	"	4.494	410	290	700
Round					
400w	EA.	3.478	550	230	780
1000w	"	4.494	860	290	1,150
Round, metal halide					
400w	EA.	3.478	600	230	830
1000w	"	4.494	900	290	1,190
Light fixture arms, cobra head, 6', high press.					
100w	EA.	2.000	330	130	460
150w	"	2.500	520	160	680
250w	"	2.500	540	160	700
400w	"	2.963	560	190	750
Flood, metal halide					
400w	EA.	3.478	540	230	770
1000w	"	4.494	740	290	1,030
1500w	"	6.015	930	390	1,320
Mercury vapor					

LIGHTING

16510.30 EXTERIOR LIGHTING, Cont'd...	UNIT	HOURS	MAT.	INST.	TOTAL
250w	EA.	2.759	360	180	540
400w	"	3.478	400	230	630
Incandescent					
300w	EA.	1.739	83.00	110	193
500w	"	2.000	150	130	280
1000w	"	3.200	160	210	370
16510.90 POWER LINE FILTERS					
Heavy duty power line filter, 240v					
100a	EA.	10.000	4,510	650	5,160
300a	"	16.000	14,970	1,040	16,010
600a	"	24.242	20,750	1,570	22,320
16600.20 CENTRAL INVERTER SYSTEMS					
Central inverter systems					
500va	EA.	2.963	9,830	190	10,020
1000va	"	4.000	10,750	260	11,010
1500va	"	5.333	12,570	350	12,920
2400va	"	6.667	16,210	430	16,640
3000va	"	8.502	17,130	550	17,680
4500va	"	10.000	26,060	650	26,710
6000va	"	11.004	32,800	710	33,510
7500va	"	14.011	37,910	910	38,820
10,000va	"	16.000	43,740	1,040	44,780
16,600va	"	22.989	75,810	1,490	77,300
25,000va	"	34.934	90,390	2,260	92,650
16610.30 UNINTERRUPTIBLE POWER					
Uninterruptible power systems, (U.P.S.), 3kva	EA.	8.000	7,810	520	8,330
5 kva	"	11.004	8,760	710	9,470
7.5 kva	"	16.000	10,510	1,040	11,550
10 kva	"	21.978	13,140	1,420	14,560
15 kva	"	22.857	15,770	1,480	17,250
20 kva	"	24.024	21,900	1,560	23,460
25 kva	"	25.000	28,030	1,620	29,650
30 kva	"	25.974	28,910	1,680	30,590
35 kva	"	27.027	30,660	1,750	32,410
40 kva	"	27.972	33,290	1,810	35,100
45 kva	"	28.986	35,040	1,880	36,920
50 kva	"	29.963	37,670	1,940	39,610
62.5 kva	"	32.000	44,680	2,070	46,750
75 kva	"	34.934	51,680	2,260	53,940
100 kva	"	36.036	69,210	2,340	71,550
150 kva	"	50.000	105,130	3,240	108,370
200 kva	"	55.172	140,170	3,580	143,750
300 kva	"	74.766	210,250	4,840	215,090
400 kva	"	89.888	314,530	5,820	320,350
500 kva	"	109.589	393,170	7,100	400,270
16670.10 LIGHTNING PROTECTION					
Lightning protection					
Copper point, nickel plated, 12'					
1/2" dia.	EA.	1.000	44.00	65.00	109
5/8" dia.	"	1.000	49.50	65.00	115

COMMUNICATIONS

16720.10 FIRE ALARM SYSTEMS	UNIT	HOURS	MAT.	INST.	TOTAL
Master fire alarm box, pedestal mounted	EA.	16.000	7,110	1,040	8,150
Master fire alarm box	"	6.015	3,650	390	4,040
Box light	"	0.500	130	32.50	163
Ground assembly for box	"	0.667	100	43.25	143
Bracket for pole type box	"	0.727	130	47.00	177
Pull station					
Waterproof	EA.	0.500	65.00	32.50	97.50
Manual	"	0.400	48.50	26.00	74.50
Horn, waterproof	"	1.000	91.00	65.00	156
Interior alarm	"	0.727	61.00	47.00	108
Coded transmitter, automatic	"	2.000	930	130	1,060
Control panel, 8 zone	"	8.000	2,140	520	2,660
Battery charger and cabinet	"	2.000	720	130	850
Batteries, nickel cadmium or lead calcium	"	5.000	540	320	860
CO2 pressure switch connection	"	0.727	100	47.00	147
Annunciator panels					
Fire detection annunciator, remote type, 8	EA.	1.818	360	120	480
12 zone	"	2.000	460	130	590
16 zone		2.500	580	160	740
Fire alarm systems					
Bell	EA.	0.615	110	39.75	150
Weatherproof bell	"	0.667	71.00	43.25	114
Horn	"	0.727	65.00	47.00	112
Siren	"	2.000	660	130	790
Chime	"	0.615	81.00	39.75	121
Audio/visual	"	0.727	120	47.00	167
Strobe light	"	0.727	110	47.00	157
Smoke detector	"	0.667	180	43.25	223
Heat detection	"	0.500	30.50	32.50	63.00
Thermal detector	"	0.500	28.50	32.50	61.00
Ionization detector	"	0.533	140	34.50	175
Duct detector	"	2.759	470	180	650
Test switch	"	0.500	81.00	32.50	114
Remote indicator	"	0.571	51.00	37.00	88.00
Door holder	"	0.727	180	47.00	227
Telephone jack	"	0.296	3.30	19.25	22.55
Fireman phone	"	1.000	430	65.00	495
Speaker	"	0.800	87.00	52.00	139
Remote fire alarm annunciator panel					
24 zone	EA.	6.667	2,230	430	2,660
48 zone	"	13.008	4,470	840	5,310
Control panel					
12 zone	EA.	2.963	1,520	190	1,710
16 zone	"	4.444	1,990	290	2,280
24 zone	"	6.667	3,050	430	3,480
48 zone	"	16.000	5,690	1,040	6,730
Power supply	"	1.509	350	98.00	448
Status command	"	5.000	9,640	320	9,960
Printer	"	1.509	3,080	98.00	3,178
Transponder	"	0.899	150	58.00	208
Transformer	"	0.667	220	43.25	263
Transceiver	"	0.727	310	47.00	357
Relays	"	0.500	120	32.50	153

COMMUNICATIONS

16720.10 FIRE ALARM SYSTEMS	UNIT	HOURS	MAT.	INST.	TOTAL
Flow switch	EA.	2.000	400	130	530
Tamper switch	"	2.963	240	190	430
End of line resistor	"	0.348	17.25	22.50	39.75
Printed ckt. card	"	0.500	150	32.50	183
Central processing unit	"	6.154	10,540	400	10,940
UPS backup to c.p.u.	"	8.999	19,290	580	19,870
Smoke detector, fixed temp. & rate of rise	"	1.600	310	100	410

16720.20 FIRE ALARMS	UNIT	HOURS	MAT.	INST.	TOTAL
Fire alarm duct detector accessory, 24v D.C.	EA.	0.500	41.50	32.50	74.00
24v Remote inducator LED	"	0.500	60.00	32.50	92.50
Test probe adapter	"	0.500	44.75	32.50	77.25
Sampling tube, 3 foot	"	0.500	16.50	32.50	49.00
6 foot	"	0.500	33.25	32.50	65.75
10 foot	"	0.750	75.00	48.75	124
Form "C" 5 amp relay contacts (2)	"	1.000	85.00	65.00	150
Panel accessory, electronic type, McCullom	"	4.000	620	260	880
Dome light assembly, single	"	0.350	24.75	22.75	47.50
Double	"	0.450	32.25	29.25	61.50
Alarm tone module, wail	"	0.500	83.00	32.50	116
Whoop	"	0.500	91.00	32.50	124
Chime	"	0.500	43.50	32.50	76.00
Power transformer	"	0.750	190	48.75	239
Replacement power supply	"	1.000	560	65.00	625
Trouble circuit module	"	0.750	300	48.75	349
Trouble silence switch	"	0.350	18.25	22.75	41.00
Bell silence switch	"	0.350	18.25	22.75	41.00
Voltage regulator	"	0.400	21.75	26.00	47.75
Replacement control panel P.C. board	"	2.000	710	130	840
Power supply	"	1.000	300	65.00	365
Pre-amplifier module	"	0.750	72.00	48.75	121
Input switching module	"	0.750	90.00	48.75	139
Audio zone selector card	"	0.750	170	48.75	219
Backup switching module	"	0.350	70.00	22.75	92.75
Interface P.C. board	"	0.400	63.00	26.00	89.00
Amplifier supervisory module	"	0.500	110	32.50	143
Fireman telephone main control board	"	1.000	300	65.00	365
Dual telephone zone module	"	0.500	130	32.50	163
Diodes	"	0.350	8.29	22.75	31.04
Fuses and fuse holder	"	0.350	13.25	22.75	36.00
Metal face plate, engraving per character	"				1.66
Black plastic tags w/engraving per	"				0.81
Addressable single zone class "A" zone	"	1.501	520	97.00	617
Class "B" zone module, dual zone	"	1.501	280	97.00	377
Quad zone	"	1.501	570	97.00	667
Single class "A" bell module	"	1.000	450	65.00	515
Dual class "B"	"	1.000	370	65.00	435
Fire alarm march time coder module	"	0.750	210	48.75	259
Flow switch module	"	1.000	230	65.00	295
Tamper	"	1.000	230	65.00	295
40 watt audio module	"	1.501	1,080	97.00	1,177
Auxiliary power supply module	"	1.000	430	65.00	495
Time delay module	"	0.750	190	48.75	239
Digital voice message repeater	"	5.000	2,150	320	2,470

COMMUNICATIONS

16720.20 FIRE ALARMS, Cont'd...	UNIT	HOURS	MAT.	INST.	TOTAL
Fire fighter telephone system, 1 zone	EA.	3.008	1,360	190	1,550
4 zone	"	5.000	1,820	320	2,140
8 zone	"	6.015	2,070	390	2,460
12 zone	"	8.000	2,320	520	2,840
16 zone	"	10.000	2,580	650	3,230
20 zone	"	12.121	3,230	790	4,020
24 zone	"	13.333	3,490	860	4,350
30 zone	"	16.000	3,870	1,040	4,910
40 zone	"	18.182	4,740	1,180	5,920
48 zone	"	20.000	5,250	1,300	6,550
Portable telephone handset w/plug and cord	"	0.500	250	32.50	283
Sound powered handset w/plug and cord	"	0.500	260	32.50	293
Remote break glass telephone jack	"	0.500	75.00	32.50	108
Handset storage rack for (4) portable	"	1.000	210	65.00	275
Manual pull station w/hammer and chain	"	1.000	120	65.00	185
Dust tight enclosure	"	2.000	290	130	420
Light emitting diode	"	1.000	110	65.00	175
Telephone jack	"	1.250	120	81.00	201
Explosion proof enclosure	"	2.500	450	160	610
Radio master box w/antenna and pedestal	"	16.000	15,740	1,040	16,780
Halon control panel w/abort sw., emerg.					
Ground fault and batterys (6amp. hr.)	EA.	8.000	1,850	520	2,370
Halon releasing device module	"	1.000	210	65.00	275
Time delay module	"	1.000	190	65.00	255
Dual 4 P.D.T. relay	"	0.667	200	43.25	243
Quad switch panel	"	0.500	150	32.50	183
Utility disconnect relay w/bypass switch	"	0.500	150	32.50	183
18 amp. hr. batterys	"	1.000	550	65.00	615
Emergency manual halon release station	"	0.750	79.00	48.75	128
Abort station	"	0.750	75.00	48.75	124
Addressable fire alarm control panels, 6 zone	"	5.000	8,450	320	8,770
12 zone	"	10.000	10,800	650	11,450
16 zone	"	14.035	12,350	910	13,260
20 zone	"	18.182	13,420	1,180	14,600
24 zone	"	21.053	14,750	1,360	16,110
30 zone	"	25.000	15,740	1,620	17,360
34 zone	"	30.769	19,060	1,990	21,050
40 zone	"	38.095	21,130	2,470	23,600
48 zone	"	44.444	23,530	2,880	26,410
Remote annunciator panel, 6 zone	"	3.008	1,620	190	1,810
12 zone	"	5.000	2,600	320	2,920
16 zone	"	8.000	3,570	520	4,090
20 zone	"	10.000	4,540	650	5,190
24 zone	"	12.121	4,710	790	5,500
30 zone	"	14.035	5,360	910	6,270
34 zone	"	16.000	5,850	1,040	6,890
40 zone	"	18.182	6,170	1,180	7,350
48 zone	"	20.000	7,150	1,300	8,450
Smoke detectors	"	1.501	180	97.00	277
Manual pull stations	"	1.501	400	97.00	497

COMMUNICATIONS

16720.50 SECURITY SYSTEMS	UNIT	HOURS	MAT.	INST.	TOTAL
Sensors					
Balanced magnetic door switch, surface	EA.	0.500	150	32.50	183
With remote test	"	1.000	200	65.00	265
Flush mounted	"	1.860	140	120	260
Mounted bracket	"	0.348	11.00	22.50	33.50
Mounted bracket spacer	"	0.348	9.84	22.50	32.34
Photoelectric sensor, for fence					
6 beam	EA.	2.759	16,060	180	16,240
9 beam	"	4.255	19,630	280	19,910
Photoelectric sensor, 12 volt dc					
500' range	EA.	1.600	470	100	570
800' range	"	2.000	530	130	660
Capacitance wire grid kit					
Surface	EA.	1.000	130	65.00	195
Duct	"	1.600	98.00	100	198
Tube grid kit	"	0.500	160	32.50	193
Vibration sensor, 30 max per zone	"	0.500	200	32.50	233
Audio sensor, 30 max per zone	"	0.500	210	32.50	243
Inertia sensor					
Outdoor	EA.	0.727	150	47.00	197
Indoor	"	0.500	98.00	32.50	131
Ultrasonic transmitter, 20 max per zone					
Omni-directional	EA.	1.600	110	100	210
Directional	"	1.333	120	86.00	206
Transceiver					
Omni-directional	EA.	1.000	120	65.00	185
Directional	"	1.000	130	65.00	195
Passive infra-red sensor, 20 max per zone	"	1.600	850	100	950
Access/secure control unit, balanced magnetic	"	1.600	530	100	630
Photoelectric sensor	"	1.600	870	100	970
Photoelectric fence sensor	"	1.600	890	100	990
Capacitance sensor	"	1.739	1,030	110	1,140
Audio and vibration sensor	"	1.600	910	100	1,010
Inertia sensor	"	1.600	1,220	100	1,320
Ultrasonic sensor	"	1.739	1,400	110	1,510
Infra-red sensor	"	2.000	870	130	1,000
Monitor panel, with access/secure tone,	"	1.739	590	110	700
High security	"	2.000	870	130	1,000
Emergency power indicator	"	0.500	350	32.50	383
Monitor rack with 115v power supply					
1 zone	EA.	1.000	500	65.00	565
10 zone	"	2.500	2,520	160	2,680
Monitor cabinet, wall mounted					
1 zone	EA.	1.000	760	65.00	825
5 zone	"	1.600	2,740	100	2,840
10 zone	"	1.739	1,250	110	1,360
20 zone	"	2.000	3,820	130	3,950
Floor mounted, 50 zone	"	4.000	3,970	260	4,230
Security system accessories					
Tamper assembly for monitor cabinet	EA.	0.444	98.00	28.75	127
Monitor panel blank	"	0.348	13.25	22.50	35.75
Audible alarm	"	0.500	110	32.50	143
Audible alarm control	"	0.348	460	22.50	483

COMMUNICATIONS

16720.50 SECURITY SYSTEMS	UNIT	HOURS	MAT.	INST.	TOTAL
Termination screw, terminal cabinet					
25 pair	EA.	1.600	330	100	430
50 pair	"	2.500	530	160	690
150 pair	"	5.000	860	320	1,180
Universal termination, cabinets & panel					
Remote test	EA.	1.739	77.00	110	187
No remote test	"	0.727	55.00	47.00	102
High security line supervision termination	"	1.000	390	65.00	455
Door cord for capacitance sensor, 12"	"	0.500	13.25	32.50	45.75
Insulation block kit for capacitance sensor	"	0.348	62.00	22.50	84.50
Termination block for capacitance sensor	"	0.348	13.25	22.50	35.75
Guard alert display	"	0.615	1,400	39.75	1,440
Uninterrupted power supply	"	8.000	1,420	520	1,940
Plug-in 40kva transformer					
12 volt	EA.	0.348	56.00	22.50	78.50
18 volt	"	0.348	37.25	22.50	59.75
24 volt	"	0.348	26.25	22.50	48.75
Test relay	"	0.348	85.00	22.50	108
Coaxial cable, 50 ohm	L.F.	0.006	0.38	0.39	0.77
Door openers	EA.	0.500	98.00	32.50	131
Push buttons					
Standard	EA.	0.348	22.00	22.50	44.50
Weatherproof	"	0.444	33.00	28.75	61.75
Bells	"	0.727	84.00	47.00	131
Horns					
Standard	EA.	1.000	87.00	65.00	152
Weatherproof	"	1.250	160	81.00	241
Chimes	"	0.667	130	43.25	173
Flasher	"	0.615	92.00	39.75	132
Motion detectors	"	1.509	390	98.00	488
Intercom units	"	0.727	87.00	47.00	134
Remote annunciator	"	5.000	3,950	320	4,270
Control/communications, panels, minimum	"	6.015	1,690	390	2,080
Maximum	"	10.000	3,990	650	4,640
CPU w/shield, minimum	"	4.000	600	260	860
Maximum	"	8.000	2,900	520	3,420
Attack resistant pkg.	"	5.000	2,000	320	2,320
Fire/burglar pkg.	"	7.018	2,240	450	2,690
Standard burglar	"	6.015	1,870	390	2,260
Fire	"	5.000	1,430	320	1,750
Input/Output board	"	2.000	1,100	130	1,230
Panel accessory flushmount kit, brass	"	0.500	81.00	32.50	114
Stainless steel	"	0.500	59.00	32.50	91.50
Desk stand	"	0.500	86.00	32.50	119
Conduit box	"	0.500	40.50	32.50	73.00
Fire alarm kit	"	0.750	51.00	48.75	99.75
Lock set and key	"	0.350	11.75	22.75	34.50
Tamper switch	"	0.350	15.25	22.75	38.00
Dual battery harness	"	0.500	30.50	32.50	63.00
Powered loop interface	"	0.750	140	48.75	189
Battery 12v DC, 6 amp	"	0.500	93.00	32.50	126
Reversing, relay module	"	1.000	230	65.00	295
Dual phone line switcher	"	1.000	260	65.00	325

COMMUNICATIONS

16720.50 SECURITY SYSTEMS	UNIT	HOURS	MAT.	INST.	TOTAL
Class "A" circuit module	EA.	1.000	270	65.00	335
Plug-in relay	"	0.500	18.50	32.50	51.00
Mounting bracket	"	0.750	35.50	48.75	84.25
Tel. cord 7'-8 conductor	"	0.500	23.75	32.50	56.25
Listen-in amplifier	"	2.000	190	130	320
Listen-in pickup	"	0.500	86.00	32.50	119
Bell supervision module	"	1.000	250	65.00	315
Zone control module	"	1.501	320	97.00	417
Independ. control keypad	"	1.000	210	65.00	275
Independ. zone control	"	2.500	360	160	520
Command center	"	4.520	580	290	870
Control/commun. panel, attack resistant	"	1.501	260	97.00	357
Fire enclosure	"	1.000	170	65.00	235
Serial output module	"	1.000	210	65.00	275
Bell noise filter	"	0.350	15.25	22.75	38.00
Release module	"	1.000	240	65.00	305
Printer/ctr. interface	"	1.751	450	110	560
Battery charger module	"	1.501	350	97.00	447
Cable ribbon	"	0.500	110	32.50	143
50' printer cable	"	0.500	160	32.50	193
Local security printer	"	1.000	1,970	65.00	2,035
Printer paper	"	0.500	100	32.50	133
Inert reader system card reader insert	"	2.500	800	160	960
Magnetic cards	"	0.350	8.44	22.75	31.19
Photo ID cards	"	0.350	11.75	22.75	34.50
Proximity card reader	"	2.500	830	160	990
Decoder	"	2.000	880	130	1,010
Cards	"	0.500	25.25	32.50	57.75
Wiegand, swipe reader interface	"	3.008	920	190	1,110
Card reader	"	3.008	810	190	1,000
Swipe cards	"	0.500	160	32.50	193
Photo cards	"	0.500	190	32.50	223
System command, zone expans. ctr. control	"	4.520	890	290	1,180
Command center	"	2.500	280	160	440
Center	"	2.500	260	160	420
Transformer	"	0.500	33.75	32.50	66.25
Enclosure	"	0.750	86.00	48.75	135
Skirt	"	0.500	61.00	32.50	93.50
Bar code programmer	"	8.000	1,390	520	1,910
Wand assembly	"	4.000	380	260	640
Wand tip	"	0.350	15.25	22.75	38.00
Connector cord	"	0.500	30.50	32.50	63.00
Adapter	"	0.500	51.00	32.50	83.50
Carry case	"	0.350	100	22.75	123
Video - Intro	"	0.500	250	32.50	283
Central station receiver	"	24.242	13,510	1,570	15,080
Spares pkg.	"	16.000	5,070	1,040	6,110
Printer paper	"	0.500	40.50	32.50	73.00
Main processing unit	"	12.121	3,380	790	4,170
Terminator card	"	1.751	340	110	450
Power supply card	"	2.000	1,010	130	1,140
Receiver line card	"	2.000	1,010	130	1,140
Telco terminator card	"	1.501	170	97.00	267

COMMUNICATIONS

16720.50 SECURITY SYSTEMS	UNIT	HOURS	MAT.	INST.	TOTAL
Printer	EA.	2.500	2,030	160	2,190
Printer terminator card	"	1.501	340	97.00	437
Vital information processor software, 4000	"	24.242	55,750	1,570	57,320
8000 acct.	"	33.333	83,630	2,160	85,790
11,000 acct.	"	50.000	111,430	3,240	114,670
33,000 acct.	"	72.727	167,260	4,710	171,970
Autodial	"	2.000	840	130	970
Ready key readers, low profile reader	"	4.000	670	260	930
Vandal resistant reader	"	5.000	750	320	1,070
P.I.N. reader	"	8.000	1,180	520	1,700
Door controller, multi function, four door	"	24.242	4,760	1,570	6,330
Two door	"	16.000	3,380	1,040	4,420
Enclosure	"	1.000	84.00	65.00	149
Networked systems, M.S. Dos P.C. software	"	18.182	2,050	1,180	3,230
Remote	"	18.182	2,050	1,180	3,230
Windows P.C. software upgrade	"	12.121	680	790	1,470
Central network, single site controller, MS	"	40.000	9,590	2,590	12,180
Multi site	"	61.538	18,900	3,990	22,890
Single, windows	"	40.000	9,620	2,590	12,210
Ancillary products, Wiegand interface	"	2.000	230	130	360
Alarm module	"	1.751	890	110	1,000
Reader mounting bracket	"	1.000	45.50	65.00	111
16730.20 CLOCK SYSTEMS					
Clock systems					
Single face	EA.	0.800	130	52.00	182
Double face	"	0.800	360	52.00	412
Skeleton	"	2.759	280	180	460
Master	"	5.000	2,860	320	3,180
Signal generator	"	4.000	2,480	260	2,740
Elapsed time indicator	"	0.800	490	52.00	542
Controller	"	0.533	110	34.50	145
Clock and speaker	"	1.096	210	71.00	281
Bell					
Standard	EA.	0.533	77.00	34.50	112
Weatherproof	"	0.800	94.00	52.00	146
Horn					
Standard	EA.	0.727	49.50	47.00	96.50
Weatherproof	"	0.952	61.00	62.00	123
Chime	"	0.533	55.00	34.50	89.50
Buzzer	"	0.533	19.75	34.50	54.25
Flasher	"	0.615	77.00	39.75	117
Control Board	"	3.478	320	230	550
Program unit	"	5.000	350	320	670
Block back box	"	0.500	19.75	32.50	52.25
Double clock back box	"	0.667	44.00	43.25	87.25
Wire guard	"	0.200	13.25	13.00	26.25
16740.10 TELEPHONE SYSTEMS					
Communication cable					
25 pair	L.F.	0.026	0.93	1.67	2.60
100 pair	"	0.029	4.45	1.85	6.30
150 pair	"	0.033	6.76	2.16	8.92
200 pair	"	0.040	9.13	2.59	11.72
300 pair	"	0.042	11.50	2.72	14.22

COMMUNICATIONS

16740.10 TELEPHONE SYSTEMS, Cont'd...	UNIT	HOURS	MAT.	INST.	TOTAL
400 pair	L.F.	0.044	15.75	2.88	18.63
Cable tap in manhole or junction box					
25 pair cable	EA.	3.810	6.49	250	256
50 pair cable	"	7.547	13.25	490	503
75 pair cable	"	11.268	19.75	730	750
100 pair cable	"	15.094	26.25	980	1,006
150 pair cable	"	22.222	39.25	1,440	1,479
200 pair cable	"	29.630	52.00	1,920	1,972
300 pair cable	"	44.444	79.00	2,880	2,959
400 pair cable	"	61.538	110	3,990	4,100
Cable terminations, manhole or junction box					
25 pair cable	EA.	3.756	6.49	240	246
50 pair cable	"	7.477	13.25	480	493
100 pair cable	"	15.094	26.25	980	1,006
150 pair cable	"	22.222	39.25	1,440	1,479
200 pair cable	"	29.630	52.00	1,920	1,972
300 pair cable	"	44.444	79.00	2,880	2,959
400 pair cable	"	61.538	81.00	3,990	4,071
Telephones, standard					
1 button	EA.	2.963	120	190	310
2 button	"	3.478	180	230	410
6 button	"	5.333	260	350	610
12 button	"	7.619	670	490	1,160
18 button	"	8.889	700	580	1,280
Hazardous area					
Desk	EA.	7.273	2,010	470	2,480
Wall	"	5.000	930	320	1,250
Accessories					
Standard ground	EA.	1.600	33.25	100	133
Push button	"	1.600	34.00	100	134
Buzzer	"	1.600	35.50	100	136
Interface device	"	0.800	18.75	52.00	70.75
Long cord	"	0.800	20.00	52.00	72.00
Interior jack	"	0.400	12.25	26.00	38.25
Exterior jack	"	0.615	24.25	39.75	64.00
Hazardous area					
Selector switch	EA.	3.200	200	210	410
Bell	"	3.200	300	210	510
Horn	"	4.211	450	270	720
Horn relay	"	3.077	370	200	570
16740.30 CALL SYSTEMS					
Call systems, single bed station	EA.	0.533	200	34.50	235
Double bed station	"	0.727	360	47.00	407
Call-in cord	"	0.200	69.00	13.00	82.00
Pull cord	"	0.200	110	13.00	123
Pillow speaker	"	0.276	220	17.75	238
Dome light	"	0.533	58.00	34.50	92.50
Zone light	"	0.533	51.00	34.50	85.50
Stake station	"	0.615	150	39.75	190
Duty station	"	0.500	200	32.50	233
Utility station	"	0.615	150	39.75	190
Nurses station	"	0.533	160	34.50	195
Surgical station	"	0.727	370	47.00	417

COMMUNICATIONS

16740.30 CALL SYSTEMS, Cont'd...	UNIT	HOURS	MAT.	INST.	TOTAL
Master station	EA.	2.500	3,920	160	4,080
Control station	"	8.000	1,380	520	1,900
Annunciator	"	2.000	520	130	650
Power supply	"	1.538	390	100	490
Speakers	"	0.800	58.00	52.00	110
Foot switch	"	0.296	69.00	19.25	88.25
Code blue systems					
Bed station	EA.	0.727	370	47.00	417
Dome light	"	0.667	58.00	43.25	101
Zone light	"	0.727	100	47.00	147
Pull cord	"	0.250	110	16.25	126
Nurses station	"	0.533	160	34.50	195
Annunciator	"	2.000	520	130	650
Power supply	"	1.455	390	94.00	484
Nurse station indicator, alarm annunciators,					
4 circuit	EA.	4.000	3,340	260	3,600
6 circuit	"	8.000	3,920	520	4,440
12 circuit	"	12.012	6,670	780	7,450
Desktop					
4 circuit	EA.	3.478	3,690	230	3,920
6 circuit	"	3.478	4,600	230	4,830
12 circuit	"	5.000	7,130	320	7,450
16750.20 SIGNALING SYSTEMS					
Signaling systems					
4" bell	EA.	0.602	120	39.00	159
6" bell	"	0.650	140	42.25	182
10" bell	"	0.748	160	48.50	209
Buzzer					
Size 0	EA.	0.444	32.00	28.75	60.75
Size 1	"	0.444	34.00	28.75	62.75
Size 2	"	0.500	36.25	32.50	68.75
Size 3	"	0.533	38.50	34.50	73.00
Horn	"	0.615	110	39.75	150
Chime	"	0.533	160	34.50	195
Push button					
Standard	EA.	0.400	36.25	26.00	62.25
Weatherproof	"	0.500	55.00	32.50	87.50
Door opener					
Mortise	EA.	0.500	38.50	32.50	71.00
Rim	"	0.400	54.00	26.00	80.00
Transformer	"	0.444	19.25	28.75	48.00
Contractor grade doorbell chime kit					
Chime	EA.	1.000	36.75	65.00	102
Doorbutton	"	0.320	5.11	20.75	25.86
Transformer	"	0.500	16.25	32.50	48.75
16770.30 SOUND SYSTEMS					
Power amplifiers	EA.	3.478	1,060	230	1,290
Pre-amplifiers	"	2.759	840	180	1,020
Tuner	"	1.455	540	94.00	634
Horn					
Equalizer	EA.	1.600	1,360	100	1,460
Mixer	"	2.222	560	140	700
Tape recorder	"	1.860	1,780	120	1,900

COMMUNICATIONS

16770.30 SOUND SYSTEMS, Cont'd...	UNIT	HOURS	MAT.	INST.	TOTAL
Microphone	EA.	1.000	150	65.00	215
Cassette Player	"	2.162	900	140	1,040
Record player	"	1.905	79.00	120	199
Equipment rack	"	1.290	100	84.00	184
Speaker					
Wall	EA.	4.000	560	260	820
Paging	"	0.800	200	52.00	252
Column	"	0.533	300	34.50	335
Single	"	0.615	68.00	39.75	108
Double	"	4.444	210	290	500
Volume control	"	0.533	68.00	34.50	103
Plug-in	"	0.800	210	52.00	262
Desk	"	0.400	160	26.00	186
Outlet	"	0.400	33.75	26.00	59.75
Stand	"	0.296	68.00	19.25	87.25
Console	"	8.000	15,920	520	16,440
Power supply	"	1.290	300	84.00	384
16780.10 ANTENNAS AND TOWERS					
Guy cable, alumaweld					
1x3, 7/32"	L.F.	0.050	0.45	3.24	3.69
1x3, 1/4"	"	0.050	0.52	3.24	3.76
1x3, 25/64"	"	0.059	0.74	3.84	4.58
1x19, 1/2"	"	0.070	1.87	4.50	6.37
1x7, 35/64"	"	0.080	2.14	5.18	7.32
1x19, 13/16"	"	0.100	2.31	6.48	8.79
Preformed alumaweld end grip					
1/4" cable	EA.	0.100	3.41	6.48	9.89
3/8" cable	"	0.100	4.51	6.48	10.99
1/2" cable	"	0.145	5.66	9.42	15.08
9/16" cable	"	0.200	7.04	13.00	20.04
5/8" cable	"	0.250	8.63	16.25	24.88
Fiberglass guy rod, white epoxy coated					
1/4" dia.	L.F.	0.145	2.31	9.42	11.73
3/8" dia	"	0.145	3.46	9.42	12.88
1/2" dia	"	0.200	4.62	13.00	17.62
5/8" dia	"	0.250	5.77	16.25	22.02
Preformed glass grip end grip, guy rod					
1/4" dia.	EA.	0.145	12.75	9.42	22.17
3/8" dia.	"	0.200	14.75	13.00	27.75
1/2" dia.	"	0.250	18.00	16.25	34.25
5/8" dia.	"	0.250	20.25	16.25	36.50
Spelter socket end grip, 1/4" dia. guy rod					
Standard strength	EA.	0.500	37.75	32.50	70.25
High performance	"	0.500	46.50	32.50	79.00
3/8" dia. guy rod					
Standard strength	EA.	0.348	36.75	22.50	59.25
High performance	"	0.500	46.50	32.50	79.00
Timber pole, Douglas Fir					
80-85 ft	EA.	19.512	3,530	1,260	4,790
90-95 ft	"	22.222	4,420	1,440	5,860
Southern yellow pine					
35-45 ft	EA.	10.959	2,110	710	2,820
50-55 ft	"	14.035	2,950	910	3,860

COMMUNICATIONS

16780.50 TELEVISION SYSTEMS	UNIT	HOURS	MAT.	INST.	TOTAL
TV outlet, self terminating, w/cover plate	EA.	0.308	5.97	20.00	25.97
Thru splitter	"	1.600	13.00	100	113
End of line	"	1.333	10.75	86.00	96.75
In line splitter multitap					
4 way	EA.	1.818	21.75	120	142
2 way	"	1.702	16.25	110	126
Equipment cabinet	"	1.600	54.00	100	154
Antenna					
Broad band uhf	EA.	3.478	110	230	340
Lightning arrester	"	0.727	33.00	47.00	80.00
TV cable	L.F.	0.005	0.49	0.32	0.81
Coaxial cable rg	"	0.005	0.33	0.32	0.65
Cable drill, with replacement tip	EA.	0.500	5.44	32.50	37.94
Cable blocks for in-line taps	"	0.727	10.75	47.00	57.75
In-line taps ptu-series 36 tv system	"	1.143	13.00	74.00	87.00
Control receptacles	"	0.449	8.52	29.00	37.52
Coupler	"	2.424	16.25	160	176
Head end equipment	"	6.667	2,050	430	2,480
TV camera	"	1.667	1,110	110	1,220
TV power bracket	"	0.800	99.00	52.00	151
TV monitor	"	1.455	850	94.00	944
Video recorder	"	2.105	1,650	140	1,790
Console	"	8.502	3,420	550	3,970
Selector switch	"	1.379	530	89.00	619
TV controller	"	1.404	250	91.00	341
16780.60 CLOSED CIRCUIT TV SYSTEMS					
Camera color, minimum	EA.	1.600	280	100	380
Maximum	"	1.600	2,000	100	2,100
Black and white, minimum	"	1.600	220	100	320
Maximum	"	1.600	1,400	100	1,500
Lens, auto tris, minimum	"	1.000	910	65.00	975
Maximum	"	1.000	1,380	65.00	1,445
Zoom, minimum	"	1.000	2,640	65.00	2,705
Maximum	"	1.000	9,650	65.00	9,715
Fixed, minimum	"	1.000	48.75	65.00	114
Maximum	"	1.000	100	65.00	165
Pinhole, minimum	"	1.000	550	65.00	615
Maximum	"	1.000	1,060	65.00	1,125
Low light level, minimum	"	1.000	570	65.00	635
Maximum	"	1.000	1,390	65.00	1,455
Enclosure indoor, minimum	"	1.501	240	97.00	337
Maximum	"	3.509	3,580	230	3,810
Outdoor, minimum	"	2.500	410	160	570
Maximum	"	5.517	1,870	360	2,230
Wiper kit	"	0.750	28.50	48.75	77.25
Lube kit	"	0.500	110	32.50	143
O-Ring kit	"	1.000	30.00	65.00	95.00
Recharge kit	"	2.500	760	160	920
Automatic washer/wiper	"	3.509	890	230	1,120
Mount, minimum	"	1.000	33.00	65.00	98.00
Maximum	"	8.000	550	520	1,070
Defroster, minimum	"	1.000	67.00	65.00	132
Maximum	"	2.000	360	130	490

COMMUNICATIONS

16780.60 CLOSED CIRCUIT TV SYSTEMS, Cont'd...	UNIT	HOURS	MAT.	INST.	TOTAL
Alarm thermostat kit	EA.	1.501	580	97.00	677
Shroud, minimum	"	0.750	55.00	48.75	104
Maximum	"	1.501	220	97.00	317
Heater, maximum	"	1.751	340	110	450
Air funnel	"	1.501	400	97.00	497
Visor, minimum	"	0.500	66.00	32.50	98.50
Maximum	"	0.500	130	32.50	163
Camera enclosure dome indoor, minimum	"	1.751	240	110	350
Maximum	"	3.756	1,380	240	1,620
Outdoor, minimum	"	2.759	490	180	670
Maximum	"	6.504	1,180	420	1,600
Pan/tilt indoor, minimum	"	4.520	420	290	710
Maximum	"	7.767	1,660	500	2,160
Outdoor, minimum	"	5.000	420	320	740
Maximum	"	9.756	2,790	630	3,420
Insulation, minimum	"	1.000	55.00	65.00	120
Maximum	"	2.500	530	160	690
Dome tamper switch	"	0.500	55.00	32.50	87.50
Blower, minimum	"	1.000	120	65.00	185
Maximum	"	1.501	210	97.00	307
Heater, minimum	"	0.500	85.00	32.50	118
Ceiling adapter	"	0.500	53.00	32.50	85.50
Lock, minimum	"	0.350	21.50	22.75	44.25
Maximum	"	0.750	130	48.75	179
Monitor color, minimum	"	1.501	290	97.00	387
Maximum	"	2.000	2,310	130	2,440
Black and white, minimum	"	1.501	370	97.00	467
Maximum	"	2.000	550	130	680
Rack, minimum	"	1.000	190	65.00	255
Maximum	"	1.751	450	110	560
Time lapse recorder, minimum	"	1.000	290	65.00	355
Maximum	"	4.000	2,840	260	3,100
Scanner, minimum	"	1.000	440	65.00	505
Maximum	"	1.501	1,270	97.00	1,367
Camera switcher, minimum	"	1.501	500	97.00	597
Maximum	"	4.520	6,400	290	6,690
Control, minimum	"	0.750	150	48.75	199
Maximum	"	4.520	5,990	290	6,280
Seq. processor	"	2.500	330	160	490
Screen splitter	"	1.501	740	97.00	837
Wireless video, minimum	"	6.504	1,290	420	1,710
Maximum	"	12.121	5,730	790	6,520
Control equalizing amp., minimum	"	1.751	510	110	620
Maximum	"	2.500	570	160	730
Relay box	"	1.501	950	97.00	1,047
Generator	"	2.000	830	130	960
Transformer	"	1.000	58.00	65.00	123
Camera power supply	"	1.501	330	97.00	427
Motion detector	"	2.000	120	130	250
Control test board	"	0.750	210	48.75	259
Receiver, minimum	"	1.000	420	65.00	485
Maximum	"	2.759	1,610	180	1,790
Keyboard control, minimum	"	2.000	540	130	670

COMMUNICATIONS

16780.60 CLOSED CIRCUIT TV SYSTEMS, Cont'd...	UNIT	HOURS	MAT.	INST.	TOTAL
Maximum	EA.	3.008	1,580	190	1,770
Matrix CPU, minimum	"	2.000	1,990	130	2,120
Maximum	"	8.000	7,100	520	7,620
Relay interface, minimum	"	1.000	950	65.00	1,015
Maximum	"	2.500	1,810	160	1,970
Alarm interface, minimum	"	1.000	410	65.00	475
Maximum	"	2.000	1,100	130	1,230
Video input card, minimum	"	1.000	290	65.00	355
Maximum	"	2.500	2,320	160	2,480
Transmitter/CPU, minimum	"	8.000	2,650	520	3,170
Maximum	"	12.121	5,630	790	6,420
Output card	"	1.000	310	65.00	375
Input card	"	1.000	390	65.00	455
Interface card	"	1.000	460	65.00	525
Auto/random scan	"	0.500	230	32.50	263
Pretested cable, minimum	"	0.500	110	32.50	143
Maximum	"	0.750	260	48.75	309
Wiring harness	"	0.350	8.29	22.75	31.04

RESISTANCE HEATING

16850.10 ELECTRIC HEATING	UNIT	HOURS	MAT.	INST.	TOTAL
Baseboard heater					
2', 375w	EA.	1.000	41.75	65.00	107
3', 500w	"	1.000	49.50	65.00	115
4', 750w	"	1.143	55.00	74.00	129
5', 935w	"	1.333	78.00	86.00	164
6', 1125w	"	1.600	92.00	100	192
7', 1310w	"	1.818	100	120	220
8', 1500w	"	2.000	120	130	250
9', 1680w	"	2.222	130	140	270
10', 1875w	"	2.286	180	150	330
Unit heater, wall mounted					
750w	EA.	1.600	160	100	260
1500w	"	1.667	220	110	330
2000w	"	1.739	230	110	340
2500w	"	1.818	240	120	360
3000w	"	2.000	280	130	410
4000w	"	2.286	320	150	470
Thermostat					
Integral	EA.	0.500	37.50	32.50	70.00
Line voltage	"	0.500	38.50	32.50	71.00
Electric heater connection	"	0.250	1.65	16.25	17.90
Fittings					
Inside corner	EA.	0.400	24.25	26.00	50.25
Outside corner	"	0.400	26.50	26.00	52.50
Receptacle section	"	0.400	27.50	26.00	53.50
Blank section	"	0.400	34.00	26.00	60.00
Infrared heaters					
600w	EA.	1.000	150	65.00	215
2000w	"	1.194	160	77.00	237
3000w	"	2.000	240	130	370
4000w	"	2.500	340	160	500
Controller	"	0.667	65.00	43.25	108

RESISTANCE HEATING

16850.10 ELECTRIC HEATING, Cont'd...	UNIT	HOURS	MAT.	INST.	TOTAL
Wall bracket	EA.	0.727	130	47.00	177
Radiant ceiling heater panels					
500w	EA.	1.000	290	65.00	355
750w	"	1.000	320	65.00	385
Unit heaters, suspended, single phase					
3.0 kw	EA.	2.759	470	180	650
5.0 kw	"	2.759	490	180	670
7.5 kw	"	3.200	790	210	1,000
10.0 kw	"	3.810	850	250	1,100
Three phase					
5 kw	EA.	2.759	480	180	660
7.5 kw	"	3.200	630	210	840
10 kw	"	3.810	680	250	930
15 kw	"	4.211	1,150	270	1,420
20 kw	"	5.333	1,540	350	1,890
25 kw	"	6.400	1,850	410	2,260
30 kw	"	8.000	2,160	520	2,680
35 kw	"	8.000	2,620	520	3,140
Unit heater thermostat	"	0.533	49.75	34.50	84.25
Mounting bracket	"	0.727	51.00	47.00	98.00
Relay	"	0.615	65.00	39.75	105
Duct heaters, three phase					
10 kw	EA.	3.810	930	250	1,180
15 kw	"	3.810	1,110	250	1,360
17.5 kw	"	4.000	1,170	260	1,430
20 kw	"	6.154	1,250	400	1,650

CONTROLS

16910.40 CONTROL CABLE	UNIT	HOURS	MAT.	INST.	TOTAL
Control cable, 600v, #14 THWN, PVC jacket					
2 wire	L.F.	0.008	0.31	0.51	0.82
4 wire	"	0.010	0.53	0.64	1.17
6 wire	"	0.131	0.93	8.49	9.42
8 wire	"	0.145	1.15	9.42	10.57
10 wire	"	0.160	1.32	10.25	11.57
12 wire	"	0.182	1.59	11.75	13.34
14 wire	"	0.211	1.87	13.75	15.62
16 wire	"	0.222	2.03	14.50	16.53
18 wire	"	0.242	2.20	15.75	17.95
20 wire	"	0.250	2.58	16.25	18.83
22 wire	"	0.286	2.58	18.50	21.08
Audio cables, shielded, #24 gauge					
3 conductor	L.F.	0.004	0.26	0.25	0.51
4 conductor	"	0.006	0.31	0.38	0.69
5 conductor	"	0.007	0.37	0.45	0.82
6 conductor	"	0.009	0.41	0.58	0.99
7 conductor	"	0.011	0.47	0.71	1.18
8 conductor	"	0.012	0.52	0.77	1.29
9 conductor	"	0.014	0.55	0.90	1.45
10 conductor	"	0.015	0.61	0.96	1.57
15 conductor	"	0.018	1.05	1.16	2.21
20 conductor	"	0.023	1.40	1.48	2.88
25 conductor	"	0.027	1.71	1.75	3.46

CONTROLS

16910.40 CONTROL CABLE, Cont'd...	UNIT	HOURS	MAT.	INST.	TOTAL
30 conductor	L.F.	0.030	2.11	1.95	4.06
40 conductor	"	0.036	2.72	2.35	5.07
50 conductor	"	0.042	3.43	2.72	6.15
#22 gauge					
3 conductor	L.F.	0.004	0.38	0.25	0.63
4 conductor	"	0.006	0.49	0.38	0.87
#20 gauge					
3 conductor	L.F.	0.004	0.28	0.25	0.53
10 conductor	"	0.015	0.92	0.96	1.88
15 conductor	"	0.018	1.18	1.16	2.34
#18 gauge					
3 conductor	L.F.	0.004	0.37	0.25	0.62
4 conductor	"	0.006	0.55	0.38	0.93
Microphone cables, #24 gauge					
2 conductor	L.F.	0.004	0.37	0.25	0.62
3 conductor	"	0.005	0.41	0.32	0.73
#20 gauge					
1 conductor	L.F.	0.004	0.40	0.25	0.65
2 conductor	"	0.004	0.63	0.25	0.88
2 conductor	"	0.004	0.72	0.25	0.97
3 conductor	"	0.006	0.88	0.38	1.26
4 conductor	"	0.007	1.23	0.45	1.68
5 conductor	"	0.009	1.49	0.58	2.07
7 conductor	"	0.011	1.67	0.71	2.38
8 conductor	"	0.012	1.84	0.77	2.61
Computer cables shielded, #24 gauge					
1 pair	L.F.	0.004	0.24	0.25	0.49
2 pair	"	0.004	0.33	0.25	0.58
3 pair	"	0.006	0.40	0.38	0.78
4 pair	"	0.007	0.47	0.45	0.92
5 pair	"	0.009	0.61	0.58	1.19
6 pair	"	0.011	0.72	0.71	1.43
7 pair	"	0.012	0.75	0.77	1.52
8 pair	"	0.014	0.88	0.90	1.78
50 pair	"	0.039	5.06	2.52	7.58
Coaxial cables					
RG 6/u	L.F.	0.006	0.37	0.38	0.75
RG 6a/u	"	0.006	0.58	0.38	0.96
RG 8/u	"	0.006	0.67	0.38	1.05
RG 8a/u	"	0.006	0.81	0.38	1.19
RG 9/u	"	0.006	1.45	0.38	1.83
RG 11/u	"	0.006	1.80	0.38	2.18
RG 58/u	"	0.006	1.98	0.38	2.36
RG 59/u	"	0.006	2.15	0.38	2.53
RG 62/u	"	0.006	2.37	0.38	2.75
RG 174/u	"	0.006	2.55	0.38	2.93
RG 213/u	"	0.006	2.72	0.38	3.10
MATV and CCTV camera cables					
1 conductor	L.F.	0.004	0.37	0.25	0.62
2 conductor	"	0.005	0.47	0.32	0.79
4 conductor	"	0.006	1.01	0.38	1.39
7 conductor	"	0.009	1.40	0.58	1.98
12 conductor	"	0.015	2.15	0.96	3.11

CONTROLS

16910.40 CONTROL CABLE, Cont'd...	UNIT	HOURS	MAT.	INST.	TOTAL
13 conductor	L.F.	0.016	2.33	1.03	3.36
14 conductor	"	0.018	2.37	1.16	3.53
28 conductor	"	0.027	5.67	1.75	7.42
Fire alarm cables, #22 gauge					
6 conductor	L.F.	0.010	0.92	0.64	1.56
9 conductor	"	0.015	1.18	0.96	2.14
12 conductor	"	0.016	1.36	1.03	2.39
#18 gauge					
2 conductor	L.F.	0.005	0.92	0.32	1.24
4 conductor	"	0.007	1.18	0.45	1.63
#16 gauge					
2 conductor	L.F.	0.007	0.92	0.45	1.37
4 conductor	"	0.008	1.27	0.51	1.78
#14 gauge					
2 conductor	L.F.	0.008	1.36	0.51	1.87
#12 gauge					
2 conductor	L.F.	0.010	1.67	0.64	2.31
Plastic jacketed thermostat cable					
2 conductor	L.F.	0.004	0.12	0.25	0.37
3 conductor	"	0.005	0.16	0.32	0.48
4 conductor	"	0.006	0.22	0.38	0.60
5 conductor	"	0.008	0.27	0.51	0.78
6 conductor	"	0.009	0.33	0.58	0.91
7 conductor	"	0.012	0.36	0.77	1.13
8 conductor	"	0.013	0.52	0.84	1.36

Supporting Construction Reference Data

This section contains information, graphics, and schematics on various aspects of projects. The intent is to provide the user with a better understanding of unfamiliar areas in order to be able to estimate better. This information includes actual code data for some areas and also selected explanations of common electrical materials, methods and practices.

NEC® Handbook Reference Pages

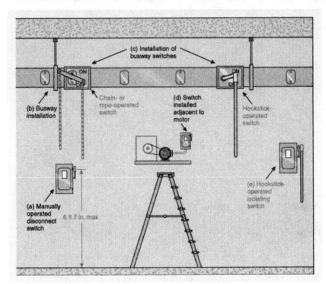

Exhibit 100.1 Example of busway and of switches considered accessible even if located above 6 ft 7 in.

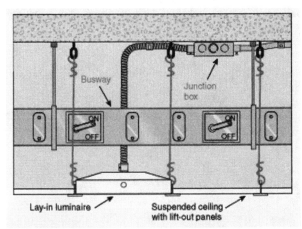

Exhibit 100.2 Example of busway and junction boxes considered accessible even if located behind hung ceilings having lift-out panels.

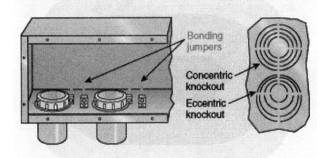

Exhibit 100.3 Bonding jumpers installed around concentric or eccentric knockouts.

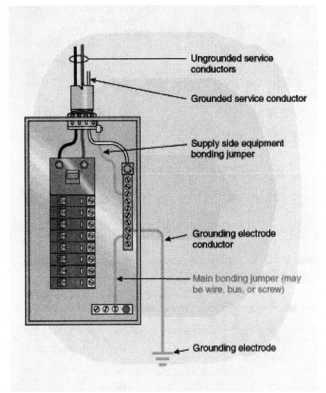

Exhibit 100.4 A main bonding jumper installed at the service between the grounded service conductor and the equipment grounding conductor.

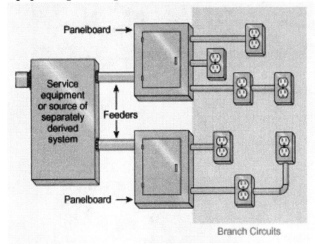

Exhibit 100.6 Feeder (circuits) and branch circuits.

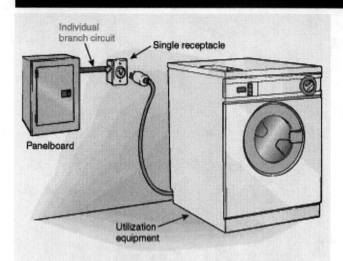

Exhibit 100.7 An individual branch circuit, which supplies only one utilization equipment via a single receptacle.

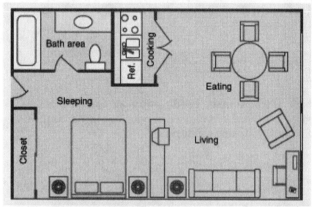

Exhibit 100.8 Example of motel or hotel room considered to be a dwelling unit.

Exhibit 100.11 Receptacles.

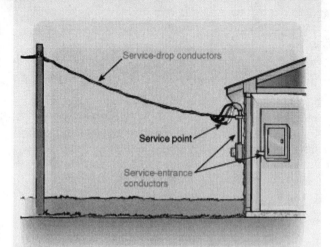

Exhibit 100.13 Overhead system showing a service drop from a utility pole to attachment on a house and service-entrance conductors from point of attachment (spliced to service-drop conductors), down the side of the house, through the meter socket, and terminating in the service equipment.

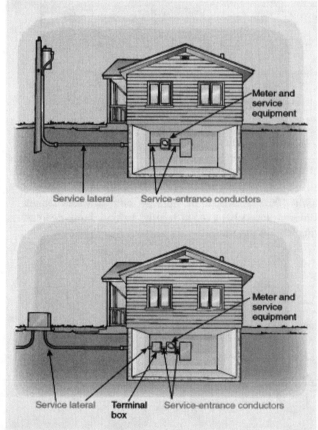

Exhibit 100.14 Underground systems showing service laterals run from a pole and from a transformer.

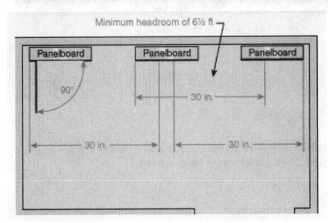

Exhibit 110.12 The 30 in. wide front working space, which is not required to be directly centered on the electrical equipment if space is sufficient for safe operation and maintenance of such equipment.

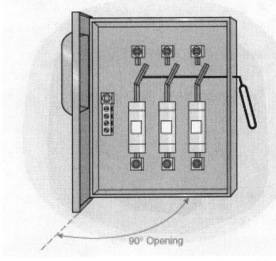

Exhibit 110.13 Illustration of requirement that working space must be sufficient to allow a full 90 degree opening of equipment doors in order to ensure a safe working approach.

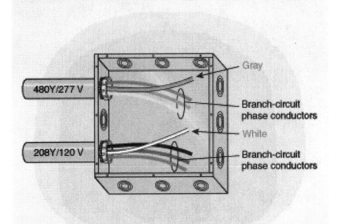

Exhibit 200.2 Grounded conductors of different systems in the same enclosure. The grounded conductors of the different systems are identified by color through the use of white and gray colored insulation, one of the methods specified by 200.6(D).

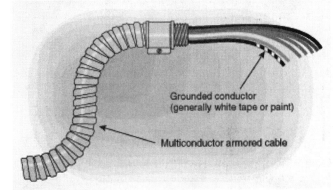

Exhibit 200.3 Field-applied identification to the conductor of a multiconductor armored cable that will be used as the grounded conductor as permitted by 200.6(E), Exception No. 1.

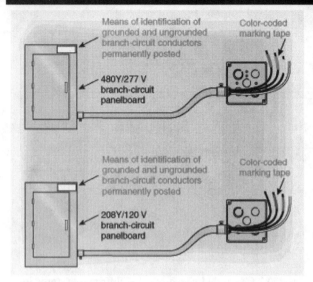

Exhibit 210.3 Examples of accessible (ungrounded) phase conductors identified by marking tape.

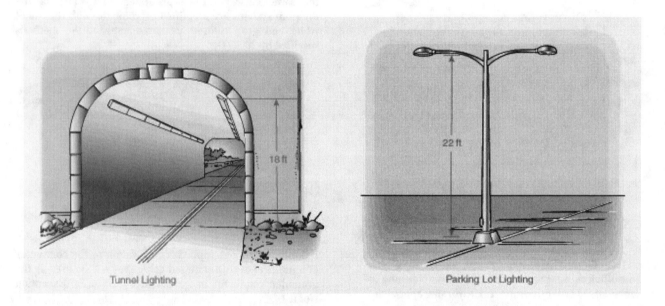

Tunnel Lighting

Parking Lot Lighting

Exhibit 210.5 Minimum mounting heights for tunnel and parking lot lighting as required by 210.6(D)(1) for circuits exceeding 277 volts to ground and not exceeding 600 volts between conductors supplying auxiliary equipment of electric-discharge lampholders.

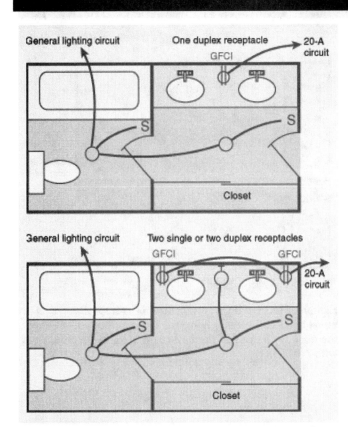

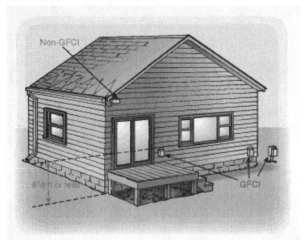

Exhibit 210.9 GFCI-protected receptacles in bathrooms in accordance with 210.8(A)(1).

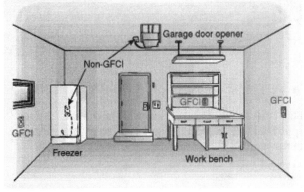

Exhibit 210.10 Examples of receptacles in a garage that are required by 210.8(A)(2) to have GFCI protection. Some receptacles are exempt because they are not readily accessible or are for an appliance that occupies dedicated space.

Exhibit 210.11 A dwelling unit with three receptacles that are required by 210.8(A)(3) to have GFCI protection and one that is exempt because it supplies a roof heating tape and is covered by the requirement of 426.28.

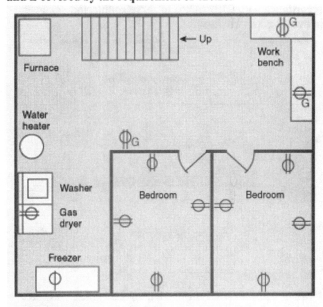

G = GFCI protection required

Exhibit 210.12 A basement floor plan with GFCI-protected receptacles in the work area, in accordance with 210.8(A)(5), and non-GFCI receptacles elsewhere.

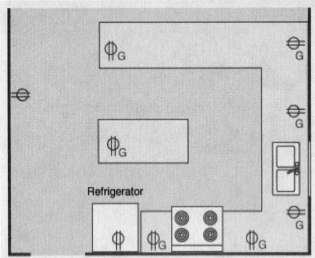

G = GFCI protection required

Exhibit 210.13 GFCI-protected receptacles shown in accordance with 210.8(A)(6) to serve countertop surfaces in dwelling unit kitchens.

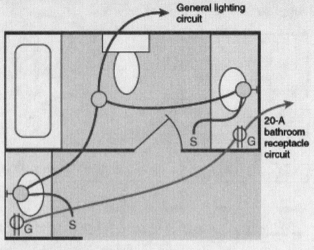

Ǝ = GFCI protection required

Exhibit 210.15 GFCI protection of receptacles in a motel/hotel bathroom where one basin is located outside the door to the rest of the bathroom area, in accordance with 210.8(B)(1).

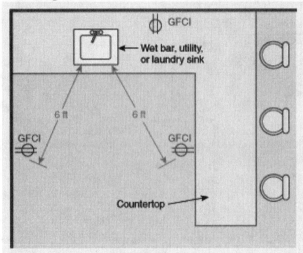

Exhibit 210.14 GFCI protection of receptacles located within 6 ft of a wet bar sink in accordance with 210.8(A)(7).

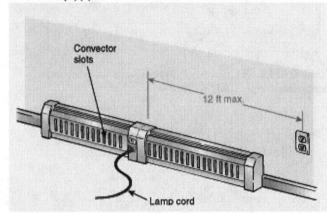

Exhibit 210.23 Permanent electric baseboard heater equipped with a receptacle outlet to meet the spacing requirements of 210.52(A).

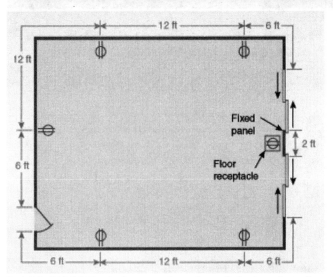

Exhibit 210.24 Typical room plan view of the location of dwelling unit receptacles meeting the requirements of 210.52(A).

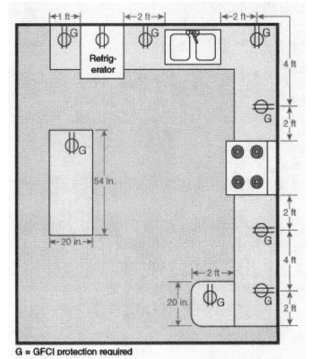

G = GFCI protection required

Exhibit 210.26 Dwelling unit receptacles serving countertop spaces in a kitchen and installed in accordance with 210.52(C).

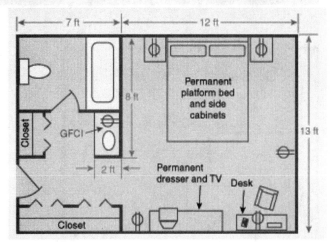

Exhibit 210.28 Floor plan of a hotel guest room with receptacles located as permitted by 210.60(B) with respect to permanent furniture.

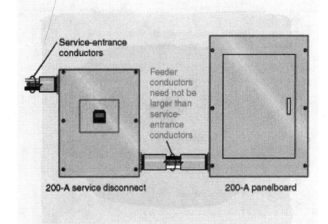

200-A service disconnect   200-A panelboard

Exhibit 215.1 A 3-wire, single-phase dwelling service with an ampacity of 200 amperes for 2/0 AWG copper or 4/0 AWG aluminum conductors used as service-entrance conductors and feeder conductors, according to 215.2(A)(3).

200 VA per linear ft × 10 ft = 2000 VA

Exhibit 220.1 An example of the linear-foot load calculation for branch circuits serving a show window.

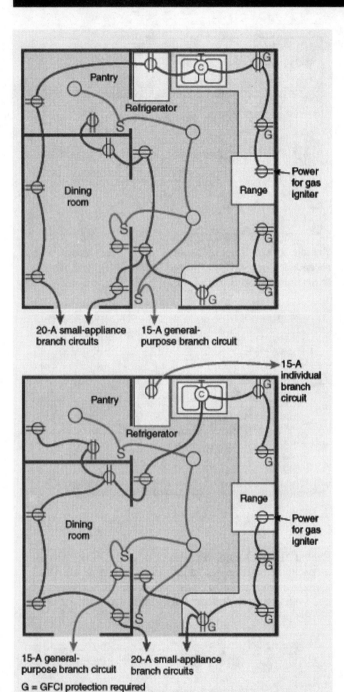

Exhibit 210.25 Small-appliance branch circuits as required by 210.52(B)(1), 210.52(B)(2), and 210.52(B)(3) for all receptacle outlets in the kitchen (including refrigerator), pantry, and dining room.

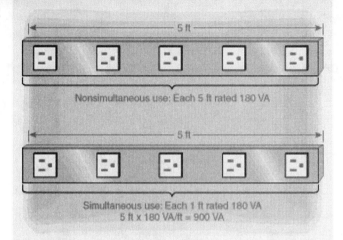

Exhibit 220.2 The requirements of 220.14(H)(1) and (H)(2) as applied to fixed multioutlet assemblies.

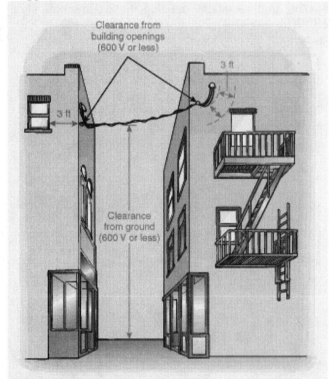

Exhibit 225.5 Examples of the requirements in 225.11, which references 230.52 and 230.54; the requirements in 225.18 for clearances from ground for conductors not over 600 volts; the requirements in 225.19 for clearances from buildings for conductors not over 600 volts; and the requirements in 225.19(D) for clearances from windows, doors, fire escapes, and so on.

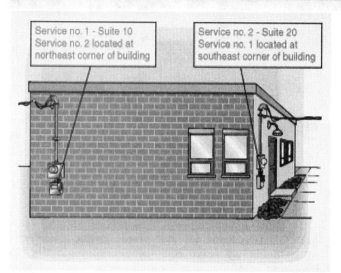

Exhibit 230.1 An example of more than one service installed for one building and permanent plaques or directories denoting all other services and the area served by each.

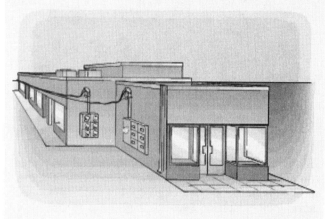

Exhibit 230.2 Two services. Two service drops supplying two services installed at separate locations for a building where there is no available space for service equipment accessible to all occupants. Maximum of six service disconnecting means for each service.

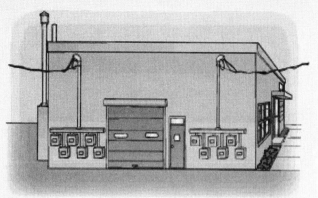

A single-occupancy building with more than one service

Exhibit 230.3 Two services. Two service drops supplying two services installed at separate locations for a building with capacity requirements exceeding 2000 amperes. Maximum of six service disconnecting means for each service.

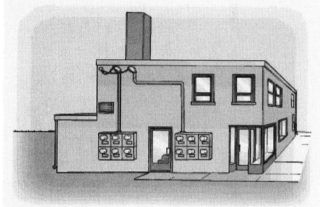

One building with two groups of occupancies

Exhibit 230.4 One service. One service drop supplying two service equipment enclosures installed at separate locations, each with maximum of six service disconnecting means.

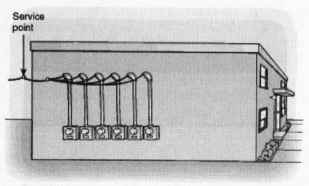

One building with more than one occupancy with separate loads

Exhibit 230.5 One service. One service drop supplying maximum of six service equipment enclosures grouped at one location.

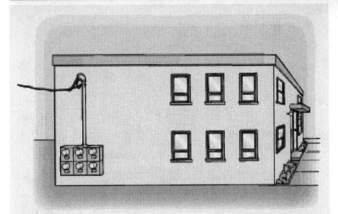

One building with more than one occupancy with separate loads

Exhibit 230.6 One service. One service drop supplying a single service equipment enclosure with maximum of six service disconnecting means grouped at one location. Optional arrangement to that in Exhibit 230.5.

One building with more than one occupancy with separate loads

Exhibit 230.7 One service. One service lateral consisting of six sets of conductors 1/0 AWG or larger, terminating in a single service equipment enclosure with maximum of six service disconnecting means.

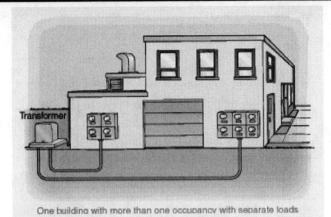

One building with more than one occupancy with separate loads

Exhibit 230.8 Two services. Two service laterals, terminating in two service equipment enclosures installed at separate locations, with each enclosure permitted to have maximum of six service disconnecting means.

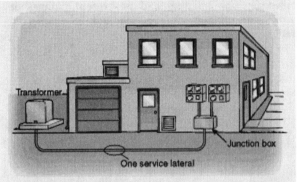

One building with more than one occupancy with separate loads

Exhibit 230.9 One service. One service lateral supplying two sets of service-entrance conductors terminating in two service equipment enclosures grouped in one location. Not more than six service disconnecting means permitted at this service location.

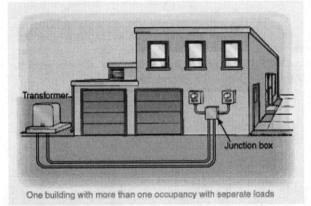

One building with more than one occupancy with separate loads

Exhibit 230.10 One service. Two service laterals, each consisting of conductors 1/0 AWG or larger, supplying two sets of service-entrance conductors terminating in two service equipment enclosures grouped in one location. Not more than six service disconnecting means permitted at this service location.

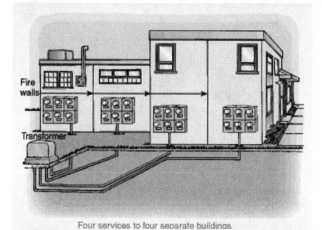

Four services to four separate buildings

Exhibit 230.11 Four services. Four service laterals supplying four service equipment enclosures installed at separate locations on a contiguous structure, each enclosure with a maximum of six service disconnecting means. Note presence of firewalls. See definition of *building* in Article 100.

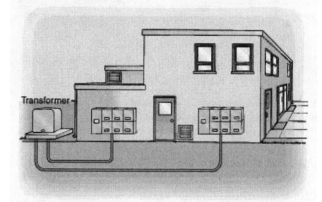

One building with more than one occupancy with separate loads

Exhibit 230.12 Two services. Two service laterals supplying two service equipment enclosures installed at separate locations, each enclosure with a maximum of six service disconnecting means.

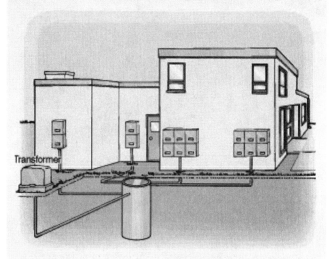

One building with more than one occupancy with separate loads

Exhibit 230.13 One service. One service lateral supplying four service equipment enclosures installed at different locations, with each enclosure permitted to have a maximum of six service disconnecting means.

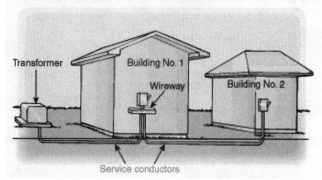

Service conductors

Exhibit 230.14 Service conductors installed in accordance with 230.3 so as not to pass through the interior of Building No. 1 to supply Building No. 2.

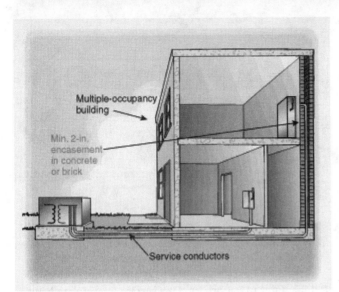

Exhibit 230.15 Service conductors considered outside a building where installed under not less than 2 in. of concrete beneath the building or in a raceway encased by not less than 2 in. of concrete or brick within the building.

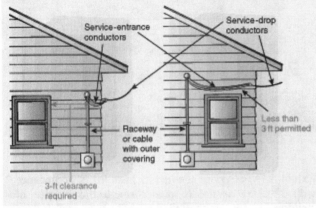

Exhibit 230.16 Required dimensions for service conductors located alongside a window (left) and service conductors above the top level of a window designed to be opened (right).

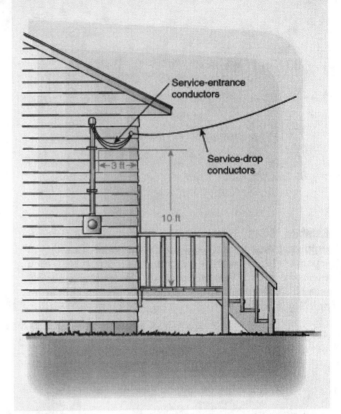

Exhibit 230.17 Required dimensions for service conductors located above a stair landing, according to 230.9(B) and 230.24(B).

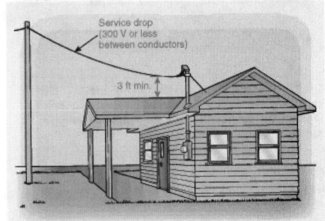

Exhibit 230.19 Reduction in clearance above a roof as permitted by 230.24(A), Exception No. 2.

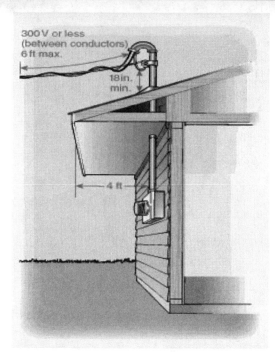

Exhibit 230.20 Reduction in clearance above a roof as permitted by 230.24(A), Exception No. 3.

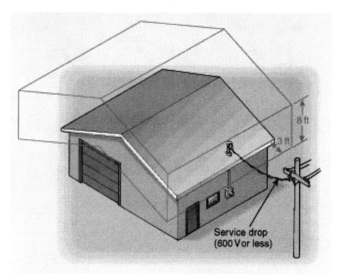

Exhibit 230.21 Clearance of the final span of a service drop, as permitted by 230.24(A), Exception No. 4.

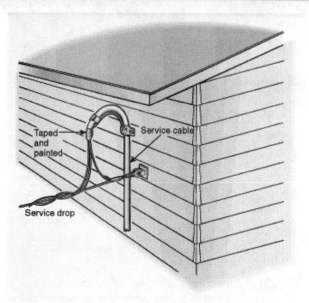

Exhibit 230.25 A service-entrance cable that terminates in a gooseneck without a raintight service head (weatherhead).

Exhibit 230.26 An enclosure for grouping service equipment consisting of six circuit breakers or six fused switches.

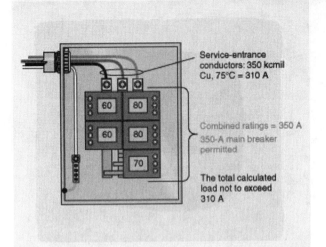

Exhibit 230.27 An example in which the combined ratings of the overcurrent devices are permitted to exceed the ampacity of the service conductors.

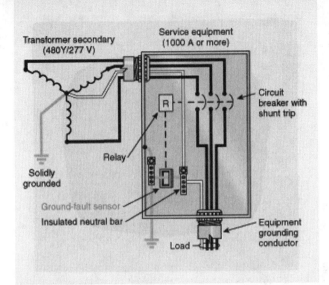

Exhibit 230.29 A ground-fault sensor encircling only the bonding jumper conductor.

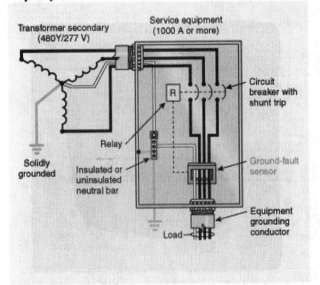

Exhibit 230.28 A ground-fault sensor encircling all circuit conductors, including the neutral.

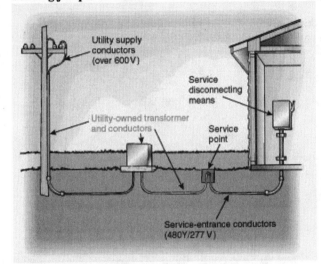

Exhibit 230.30 Service rated over 600 volts supplying a utility-owned transformer.

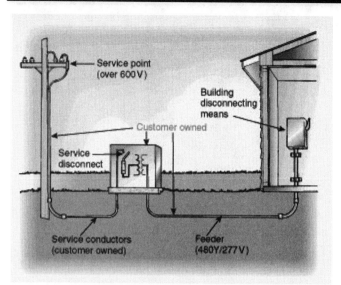

Exhibit 230.31 Service rated over 600 volts supplying a customer-owned transformer.

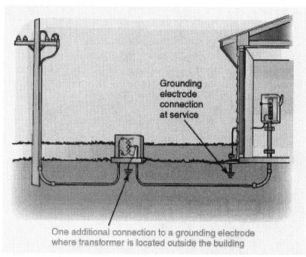

Outdoor Transformer. Where the transformer supplying the service is located outside the building, at least one additional grounding connection shall be made from the grounded service conductor to a grounding electrode, either at the transformer or elsewhere outside the building.

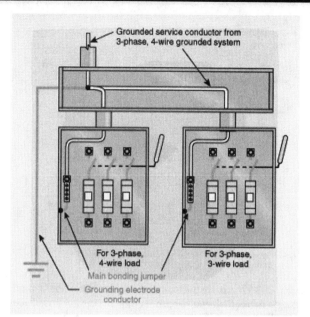

Exhibit 250.10 A grounded system in which the grounded service conductor is brought into a 3-phase, 4-wire service equipment enclosure and to the 3-phase, 3-wire service equipment enclosure, where it is bonded to each service disconnecting means.

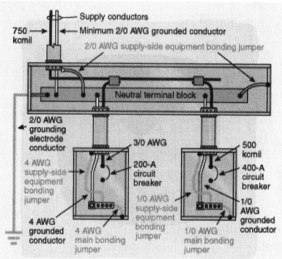

Exhibit 250.12 An example of the bonding requirements for service equipment.

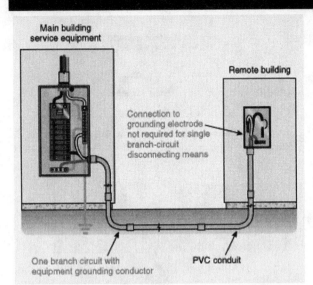

Exhibit 250.17 An installation where a connection from the single branch-circuit disconnecting means enclosure to a grounding electrode system is not required at the remote building because an equipment grounding conductor is installed with the circuit conductors.

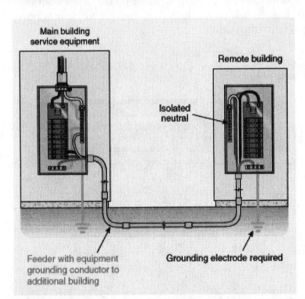

Exhibit 250.18 An installation in which connection between the grounded conductor (neutral) and equipment grounding terminal bar is not allowed. A connection from the equipment grounding terminal bus to the grounding electrode is required.

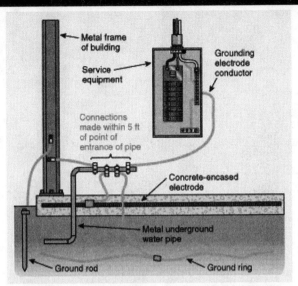

Exhibit 250.21 A grounding electrode system that uses the metal frame of a building, a ground ring, a concrete-encased electrode, a metal underground water pipe, and a ground rod.

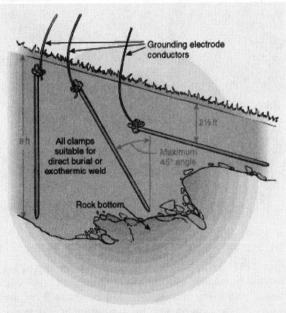

Exhibit 250.23 Installation requirements for rod and pipe electrodes as specified by 250.53(G).

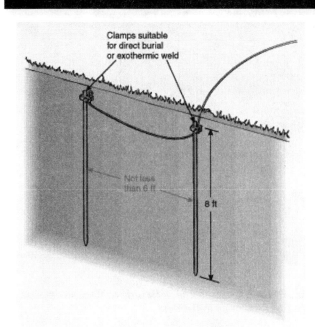

Exhibit 250.24 The 6-ft spacing between electrodes required by 250.53(B) and 250.56.

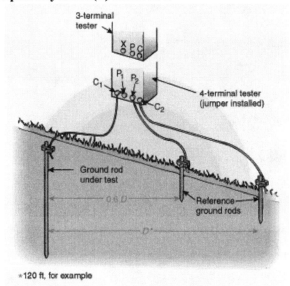

*120 ft, for example

Exhibit 250.25 The resistance to ground of a ground rod being measured by a ground tester.

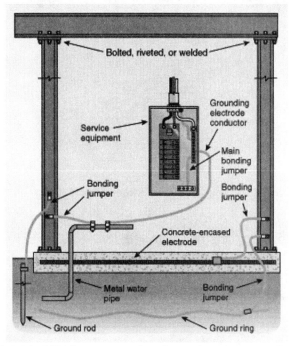

Exhibit 250.27 An example of running the grounding electrode conductor to any convenient electrode available as well as bonding electrodes together to form the grounding electrode system required by 250.50.

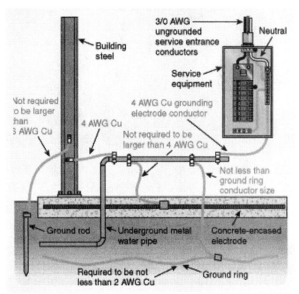

Exhibit 250.29 Grounding electrode conductor and bonding jumpers sized in accordance with 250.66 for a service supplied by 3/0 AWG ungrounded conductors.

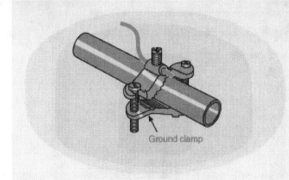

Exhibit 250.30 An application of a listed ground clamp.

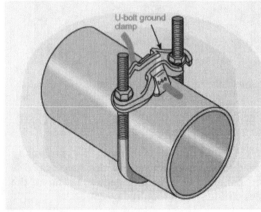

Exhibit 250.31 An application of a listed U-bolt ground clamp.

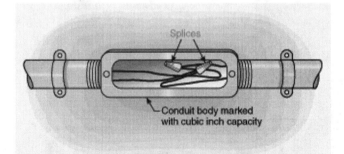

Exhibit 314.4 An example of splices in a raceway-supported conduit body.

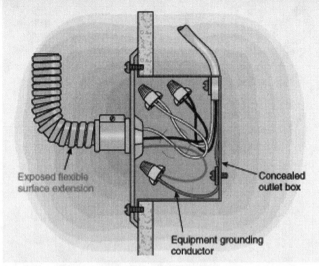

Exhibit 314.5 An example of a flexible surface extension from a flush-mounted outlet box.

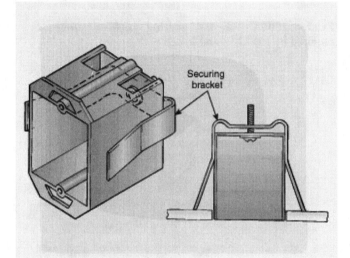

Exhibit 314.6 One type of device box used for old work.

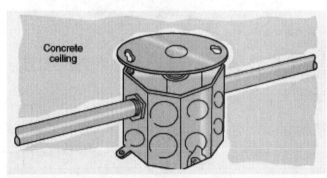

Exhibit 314.7 A mud box installed in a concrete ceiling.

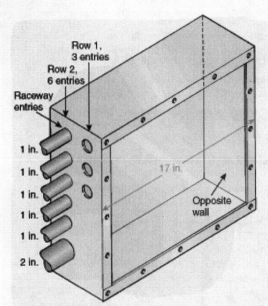

6 × 2 in. (trade diameter of largest raceway) = 12 in.
12 in. + 5 in. (sum of diameters of other entries, row 2 only)
= 17 in. (min. required from each entry to opposite wall)

Exhibit 314.10 An example showing calculations required by 314.28(A)(2) for splices, angle pulls, or U pulls.

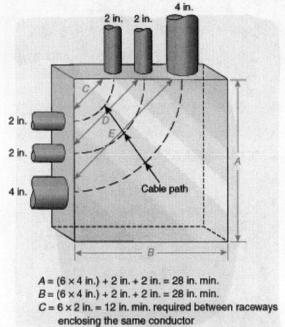

A = (6 × 4 in.) + 2 in. + 2 in. = 28 in. min.
B = (6 × 4 in.) + 2 in. + 2 in. = 28 in. min.
C = 6 × 2 in. = 12 in. min. required between raceways enclosing the same conductor
D = 6 × 2 in. = 12 in. min. required between raceways enclosing the same conductor
E = 6 × 4 in. = 24 in. min. required between raceways enclosing the same conductor

Exhibit 314.11 An example showing calculations required by 314.28(A)(2) for raceways enclosing the same conductor.

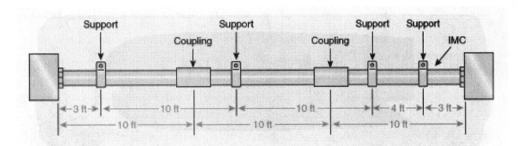

Exhibit 342.1 Minimum fastening requirements for intermediate metal conduit according to 342.30(A).

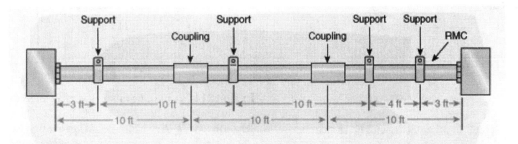

Exhibit 344.1 Minimum support required for rigid metal conduit according to 344.30(A).

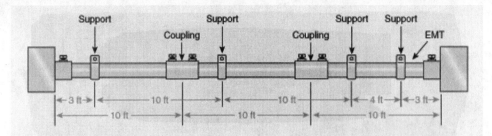

Exhibit 358.1 Minimum requirements for securely fastening electrical metallic tubing (EMT) unless an exception applies.

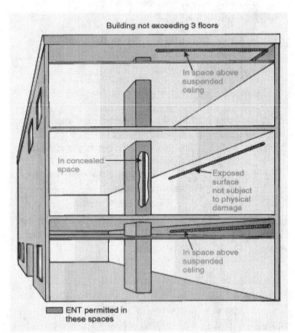

Exhibit 362.2 Examples of permitted uses of ENT in a building not exceeding three floors.

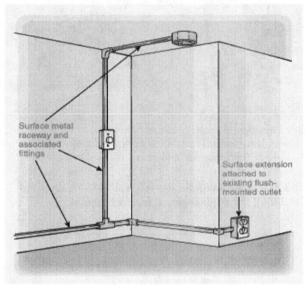

Exhibit 386.1 An example of a surface metal raceway extending from an existing receptacle outlet.

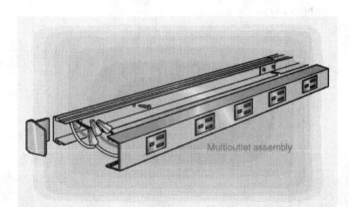

Exhibit 380.1 A typical multioutlet assembly shown in assembly form.

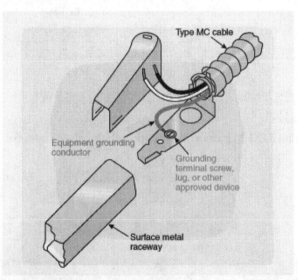

Exhibit 386.2 An example of providing a means for terminating an equipment grounding conductor at a surface metal raceway.

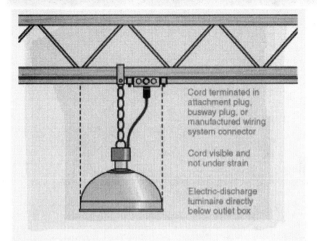

Exhibit 410.5 A listed cord-and-plug-connected electric-discharge luminaire.

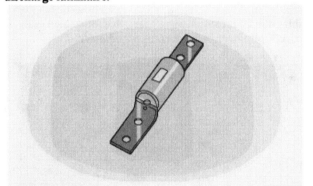

Exhibit 450.12 A current limiter (a special type of high-interrupting-capacity fuse).

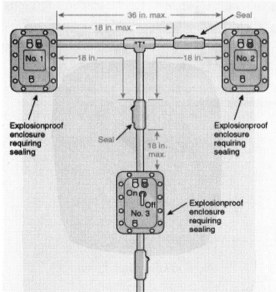

Exhibit 501.6 Two seals required so that the run of conduit between Enclosure No. 1 and Enclosure No. 2 is sealed. Even if Enclosure No. 3 were not required to be sealed, the

vertical seal in the vertical run of conduit to Enclosure No. 3 would be required to be sealed within 18 in. of Enclosure No. 1, because the vertical conduit run to the "T" fitting is a conduit run to Enclosure No. 1.

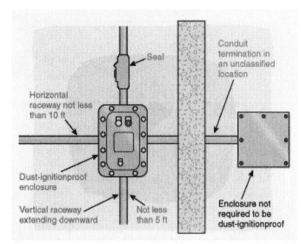

Exhibit 502.2 Three methods for preventing dust from entering a dust-ignitionproof enclosure through the raceway.

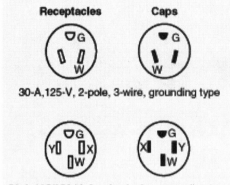

Exhibit 552.44(C) Attachment Cap and Receptacle Configurations

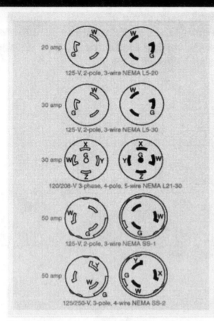

Exhibit 555.1 Typical configurations for single locking- and grounding-type receptacles and attachment plug caps used to provide shore power for boats in marinas and boatyards. These configurations are 30 amperes to 50 amperes.

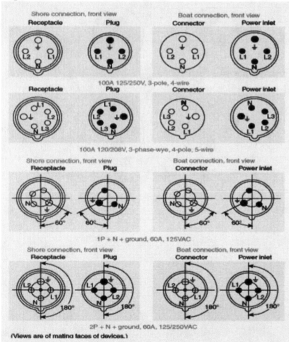

Exhibit 555.2 Typical configurations for safety pin-and-sleeve-type receptacles, plugs, connectors, and power inlets used to provide shore power for boats in marinas and boatyards. These configurations are 60 amperes or 100 amperes.

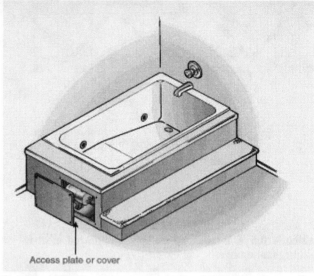

Exhibit 680.19 Access plate for hydromassage tub electrical equipment, located as described in 680.73.

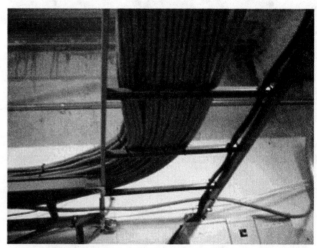

Exhibit 800.7 Overhead ladder–type cable tray containing communications cables.

City Multipliers

The costs presented in this Costbook attempt to represent national averages. Costs, however, vary among regions, states and even between adjacent localities.

This table of City Multipliers is provided in order to more closely approximate the probable costs for specific locations throughout the U.S. These adjustment factors are used to modify costs obtained from this book to help account for construction costs regional variations and therefore provide a more accurate estimate for specific areas. The factors are formulated by comparing costs in a specific area to the costs presented in this Costbook. An example of how to use these factors is shown below. Whenever local current costs are known, whether material prices or labor rates, they should be used when more accuracy is required.

$$\text{Cost Obtained from Costbook Pages} \quad X \quad \text{City Multiplier Divided by 100} \quad = \quad \textbf{Adjusted Cost}$$

For example, a project estimated to cost $1,000,000 using the Costbook can be adjusted to more closely approximate the cost in Los Angeles where the Multiplier is 105:

$$1,000,000 \; X \; \frac{105}{100} = \textbf{1,050,000}$$

City Multipliers

City Multipliers

State	City	Multiplier
AK	ANCHORAGE	123
AL	ANNISTON	81
	AUBURN-OPELIKA	81
	BIRMINGHAM	79
	DECATUR	78
	DOTHAN	77
	FLORENCE	78
	GADSDEN	77
	HUNTSVILLE	79
	MOBILE	81
	MONTGOMERY	77
	TUSCALOOSA	79
AR	FAYETTEVILLE-SPRINGDALE	72
	FORT SMITH	77
	JONESBORO	77
	LITTLE ROCK	78
	PINE BLUFF	78
	TEXARKANA	77
AZ	YUMA	89
	PHOENIX-MESA	88
	TUCSON	87
	FLAGSTAFF	88
CA	REDDING	100
	BAKERSFIELD	101
	RIVERSIDE-SAN BERNARDINO	101
	SACRAMENTO	103
	SAN DIEGO	102
	ORANGE COUNTY	103
	LOS ANGELES-LONG BEACH	105
	SAN JOSE	110
	SAN FRANCISCO	113
	SAN LUIS OBISPO	99
	STOCKTON-LODI	102
	FRESNO	103
	MODESTO	100
	SALINAS	105
	SANTA CRUZ-WATSONVILLE	105
	VALLEJO-FAIRFIELD-NAPA	105
	SANTA ROSA	105
	OAKLAND	108
	CHICO-PARADISE	101
	MERCED	100
	VENTURA	101
	VISALIA-TULARE-PORTERVILLE	100
	YOLO	102
	YUBA CITY	101
	SANTA BARBARA	104

State	City	Multiplier
CO	GRAND JUNCTION	86
	PUEBLO	88
	BOULDER-LONGMONT	86
	COLORADO SPRINGS	91
	DENVER	91
	GREELEY	85
	FORT COLLINS-LOVELAND	85
CT	WATERBURY	100
	NEW LONDON-NORWICH	98
	HARTFORD	100
	BRIDGEPORT	101
	STAMFORD-NORWALK	104
	NEW HAVEN-MERIDEN	101
	DANBURY	101
DC	WASHINGTON	94
DE	DOVER	94
	WILMINGTON-NEWARK	95
FL	ORLANDO	86
	JACKSONVILLE	85
	TAMPA-ST. PETERSBURG	84
	WEST PALM BEACH-BOCA	86
	MIAMI	86
	PANAMA CITY	75
	TALLAHASSEE	77
	FORT MYERS-CAPE CORAL	79
	SARASOTA-BRADENTON	80
	LAKELAND-WINTER HAVEN	81
	PENSACOLA	79
	GAINESVILLE	81
	FORT LAUDERDALE	86
	DAYTONA BEACH	83
	MELBOURNE-TITUSVILLE	88
	FORT PIERCE-PORT ST. LUCIE	86
	OCALA	86
	FORT WALTON BEACH	87
	NAPLES	88
	PUNTA GORDA	79
GA	AUGUSTA	75
	COLUMBUS	76
	MACON	78
	SAVANNAH	80
	ATLANTA	86
	ALBANY	77
	ATHENS	78
HI	HONOLULU	122

City Multipliers

State	City	Multiplier
IA	SIOUX CITY	86
	WATERLOO-CEDAR FALLS	85
	DAVENPORT	90
	DES MOINES	91
	DUBUQUE	86
	CEDAR RAPIDS	87
	IOWA CITY	90
ID	POCATELLO	87
	BOISE CITY	89
IL	SPRINGFIELD	94
	PEORIA-PEKIN	95
	ROCKFORD	95
	CHICAGO	104
	DECATUR	94
	BLOOMINGTON-NORMAL	95
	CHAMPAIGN-URBANA	95
	KANKAKEE	96
IN	TERRE HAUTE	90
	FORT WAYNE	90
	EVANSVILLE	90
	INDIANAPOLIS	94
	GARY	97
	KOKOMO	90
	LAFAYETTE	90
	MUNCIE	90
	SOUTH BEND	91
	BLOOMINGTON	91
	ELKHART-GOSHEN	91
KS	WICHITA	84
	TOPEKA	84
	KANSAS CITY	89
	LAWRENCE	85
KY	LEXINGTON	84
	LOUISVILLE	86
	OWENSBORO	85
LA	MONROE	79
	SHREVEPORT-BOSSIER CITY	80
	LAKE CHARLES	83
	BATON ROUGE	83
	NEW ORLEANS	86
	ALEXANDRIA	79
	LAFAYETTE	81
	HOUMA	83

State	City	Multiplier
MA	SPRINGFIELD	99
	LOWELL	98
	WORCESTER	98
	BOSTON	106
	PITTSFIELD	99
	FITCHBURG-LEOMINSTER	100
	BROCKTON	103
	NEW BEDFORD	103
	LAWRENCE	103
	BARNSTABLE-YARMOUTH	104
MD	CUMBERLAND	86
	HAGERSTOWN	82
	BALTIMORE	88
ME	BANGOR	86
	LEWISTON-AUBURN	86
	PORTLAND	87
MI	GRAND RAPIDS-MUSKEGON	90
	LANSING-EAST LANSING	94
	SAGINAW-BAY CITY-MIDLAND	92
	DETROIT	100
	KALAMAZOO-BATTLE CREEK	86
	JACKSON	94
	FLINT	95
	ANN ARBOR	95
	BENTON HARBOR	90
MN	ROCHESTER	95
	DULUTH	95
	MINNEAPOLIS-ST. PAUL	100
	ST. CLOUD	97
MO	JOPLIN	86
	SPRINGFIELD	87
	ST. JOSEPH	89
	KANSAS CITY	92
	ST. LOUIS	89
	COLUMBIA	89
MS	BILOXI-GULFPORTAGOULA	78
	JACKSON	77
	HATTIESBURG	78
MT	MISSOULA	87
	BILLINGS	88
	GREAT FALLS	89

City Multipliers

State	City	Multiplier
NC	WILMINGTON	76
	GREENSBORO-HIGH POINT	75
	ASHEVILLE	74
	RALEIGH-DURHAM-CHAPEL HILL	75
	CHARLOTTE	75
	HICKORY-MORGANTON-LENOIR	71
	ROCKY MOUNT	71
	FAYETTEVILLE	76
	GOLDSBORO	74
	GREENVILLE	75
	JACKSONVILLE	76
ND	BISMARCK	86
	GRAND FORKS	85
	FARGO	86
NE	LINCOLN	83
	OMAHA	86
NH	MANCHESTER	90
	NASHUA	88
	PORTSMOUTH	83
NJ	ATLANTIC-CAPE MAY	99
	TRENTON	100
	NEWARK	103
	VINELAND-MILLVILLE	98
	JERSEY CITY	101
	MONMOUTH-OCEAN	100
	BERGEN-PASSAIC	102
	MIDDLESEX-SOMERSET	97
NM	LAS CRUCES	83
	ALBUQUERQUE	86
	SANTA FE	88
NV	LAS VEGAS	97
	RENO	96
NY	BINGHAMTON	90
	ALBANY-SCHENECTADY-TROY	92
	SYRACUSE	93
	ROCHESTER	95
	BUFFALO-NIAGARA FALLS	97
	NEW YORK	119
	GLENS FALLS	85
	UTICA-ROME	93
	ELMIRA	86
	JAMESTOWN	92
	DUTCHESS COUNTY	91
	NASSAU-SUFFOLK	104
	NEWBURGH	94

State	City	Multiplier
OH	CINCINNATI	88
	YOUNGSTOWN-WARREN	90
	COLUMBUS	91
	TOLEDO	93
	CLEVELAND-LORAIN-ELYRIA	95
	DAYTON-SPRINGFIELD	89
	LIMA	91
	MANSFIELD	87
	CANTON-MASSILLON	91
	AKRON	93
	STEUBENVILLE	94
	HAMILTON-MIDDLETOWN	88
OK	ENID	79
	LAWTON	80
	TULSA	81
	OKLAHOMA CITY	82
OR	EUGENE-SPRINGFIELD	95
	MEDFORD-ASHLAND	94
	SALEM	96
	PORTLAND	97
	CORVALLIS	95
PA	HARRISBURG-LEBANON	91
	SCRANTON--WILKES-BARRE	92
	PITTSBURGH	94
	ALLENTOWN-BETHLEHEM	95
	PHILADELPHIA	103
	WILLIAMSPORT	90
	LANCASTER	91
	YORK	92
	ALTOONA	93
	STATE COLLEGE	88
	ERIE	93
	READING	93
	JOHNSTOWN	94
	SHARON	91
PR	SAN JUAN	74
	PONCE	73
	MAYAGUEZ	72
RI	PROVIDENCE	98
SC	FLORENCE	74
	CHARLESTON	77
	GREENVILLE-SPARTANBURG	76
	COLUMBIA	77
	AIKEN	82
	MYRTLE BEACH	81
	SUMTER	76

City Multipliers

State	City	Multiplier
SD	RAPID CITY	80
	SIOUX FALLS	81
TN	JOHNSON CITY	76
	CHATTANOOGA	79
	KNOXVILLE	79
	MEMPHIS	84
	NASHVILLE	83
	JACKSON	78
	CLARKSVILLE	81
TX	LUBBOCK	79
	AUSTIN-SAN MARCOS	79
	SAN ANTONIO	80
	DALLAS	82
	HOUSTON	83
	FORT WORTH-ARLINGTON	82
	LONGVIEW-MARSHALL	75
	SAN ANGELO	75
	MCALLEN-EDINBURG-MISSION	76
	ODESSA-MIDLAND	77
	TEXARKANA	77
	LAREDO	70
	CORPUS CHRISTI	77
	EL PASO	77
	VICTORIA	77
	ABILENE	77
	TYLER	77
	WACO	77
	WICHITA FALLS	77
	AMARILLO	78
	BRYAN-COLLEGE STATION	78
	BEAUMONT-PORT ARTHUR	79
	GALVESTON-TEXAS CITY	81
	BRAZORIA	82
	BROWNSVILLE-HARLINGEN	80
	KILLEEN-TEMPLE	75
	SHERMAN-DENISON	81
UT	PROVO-OREM	85
	SALT LAKE CITY-OGDEN	84
VA	ROANOKE	77
	LYNCHBURG	78
	NORFOLK-VIRGINIA BEACH	82
	RICHMOND-PETERSBURG	82
	CHARLOTTESVILLE	79
	DANVILLE	76
VT	BURLINGTON	88
WA	YAKIMA	95
	SPOKANE	97
	BELLINGHAM	101
	TACOMA	100
	SEATTLE-BELLEVUE-EVERETT	100
	RICHLAND-KENNEWICK-PASCO	95
	OLYMPIA	97
	BREMERTON	99
WI	WAUSAU	90
	EAU CLAIRE	90
	MADISON	90
	GREEN BAY	91
	MILWAUKEE-WAUKESHA	96
	LA CROSSE	89
	KENOSHA	93
	RACINE	93
	APPLETON-OSHKOSH-NEENAH	91
	JANESVILLE-BELOIT	91
	SHEBOYGAN	93
WV	PARKERSBURG	88
	CHARLESTON	89
	HUNTINGTON	90
	WHEELING	90
WY	CASPER	83
	CHEYENNE	84

Index

Index

Index

Index

229

Index

Index

Index

Notes

Notes

Notes

Notes